THE ACENTRIC LABYRINTH

Ramon G. Mendoza is Director of the Humanities Program at Florida International University. A Cuban-born ex-Jesuit priest, he became Professor at the Latin American Institute of the Free University of Berlin and later Professor of Modern Languages at F.I.U. His books on Heidegger, Ignatius Loyola, and Franz Kafka have been acclaimed as important contributions to the Humanities.

The
Acentric Labyrinth

GIORDANO BRUNO'S PRELUDE
TO CONTEMPORARY COSMOLOGY

Ramon G. Mendoza

ELEMENT
Shaftesbury, Dorset ● Rockport, Massachusetts
Brisbane, Queensland

© Ramon G. Mendoza 1995

First published in Great Britain in 1995 by
Element Books Limited
Shaftesbury, Dorset SP7 8BP

Published in the USA in 1995 by
Element Books, Inc.
P.O. Box 830, Rockport, MA 01966

Published in Australia in 1995 by
Element Books Limited
for Jacaranda Wiley Limited
33 Park Road, Milton, Brisbane 4064

Cover design by Max Fairbrother
Design by Roger Lightfoot
Typeset by WestKey Ltd
Printed and bound in the USA by Edwards Brothers Inc

British Library Cataloguing in Publication
data available

Library of Congress Cataloging in Publication
data available

ISBN 1-85230-640-8

To my friend and colleague Gregory Olson

Since Copernicus man is rolling out of the center unto X.

FRIEDRICH NIETZSCHE

Acknowledgments

There are several people and institutions who deserve my deepest gratitude for their support and assistance to me in bringing to successful completion the lengthy and laborious undertaking of writing and publishing this book.

Above all I am deeply indebted to the Warburg Institute of the University of London for having given me free and easy access to the impressive literature on Bruno collected there thanks to the efforts mainly of the late Frances Yates, who dedicated many years of research to the life and thought of the Italian Renaissance philosopher, and who is still widely recognized as one of the world's leading authorities on Bruno. In no other European library have I found such friendly and efficient assistance for research than at the Warburg Institute Library, and I don't think this book would have been possible without the copious information I was able to gather there and the insights that I gained from it.

On a more personal level, I wish to express my deepest gratitude to those colleagues of mine at Florida International University who gave me their precious time to read and edit the manuscript, discussed with me the ideas expressed in it, and gave me invaluable advice concerning style and structure. I am particularly indebted to Dr. Thomas Breslin, Vice Provost of Florida International University, who took the trouble to read my manuscript several times and to edit it most scrupulously. As Director of Sponsored Research at F.I.U., Professor Breslin has always strongly encouraged my work and given me wise directives concerning its publication. Four other colleagues of mine also read and edited the manuscript: Professors Florence Yudin, Danielle Johnson-Cousin, Richard Sugg, and Steve Fjellman. For their work, strong encouragement, and valuable suggestions I am especially grateful.

Among my closest friends I am particularly indebted to Margaret B. Harris for the help and encouragement I have constantly received from her. She also read and edited my manuscript and made valuable suggestions concerning both style and content. Dr. Meyer Halperin also deserves my deepest gratitude for several very careful editions of the manuscript.

I also wish to acknowledge a very special inspiration that I received from Barry Kihl, a former student of mine with whom I held lively discussions during the time I was writing the book. He had a way of challenging my ideas that proved to be most useful in bringing out a lot that would otherwise have remained submerged had he not prodded me.

I also wish to thank Maria Menna and my friend, Faber Carmona, for their generous assistance in procuring for me most valuable material on Bruno.

Finally my deepest gratitude goes to my editor Ian Fenton, and to Element Books, who made possible the publication of this book.

Hollywood, Florida

Contents

Introduction

In a world that in the last fifty years has incessantly expanded its frontiers to comprehend the immeasurably large and the infinitesimally small – galaxies and quarks – not enough attention has been paid to Giordano Bruno (1548–1600), the man who for the first time after Lucretius (100–55 B.C.) expanded the mind's exploratory horizons to embrace both maxima and minima in what rightfully deserves to be regarded as the first full-fledged cosmological speculation of modern times.

This neglect is all the more surprising considering the fact that contemporary science has recently deemed it indispensable to link its most compelling theory of the immeasurably large – Einstein's general theory of relativity – to the only theory of the infinitesimally small unanimously accepted by the scientific community – quantum mechanics – in order to advance its own speculations about the origin, size, structure, and fate of the universe. As a result of these speculations an entirely new science was born – quantum cosmology. The recent happy encounter and successful marriage of nuclear physics with astrophysics invites us to reflect on Giordano Bruno, the man who insightfully anticipated some of their basic presuppositions four hundred years ago.

Most contemporary physical theories about the universe are based upon several non-empirical, downright metaphysical assumptions. Perhaps the most important and fundamental one is that our universe constitutes a system – an organized array of individual elements and parts forming and working as a unit. Equally important for most contemporary cosmologies are the assumptions that the laws of nuclear physics and astrophysics are valid throughout the entire universe and that all the laws of nature, operative on earth, have unrestricted universal applicability.

It generally escapes the notice of most contemporary historians of science that it was Giordano Bruno who, for the first time in the history of thought, both Western and Oriental, clearly and explicitly formulated precisely these three fundamental metaphysical assumptions of contemporary cosmology: the unity of the universe, its uniformity, homogeneity and isotropy, and the universal validity and applicability of its laws.

For yet another reason does Bruno deserve to be regarded not only as a precursor, but as the real founder of contemporary cosmology. There is today a common persuasion among cosmologists and astrophysicists that there must be some form of extraterrestrial life, indeed of intelligence, in other parts of the universe. This belief has now become so popular that it almost dominates the world of science fiction. Moreover, this persuasion has been taken most seriously by the space programs of the great powers, which are currently involved in joint efforts of extraterrestrial-life exploration.[1] It was Bruno's firm conviction, against the opinions of his contemporaries, that life existed elsewhere in the universe. This was not Bruno's original idea; before him, Nicholas of Cusa (1401–1464) had expressed this view. However, it was Bruno who, for the first time, gave this idea an entirely rational and compelling justification. If the universe was, as he asserted, acentric and infinite, and if homogeneity and isotropy were the properties of such a universe, then it was most natural and logical that life would exist elsewhere as well. Even theologically this conclusion was most plausible, for to limit life and intelligence exclusively to the planet Earth, Bruno argued, would amount to a rationally unjustifiable self-imposed limitation of God's omnipotence.

In yet another way must Bruno be considered the founder of contemporary cosmology. He envisioned an eternally changing and evolving universe – a Heracleitan universe in perpetual flux – thereby anticipating Laplace's concept of cosmic evolution.

Thus, from the perspective of contemporary cosmology, Bruno deserves to be regarded as the most modern and insightful of all Renaissance thinkers; he was the first to be interested in precisely the three things that characterize and fascinate our atomic and cybernetic age: memory and the mind, sub-atomic particles (Bruno's minima), and the cosmos (Bruno's maxima). He was the first great theoretical explorer concurrently of the very large and the very small, as Newton, Dirac, Einstein, and Hawking would be after him. Also Einstein's question whether God had any choice in creating the universe had already been asked by Bruno . . . and answered negatively! In sum, most of the great contemporary cosmologists after Einstein are simply following Bruno's footsteps in the most important and fascinating business the human mind can possibly undertake – 'reading God's mind'. As Stephen Hawking observes:

> If we do discover a complete theory, it should in time be under-
> standable in broad principle by everyone, not just a few scientists.
> Then we shall all, philosophers, scientists, and just ordinary peo-
> ple, be able to take part in the discussion of why it is that we and
> the universe exist. If we find the answer to that, it would be the
> ultimate triumph of human reason – for then we would truly know
> the mind of God.[2]

Bruno's merits as the true founder of modern cosmology have not yet been properly recognized. A most revealing sign of the inadequate estimation contemporary science has for Bruno is the fact that up to now the best it has been able to do in honor of his memory was to name after him one of the most inconspicuous craters on the dark side of the Moon! Perhaps not so sad after all, for ironically, at least this way Bruno has finally been awarded his much deserved immortality, for from now on his name will be indelibly written, albeit in very small letters, on the map of a tiny corner of the infinite acentric universe he was the first to conceive.

Although some justice has already been done to Bruno by recent sound and unbiased scholarship, and his badly disfigured image has been considerably restored, much remains to be done to sharpen our assessment of his role in shaping contemporary understanding of the universe, and particularly of his contributions to the development of modern cosmology. Bruno's cosmological model, by remarkably anticipating an impressive number of characteristic features of some of the most compelling contemporary cosmological models, provides the most convincing proof of his true modernity, and of his having effectively surpassed the medieval as well as the Renaissance world-views.

Many books have been written about Bruno. Very few, however, have focused on the premises and principles that guided his thinking, nor has any, to my knowledge, asked how was it possible for him to surmise, more clearly than any of the most lucid scientists of his and the following century, what present-day science claims to know about the origin, size, nature, and fate of the universe. And this he achieved without the help of advanced mathematics, experimentation, and even the most rudimentary astronomical devices, but relying exclusively on unaided sensorial observation, a most vivid imagination, and reason. This baffling power of reason to understand the universe, so conspicuously exemplified in Bruno, prompts us to wonder about the ultimate rationality of the universe, and makes Einstein's remark, 'The most incomprehensible thing about the universe is its comprehensibility,' appear all the more urgent for us to ponder.

This book explores the guiding principles that led Bruno's thinking to anticipate insights that experimental and mathematical science took more than three hundred years to arrive at, and re-examines the main features of Giordano Bruno's post-Copernican cosmology in the light of the most recent discoveries and tenets of some contemporary cosmological theories. Perhaps the elucidation of the guiding principles of Bruno's thinking and heuristic methodology may also prove useful for a better understanding of the interrelationship between cosmological science and metaphysics. This book, in sum, proposes a re-examination of Bruno's natural philosophy, particularly his cosmology, and documents his crucial role in the so-called Copernican Revolution.

Although numerous scholarly monographs discussing Bruno's natural philosophy have been published in Europe since Emile Namer's insightful work in this field appeared in 1923,[3] hardly any of these works has been translated into English. Thus, the English-speaking public has been generally deprived of the deeper understanding of Bruno's natural philosophy that these publications provide.

In fact, only two major works written in English and dealing directly with Bruno's philosophy have appeared since Dorothea Waley Singer published in 1950 her excellent book *Giordano Bruno: His Life and Thought*. This first sympathetic and finely documented study of Bruno by an American scholar was honored in Milan with an Italian translation in 1974. The second attempt by another American scholar to expound and discuss Bruno's cosmology was undertaken twenty years later by Antoinette Mann Paterson. Although Paterson's detailed and extensive study, *The Infinite Worlds of Giordano Bruno*, focuses directly and exclusively on Bruno's cosmology, it has enjoyed little, if any, international recognition, as the extremely rare references to her work in European Brunian bibliographies indicate. The reason for this spiritless reception of Paterson's study in Europe may be that it was perceived as being more systematic and expository than philosophically incisive.

In sharp contrast to the aforementioned, the book on Bruno which has received the highest international acclaim for its sound scholarship and impressive erudition is Frances Yates's *Giordano Bruno and the Hermetic Tradition*, published in London and Chicago (University of Chicago Press) in 1964. Yates, a well-known Renaissance scholar working at the Warburg Institute of the University of London, was considered in the English-speaking world for several decades as the highest authority on Bruno. Her unchallenged posthumous ascendancy has been recently evidenced by a 1991 paperback reprint, by the University of Chicago Press, of the very same edition of 1964, without any reference to the fact that Yates's interpretation of Bruno's cosmology has now been widely rejected by the most serious European (and some American) scholars. Some reference to the dramatic change that has taken place in the assessment of Bruno's merits as a philosopher should have been made, not only in all fairness to Bruno, but also in obliged acknowledgment of the copious recent scholarship which regards Yates's sweeping and unqualified judgment of Bruno as being 'nothing but a Renaissance magus' as a partial characterization of the man who, as it is now becoming increasingly clear, was one of the most insightful minds of the sixteenth century. This overly reductive assessment of Bruno's thought by one of England's most authoritative Renaissance scholars makes a re-examination of Bruno's cosmology and ontology imperative, since the recent paperback edition, lacking a critical introduction, merely continues to propagate a false image of Bruno.

In the United States, Yates's indictment of Bruno was uncritically accepted by one of her American epigones, the Hungarian-born Benedictine monk, Stanley Jaki. Upon reading Yates's book, Jaki hastened to serve to the English-speaking public a translation of Bruno's first Italian cosmological dialogue, *The Ash Wednesday Supper*, which contains just a preliminary sketch of his cosmological model. Jaki presented his impulsive translation of the dialogue in an introduction heavily seasoned with abundant monotonously unkind footnotes.

For this most damaging disservice to Bruno's reputation as a serious thinker, both Yates and Jaki cannot avoid being ranked among the latest representatives of a long lineage of devout Christian Bruno detractors, whose common (perhaps unconscious) interest has been to keep alive the black legend that was launched by the Church as soon as the embers of Bruno's pyre cooled off.

It is most interesting to observe the historical vicissitudes of the tactics of disparagement the black legend has used throughout its four-century-long history. It adapted most cleverly to the changing ideologies and values of the times. Thus, from Bruno's death to the publication of Newton's *Principia mathematica*, the black legend readily disposed of Bruno simply by holding up to the world the image of the reprobate apostate and heretic and by putting all his writings in the Holy Office's Index of Forbidden Books. Indeed, a more convincing proof of Bruno's monstrous depravity could not be presented than his turning his face away from the crucifix the priest offered him to kiss before his execution.

But things changed radically after Newton's fame spread over Europe. The second phase of the black legend lasted until shortly after the French Revolution. It was the age of the Enlightenment, as well as of the Scientific and Industrial Revolutions. For the *philosophes* and the new scientists the image of Bruno, the heretic, had lost all its punch. If anything, as in Galileo's case, Bruno's challenge of the Church's obsolete cosmological views, and his consequent punishment for his rebellion, was a title of glory rather than a stigma of disgrace. The black legend changed its tactics accordingly. From then on, Bruno became the enemy of science and mathematics, and the old image of Bruno, the reprobate heretic, changed into that of Bruno, the mystic, or Bruno, the obscurantist magician. Nobody then seemed to take notice of the fact that this obscurantist magician had inspired two of the greatest philosophers of the Age of Reason, Spinoza and Leibniz, and two of the most eminent German idealist philosophers of the following century, Schelling and Hegel. Why should anybody pay any attention anyway to an Italian hothead, who, unlike Descartes, Spinoza, and Leibniz, had shown so little respect for mathematics? This negative image of Bruno was soon to be strongly reinforced by the triumph of positivism in the middle of the nineteenth century; and one century later, in 1964, it was again vigorously revived, as the last ripples of the original eighteenth-century wave of the black legend reached us in the form of Frances Yates's thesis of 'Bruno – nothing but a Renaissance magus'.

Finally, when the time was right, a 'white' Bruno legend made its appearance as a vigorous reaction and challenge to the black legend. It has a shorter, but a far more dramatic history. It originated only after propitious historical circumstances permitted its formation in the early nineteenth century. The Germans started it, specifically those very Germans, Lutherans most of them, who had received some inspiration from Bruno's unorthodox cosmological views. Bruno was, in fact, greatly admired by Goethe, Schelling, and Hegel, and they were the first to pay close attention to Bruno as a thinker and to acknowledge his merits as a great philosopher. Ironically, it was not overly zealous and patriotic Italians, but level-headed Germans who discovered the hidden potential of Bruno's philosophy. However, the high respect the German philosophers and poets showed for Bruno was not sufficient to create the white legend that irritated Frances Yates so much. It was the Italians of the Risorgimento who transformed the German acknowledgement of Bruno's merits as a philosopher into the symbol and banner of the powerful Italian liberal antipapist and anticlerical political movement of the late nineteenth century. Monuments to Bruno were erected in Rome and Nola, Bruno's native city; fiery speeches were made in his honor all over Italy, and hundreds of articles appeared in newspapers and magazines. Bruno was praised as the innocent victim of religious intolerance, as the heroic martyr for the cause of freedom of speech, and, of course, as one of the greatest philosophical geniuses of all times. All of these claims were at first supported only by very scanty scholarship; almost all of it was pure rhetoric and apologetic polemics.

The confident, and by this time mostly dormant, supporters of the black legend were at first surprised by the sudden fanfare about Bruno, then very upset, and finally aroused and drawn into the fray. They responded with no less rhetoric and passion. Pope Leo XIII gave the tone: in a letter addressed to all the faithful on the occasion of the erection in June 1889 of a monument to Bruno on the Roman public square where he was executed, the Pope wrote:

> Bruno cannot show any scientific accomplishments whatsoever,
> nor has he gained any merits in promoting public life. His attitude
> was insincere, mendacious, and utterly egoistic, intolerant towards
> every contrary opinion, outright wicked, and full of a truth-
> disfiguring base flattery.

Seen in this historical context, Frances Yates's image of Bruno was
not merely a revival of the old image forged during the Scientific
Revolution of the late seventeenth and early eighteenth centuries.
It was a vigorous reaction of a conservative British scholar against
the white legend created by the vociferous camp of late-
nineteenth-century Italian patriots, freethinkers, and anticlerical
intellectuals. Frances Yates decided the time had come to put an
end to all that nonsense; and indeed who was better qualified than
she to carry out that mission, being, as she was, one of the most
authoritative scholars in the field of the Italian Renaissance in
England? The result of her decision was disastrous for Bruno's
reputation as a thinker. Yates's image of Bruno, the magician, was
generally accepted without further questioning in the English-
speaking world, until it was challenged by Robert Westmann in a
paper read ten years later at the Clark Library Seminar at the
University of California in Los Angeles. This lecture marked the
beginning of the end of the Brunian black legend in the English-
speaking world.

Such were the two opposing camps of the black and the white
Bruno legends. Fortunately continental European scholarship
during the last third of the twentieth century has shunned and
decidedly moved away from this rather infantile polemic. The
numerous books and articles published after 1964 dedicated to
discuss Bruno's thought, his natural philosophy, and especially
his cosmology, have become less and less polemical and apologetic. Only in America and Britain does the ghost of Frances Yates
continue to haunt the scene, as the 1991 paperback reprint of her
outdated book, and, above all, the total absence of any original
serious study of Bruno's philosophy in the English language for
almost thirty years clearly indicate. Frances Yates's ghost seems
indeed to have effectively scared away almost all American and
British scholars from the vast premises it haunts.

But if serious English-speaking scholars were scared away, not
so John Bossy. His field of historical interest is post-Reformation

English Catholicism (an interest he shared with the English Jesuits who educated him). However, judging from his latest creation, it is in the fictional world of Sir Arthur Conan Doyle where Mr. Bossy really feels at home.[4] Once again, the poltergeist of Frances Yates continues to torment Bruno. It succeeded in inspiring John Bossy to write a book with the sole purpose of demonstrating that Bruno was nothing but a spy hired by Queen Elizabeth's secretary of state, Francis Walsingham, to report to him what was going on in the French embassy. Bruno was lodging there as a special guest of the French ambassador, Michel de Castelnau. In order to prove the thesis of Bruno the mole, Bossy identifies the ambassador's guest and friend with the chaplain of the French embassy, and, to make this plausible, he was compelled to fancy that the excommunicated Bruno celebrated Mass and listened to confessions there.

Thus, almost four centuries after his death, Giordano Bruno continues to be disparaged, this time by a British novelist who, ignoring Bruno's real vocation and total dedication to philosophical speculation (so strenuous that it yielded five elaborate dialogues in less than two years) turns him into a career secret agent[5], a busy informer, a go-between intrigant in the payroll of the Queen's secretary of state, and, ironically, even into the savior of Protestant England. For, according to Bossy, Bruno was the key figure in foiling the most dangerous conspiracy Queen Elizabeth ever faced, thereby saving England from a French invasion with the purpose of putting Mary, Queen of Scots, on the throne, and bringing England back to the Papal fold.[6]

It is amusing to see the pains that some scholars with strong religious convictions and loyalties are still willing to take with the sole purpose of belittling Bruno. For this and no other is John Bossy's ultimate purpose, as it clearly transpires from the following passage:

> (Bruno) systematically betrayed his master Castelnau, who did nothing but good for him, was extremely loyal to him, and regarded him as a friend. He persuaded his secretary to betray him. He procured, in so far as it was in his power to do it, the arrest, torture, and execution of Francis Throckmorton, whom Castelnau said that he loved as himself, and by whose fate he was appallingly harrowed. He did all this while buttering up Castelnau in three dedicatory epistles with fulsome expressions of esteem, friendship

and undying gratitude for looking after him and sticking up for
him. This was quite exceptionally disgraceful conduct, and it must
gravely damage Bruno's reputation from now on.

Since Bossy's thesis has already been effectively refuted by
others,[7] his allegations will not be reviewed now, but some of them
will be discussed later on[8], in case some suspicions have crept into
the minds of some readers of Bossy's detective story.

The books about Bruno written by Yates, Jaki, and Bossy are
still practically[9] the only windows available to English-speaking
readers through which they can look at the Brunian philosophical
universe.[10] Considering the damage done by them in the English-
speaking world to Bruno's reputation as a philosopher, the temp-
tation for me was strong to take an apologetic stand. I was
annoyed by the unfairness of Yates's treatment of Bruno, all the
more objectionable in view of her authority and widely acclaimed
scholarly competence as a Renaissance scholar. A fresh, less pre-
judiced look at Bruno's thought would, I fancied, possibly serve
as a sort of thread of Ariadne by which the readers might find their
way back from their disoriented groping inside the Brunian labyrinth where they had been led astray by the confusing signs posted
by Yates and Jaki. But the more I advanced, heedless of those
misleading pointers, in the examination of Bruno's thought, the
more apparent it became to me that a straightforward presentation
and discussion of Bruno's cosmological and ontological ideas
would suffice to repair the damage done and to restore him to the
place he deserves to occupy in the history of Western thought.

Consequently, my main intention became to discuss Bruno's
post-Copernican cosmology and to show that what has been
universally hailed as the 'Copernican Revolution' was hardly a
revolution at all; that Bruno was the true revolutionary, and that
his revolution – the 'Brunian Revolution', as it rightfully deserves
to be called – was the one that really ushered in the Modern World.
Here again I could not but disagree with Hans Blumenberg's
thesis that Bruno must be considered as standing, together with
Nicholas of Cusa, at the threshold between the two epochs, Antiquity and Modernity.[11] Blumenberg's main reason for keeping
Bruno out of the Modern World and placing him merely at the
threshold between Antiquity and Modernity is his contention that
Bruno conceived his new philosophy as a mere rebirth of the old

Greek philosophy, and that this implied the vision, totally foreign to Modernity's own self-appraisal, of a cyclical, and hence unmodern, conception of history. The flaw of this argument lies in the fact that Bruno's conception of his philosophy as a rebirth of the ancient Greek philosophy in no way proves that he shared its conception of the cyclical 'eternal return'. It will become apparent in the final chapters of this book how radically Bruno's understanding of cosmic history differs from Nietzsche's conception of it as the Eternal Return of the Same, and hence how different his cosmovision is from that of both Nietzsche and the Greeks. Bruno's understanding of his own philosophy as a rebirth of the old Greek one – which indeed endorsed a cyclical conception of nature and history – does in no way prove that he shared this concept. Bruno's cosmovision is progressive, not regressive, evolutionist and non-repetitive, and consequently genuinely modern. Thus, I had no choice but to side with Bruno's own immodest but correct self-evaluation: 'If Copernicus is the dawn, then I am the sun of the New Era.' He already had his two feet squarely on the solid ground of Modernity, and was perfectly aware of it.

Bruno's intense interest in magic is undeniable. But beyond this simple acknowledgement of fact, it is important to explore further the motives for such interest. Frances Yates's cursory explanation was that Bruno was caught up in, and was blindly following, the trend of medieval and Renaissance Hermetic Tradition.[12]

It is true that, after having put the final touches to his philosophical system in Germany, around 1591, Bruno turned his attention again, and more intensely than ever before, to magic. But what were the reasons, we must ask, for this change of direction in Bruno's theoretical speculation? What is the relationship between Bruno's new philosophy and magic? A satisfactory answer to this important question may throw considerable light on Bruno's revolutionary socio-political agenda as well as on the true nature of his entire philosophical endeavor.

This is precisely the question that Frances Yates never asked, and the main reason for her misunderstanding of Bruno and his philosophy. Frances Yates was right in linking Bruno with the humanist Hermetic Tradition; he did share Pico della Mirandola's and Marsilio Ficino's interest in magic, and the reasons for their common interest were, to a large extent, the same. They were convinced that there were powerful hidden forces in nature that had not been discovered yet; that the discovery and manipulation of these forces could become a source of enormous power and an instrument of social transformation; that an entirely new world order would result from the release and efficient utilization of these forces; and that the Aristotelian logic, physics and metaphysics were totally unable to lead to the discovery and manipulation of these forces. It was also their belief that the ancient Egyptians knew about these forces, had developed means to harness them, and that these means were theurgical. They also believed that the Hermetic philosophy (in reality Neoplatonic, not pre-Platonic as they thought) contained in the Corpus Hermeticum was an archaic anticipation of the true philosophy later developed by Plato, Plotinus, and the Neoplatonists. This philosophy contained elements of a philosophy and world view on which the three great monotheistic religions, Christianity, Judaism, and Islam could agree. It would provide the basis for a mutual understanding and tolerance; and perhaps eventually it could even lead to a harmony and peaceful coexistence that would eliminate altogether the wars of religion that were then ravaging Europe and the Levant. This is the reason why Lorenzo de' Medici ordered Ficino to interrupt his translation of Plato so that he could dedicate himself entirely to the translation of some texts of the *Corpus Hermeticum* which had recently been brought to Florence from Constantinople. An acute sense of urgency transpires from this order, particularly if one takes into consideration the enormous importance the Florentine Academy placed on having all of Plato's works translated into Latin.

One thing, however, radically separates Bruno from the Italian Neoplatonic humanists. They had not developed what he had, namely an entirely new philosophical system that undermined and supplanted Aristotelianism as well as Neoplatonism. Whereas the Renaissance humanists of the Hermetic Tradition set their hopes of renewal on magic and the Hermetic philosophy (which was nothing but a late Neoplatonic elaboration), Bruno had worked out, as a result of a colossal intellectual effort, a totally new philosophy and world view in harmony with the latest discoveries of astronomical science. Consequently Bruno's renewed interest in magic after his philosophical system was completed needs to be rethought and reassessed within a totally different frame of reference from that of the Renaissance humanists, and from a completely different perspective than the one Frances Yates used to evaluate Bruno and his work.[13]

My discussion of Bruno's cosmology resulted in a clearer understanding thereof as the heart and core of a more comprehensive, far-reaching, and no less revolutionary new philosophy – the 'philosophy of the Nolan', as the native of the ancient city of Nola in Campania liked to call it. Its scope was universal, for it comprehended ethics, religion, and even the entire European political order. It was a genuinely Nietzschean overturn of all traditional values, which included the daring proposal of a new religion acceptable to all mankind, the rejection of every form of ecclesiastical, political, and intellectual despotism and tyranny, and the appeal to establish permanent peace in a commonwealth of all nations, a new world no longer ravaged by nationalistic greed and senseless religious wars.

My views concerning Bruno's comprehensive cultural revolution, although already vaguely supported by two Italian studies published in the forties by Italian scholars, A. Corsano's *Il pensiero di Giordano Bruno nel suo svolgimento storico* (Florence, 1940), and Luigi Firpo's *Il processo di Giordano Bruno* (Naples, 1949), recently received the strongest confirmation from Michele Ciliberto's insightful study of Bruno's philosophy in his book *Giordano Bruno* (Rome-Bari, 1990). Ciliberto compellingly contends that Bruno had both a mission and a well thought-out strategy to bring about a total revolution of the European *civiltà* (culture and civilization). This final revolution ultimately depended on the favorable reception in Europe of his cosmology, and of its metaphysical foundations, the new Brunian ontology.[14]

What I am sure many readers will find most interesting in Bruno is his passionate interest in knowledge of the universe in an age when the cultural environment was indifferent, if not hostile, to pioneering cosmological speculations. Most fascinating, philosophically, is his undaunted opposition to metaphysical dualism and his firm conviction that monism could provide more satisfactory answers to the questions concerning the relationship between mind, nature, and the universe – questions that have become increasingly pressing in recent years due to the latest astronomical discoveries and cosmological theories concerning the origin, structure, and fate of the universe.

Bruno's defeat was not only a personal one. It was also a severe setback for European culture and civilization. A long overdue correction of the trail blazed by dualistic Platonism – and its most popular form, Christianity, which Nietzsche called 'Platonism for the masses' – was foiled for centuries to come. The birth and development of a sound philosophy of nature was rendered virtually impossible, and the inveterate conception of an extracosmic omnipotent, providential, and benevolent pure Spirit, totally detached from the matter it created, was indelibly stamped on Western minds and allowed to continue, for a very long time, to inspire our art and literature, and to provide the principal foundation for our ethical and social behavior.

In the southern half of the European continent the consequences of Bruno's condemnation were particularly disastrous. The road to Galileo's tragedy was paved by the terror which spread over Catholic European intellectuals after Bruno's execution,[15] and, very soon after the Holy Office decided to forbid the works of Copernicus and Galileo as well, the prominent role in science and culture that Italian universities had played until then started to decline. This sort of scientific and cultural progressive paralysis afflicted not only Italy, but Spain – always in the avantgarde of the Counter-Reformation – and its vast colonial empire as well. Consequently, the center of gravity of scientific research, experimentation, and theory rapidly began to move towards Protestant northern Europe, which was soon to become the principal stage of the Scientific and Industrial Revolutions, and consequently also the zone of the highest concentration of economic and political power.

As a secular humanist, I wish to acknowledge yet another very important motive for my interest in Bruno. I see Bruno as a remarkable modern embodiment of the Greek spirit symbolized in Oedipus, a highly intelligent human being committed to the search for truth, and passionately seeking it to the bitter end, no matter what the consequences for himself might be. Bruno's passion for knowledge, particularly for the highest type of knowledge possible for human beings – of God, nature and the universe – is indeed, as the title of one of Bruno's books accurately defines it, a heroic frenzy (*eroico furore*), a frenzy that is both Apollinean and Dionysian, the former because it was a passion for truth and knowledge, the latter because it led to death and resurrection.

CHAPTER ONE

The Renaissance of Cosmology

Since the dawn of Western philosophy thinkers have been specu-
lating about the universe as a whole. Their speculations about the
cosmos were generally referred to as cosmology. However, after
experimental mathematical science was born in the seventeenth
century, philosophical speculations about the universe quickly
lost much of the authority they had enjoyed until then. They were
discarded as 'metaphysical', a term henceforth increasingly
disreputable, for it was roughly synonymous with 'merely
speculative', that is, an approach utterly incapable of providing
reliable information about the universe due to a method of inquiry
which left no room for experimentation and mathematics. By the
end of that century the philosophers seemed to have definitively
lost the universe to the scientists and those who, despite the radical
change in outlook, persisted in philosophizing about the universe,
were labeled 'cosmologists'. Since most scientists carefully
avoided the type of questions the cosmologists liked to ask, they
had no trouble in keeping those speculations at a safe distance
from their own rigorous scientific theories by dubbing them
merely 'philosophical' or 'metaphysical'.

This situation prevailed for almost two-and-a-half centuries. In
recent years, however, the attitude of physicists towards what
until then they had discarded as being merely metaphysical and
philosophical speculations has changed radically. Cosmology
was summoned out of the closet by the physicists themselves, and
her older sister, cosmogony, suddenly became the queen of the
realm after having been Cinderella for such a long time.

As long as it did not concern itself with the question regarding
the origin of the universe, astrophysics remained a purely empirical science. Cosmology, on the other hand, which had always
been a speculative 'science' (as a matter of fact, judging by

contemporary standards, hardly a science at all), was considered dead and safely buried under the avalanche of empirical data released by nineteenth-century positivistic science.

A quite unexpected comeback, actually a renaissance of cosmology, occurred by the end of the second decade of the twentieth century. It is even possible to indicate precisely the year of its rebirth. It was 1929. From then on it has been increasingly difficult to maintain in vigor the banishment of cosmology from the homeland of science onto the forbidden regions of metaphysics and theology, for a most remarkable discovery was made which put the question regarding the origin of the universe squarely on the territory of science. Even more astonishing was the fact that the discovery forced science to summon cosmology back from exile to the homeland, and, along with cosmology, the metaphysics on which it is based and which had been, until then, the target of so much positivistic contempt and derision. This eventful reversal was brought about by Edwin Hubble's discovery of the expansion of the universe, which Stephen Hawking considers one of the most important intellectual feats of the twentieth century.

It is now common knowledge how this came about. By observing the spectra of distant galaxies, Hubble noticed that, contrary to expectations, most of them were red-shifted; moreover, that the farther away the receding galaxies were from us, the more redshifted their spectra became, an observation which forced him to conclude, on the basis of the Doppler effect, that the galaxies were all moving away from each other, and that the farther away they were from us the faster they seemed to be receding. The inevitable conclusion astonished the scientific world and changed forever our views of the universe. The universe is expanding!

The view of a stable-state universe was so firmly held by all scientists and astronomers before Hubble, that even the genius of Einstein refused to challenge it. But reason had already beaten empirical observation in the race to discover the truth about the universe. Even before Hubble discovered that the universe is expanding, the great Russian physicist, Alexander Friedman, had arrived at the same conclusion.

Ironically, Friedman arrived at this conclusion by taking seriously Einstein's theory of general relativity. In fact, he took it even more seriously than Einstein himself, since for a long time Einstein had refused to believe that the universe is not static, that is, neither expanding nor contracting, but had assumed, for metaphysical (and perhaps also theological) reasons, that it was in a state of balanced equilibrium. The equations of his general theory of relativity, however, clearly postulated an expanding universe. Consequently, in order to uphold both his general theory of relativity and his prejudice that the universe had to be static, Einstein inserted in his equations the so-called 'cosmological constant', so that they would show that the cosmic bodies would not continue their expansion indefinitely. There existed a restraining force, Einstein fancied, in-built in the very fabric of spacetime and hence not attributable to any source of mass/energy, which prevented the cosmic bodies from becoming runaways when they reached a certain distance from each other. This accommodating subterfuge Einstein would later call the greatest mistake of his entire scientific career.

Despite Einstein's staggering authority, Friedman could not bring himself to accept Einstein's patching-up the equations of his general theory of relativity with the artifice of the cosmological constant. Thus, even before Hubble provided experimental evidence for the expansion of the universe, Friedman had theoretically anticipated and predicted it by sticking faithfully to Einstein's equations of general relativity after ridding them of their unwarranted metaphysical contamination.

Now, if the universe is expanding, as Friedman anticipated and Hubble empirically demonstrated, it was reasonable to conclude that, in a distant past, the expanding galaxies had been much closer to one another than they are now, so that imaginatively reversing time we would inevitably arrive at a state of the universe in which all the galaxies and all the matter of the universe had to be exceedingly close to each other, so that the volume of the universe must have been extremely small and, conversely, its density and temperature immeasurable.

Continuing this process of rational extrapolation from scanty empirical evidence, one would perforce arrive retroactively at a point in time in which all the matter of the universe would be at exactly the same point, compressed into an entity most difficult to imagine and most paradoxical, the so-called 'Big Bang singularity', where density and temperature are infinite, and the curvature of spacetime likewise infinite – a cosmic fireball infinitesimally minute, but boundlessly hot and dense, in which, notwithstanding, all the particles, forces, forms and bodies of the universe that were eventually to appear, although actually absent, must have been virtually present – a metaphysical conception remarkably reminiscent of Aristotle's doctrine of act and potency and of Nicholas of Cusa's omnipotent deity which could not but explicate, that is unfold itself, out of its original infinite implication.

In this fashion, contemporary astrophysics underwent a profound transformation; it had become cosmological once more; it dared to speculate and to allow reason to lead the way, ahead of observation and experimentation, renouncing its previous inviolable dictate to proceed exclusively on the basis of hard positive empirical evidence.

Thus, the empirical discovery of an expanding universe led scientists to speculate about the origin of the universe. It also radically changed their ideas about the age of the universe, for henceforth time had to be considered finite. Time had, like the universe, a beginning; as a matter of fact, according to general theory of relativity, spacetime is essentially linked to mass/energy: spacetime does not exist 'outside' or 'before' the appearance of mass/energy in the universe; in fact, it is mass/energy which, so to speak, carries spacetime along with it in its expansion from the initial singularity. Thus the singularity did not enter a pre- existing four-dimensional spacetime ready to accommodate all the expanding mass/energy that burst out of the singularity, as Newton's obsolete concept of absolute space suggested.

The discovery of the expanding universe also radically changed many scientists' concept of space. Thus, in numerous contemporary cosmological models based on the hypothesis of the Big Bang singularity, space, like time, is finite. This finitude, however, is very different from the finitude essential to the Aristotelian-Ptolemaic conception of the perfectly spherical and tightly bounded universe. Although finite, the universe is nevertheless boundless. In Einstein's concept of spacetime, space, in fact, is curved, so that it is possible to travel along and through it indefinitely without ever coming up against an impassable wall.

Indeed, the most notable offspring of the born-again cosmology is the famed Big Bang singularity. It came to the world thanks only to the midwifery of metaphysics, for all empirical knowledge about the origin of the universe was declared impossible by science's very own painful admission that all scientific theories

that have hitherto been developed – in particular the most successful ones to predict phenomena both in the macrocosm of astrophysics and in the microcosm of subatomic particles, namely
Einstein's general theory of relativity and quantum mechanics –
could not be legitimately applied to the Big Bang singularity. They
were utterly incapable of predicting anything certain about its
origin, or for its reasons for expanding the way it does. Einstein's
general theory of relativity, of course, could not be applied, since
the singularity is an infinitesimally small entity. Furthermore,
Einstein's theory of general relativity deals with the force of
gravity on a large scale, and it is commonly agreed that in the
initial singularity the force of gravity had not as yet individuated
itself, since the symmetry of the primordial radiation soup had not
been broken.

The other contemporary authoritative physical theory that
could conceivably be applied to the Big Bang singularity is quantum
mechanics. In contrast to the general theory of relativity, quantum
mechanics does apply to exceedingly small quantities of matter;
in fact its proper field of applicability is precisely that of subatomic
particles. If any contemporary physical theory at all could be
applied to the Big Bang singularity, it had to be quantum mechanics, since it is the only physical theory developed, to date, capable
of dealing with extremely small physical entities, such as the
particles and quanta of the subatomic world. Thus, it is not surprising that the origin of the universe and the vicissitudes of the
primordial singularity eventually became the proper and exclusive domain of speculative quantum cosmology.

Thus, cosmology was born again; but it is only under the
tutelage of quantum mechanics that it has been able to regain
respectability in the scientific world. In fact, speculative cosmology has already become the area of specialization of some of the
most brilliant minds of contemporary astrophysics – the Big Bang
theoreticians – for whom the rules of the game are dictated exclusively by the principles, tenets, and discoveries of quantum
mechanics.

Thus 1929, the year of Hubble's discovery of the expanding
universe, must be regarded as the birthyear of contemporary
cosmology. Since then, cosmology is no longer viewed as the
exclusive province of metaphysics and theology but rather as a
legitimate speculation-field of contemporary physics.

The recent, almost complete takeover of the cosmological domain by quantum mechanics evidences the strong conviction of contemporary astrophysicists that the infinitely large is inextricably linked to the infinitesimally small, and that in order to understand the former, we must first try to unravel the secrets of the latter. Thus, the hopes of gaining insight into the central cosmological problems of the origin of the universe and its probable fate have now been placed almost entirely on the information we are incessantly accumulating about the nature and behavior of the most minute subatomic particles, with the help of extremely powerful particle accelerators and supercolliders. As is well known, the main purpose of the very costly joint project of the United States and Japan to build a giant superconducting supercollider near Houston, Texas, in the next few years, was to gain more knowledge about the origin of the universe. Most unfortunately for science the project has been scrapped by short-sighted federal legislators, and the long subterranean tunnels of the superconducting supercollider are now being turned into allegedly more profitable mushroom hothouses.

But not only quantum mechanics and Einstein's general theory of relativity are forcing the scientific community to revise its habitual adverse stance towards philosophy. A most vigorous push in that direction has recently been given by the sensational discoveries made by chaos-theory. According to this theory, the traditional concept of chaos needs to be redefined. Chaos is no longer just total confusion and disorder, absence of pattern and symmetry, total randomness, and utterly lawless turbulence. Besides this conventional concept of chaos, a novel variation has come to the fore, a sort of 'scientific' chaos. Its most characteristic feature is that it can be generated by an algorithm and hence may be accurately described, for beneath its apparent turbulence it harbors hidden patterns and symmetries. Paradoxically, however, although this strange chaotic 'system' is subject to the law of causality, it does not allow exact and certain predictions about its past or future behavior.

The remarkable thing about such chaos-generating algorithms is that they can no longer be obtained by means of the traditional Laplacian mathematics of classical Newtonian mechanics. The traditional analytic method consisted in breaking down a system into its most elementary constituent parts in order to understand it fully. In a chaotic system, however, if one tries to break it down the usual way, one will see nothing but confused turbulence. On the other hand, if one tells a computer to look at it, the pattern hidden underneath the apparently anarchic turbulence starts to emerge, provided, of course, that the computer has been programmed with the algorithms of a totally different kind of geometry called fractal geometry. What then appears on the screen is indeed astounding: infinite self-containing 'Russian-doll' patterns resembling spiraling snails, ammonites, and sea-horse tails – the Mandelbrot set. Even more astonishing is the fact that similar patterns appear underlying such diverse chaotic systems as eddies of water, clouds, feathers, leaves, galaxies, insect populations, and so forth. Thus the Aristotelian 'form', or rather the Platonic *eidos* – the algorithm in this case – seems to be utterly indifferent to the matter it happens to inform.

Perhaps the most interesting feature of the Mandelbrot set underlying so many different chaotic systems is that their parts, called fractals, seem to be boundless, interrelated, serial, each one of them always including all the following, and always tending to arrange themselves in spiral form. Thus, the configuration that slowly emerges is that of an acentric, spiraling, infinite labyrinth. It is therefore not surprising that the maxima as well as the minima in the universe have such a marked propensity to reproduce this ideal limit-configuration in the spiral galaxy and the double helix of DNA. Even that other awesome acentric labyrinth of nature, the immensely complex and tangled circuitry of the seemingly chaotic system of the human brain with its one hundred billion neurons, is generated by one single algorithm. In the face of this, it is remarkable that not one single cosmological model among the dozens that have been elaborated presents the universe as an eternal, acentric, infinite, spiraling helix.[1]

The conclusion seems to be unavoidable: there is an enormous amount of order and highly complex organization in the universe; indeed there is order even in what until now seemed to us to be so disorganized and disorderly that it was totally inaccessible to any description based on conventional mathematics. But now, when we look at the universe through the eyes of a computer, programmed with the algorithms of fractal geometry, it begins to look very much like the huge integral of an infinite number of algorithms. Order, it seems, is universal and mathematically describable with remarkable precision. Although unquestionably, Newtonian determinism has been dealt a deadly blow by quantum mechanics, in some eerie way Plato's ghost is staging a remarkable comeback. This is, at least, the deep conviction of the eminent physicist, Roger Penrose, who states that when mathematicians communicate, 'communication is possible because each is directly in contact with the same externally existing Platonic world!'[2] And that Platonic world is densely populated by the algorithms responsible for generating scientific chaos as well as all biological systems of organized complexity.

These conclusions of chaos-theory pose a tremendous challenge to well-established conventional scientific views about the scope and nature of scientific discourse and inquiry. For, if we must acknowledge that the universe is saturated with order, then the question is unavoidable: How did this order get into it in the first place? Is there one single source and principle of organized complexity, or are there many? What is this source and principle of organized complexity? Where is it located? Why are new forms and patterns of increasingly complex organization constantly emerging in the universe? And, above all, how is it that in a universe which seems to be racing towards increasingly higher entropy, new oases of order are incessantly being formed?

What all these new insights of the general theory of relativity, quantum mechanics, and chaos-theory are converging towards is a new science of the universe as a whole, a new cosmology, which can no longer be merely empirical, but rather must be highly speculative and philosophical.

Indeed, the great irony of contemporary scientific cosmology is that it has again become metaphysical. If this is so, then Bruno is, for yet another reason, and not the least important one, one of its greatest precursors, for it was precisely with the help of metaphysics, common sense, and observation, that he succeeded in beating Descartes, Kepler, Galileo, and Newton – despite all their vastly superior advantages in mathematics, astronomical technology, and experimentation – to a far more accurate representation of what contemporary scientific cosmology tells us the universe is really like.

The old questions keep recurring and are becoming increasingly more pressing: How did it all begin? How will it end? Is the universe finite or infinite? Is it eternal? Is there only one or are there many, indeed countless other universes? Cosmology is now considered a science, despite its strongly theoretical bent (since it consists of theories focusing on the universe as a whole and it is, of course, impossible to conduct experiments with the universe as a whole). Notwithstanding, contemporary cosmological theories are truly scientific because they are based on the most accurate observation of the macrocosm carried out in computerized observatories equipped with extremely powerful telescopes, as well as on experimentation at the level of the microcosm conducted by powerful particle accelerators and colliders. All new theories must match the observational data, or else they must be abandoned.

Regarding the fact of Bruno's anticipation of the insights of contemporary cosmology and the means he used to attain it, the most fundamental and difficult question is: What is it that enables the human mind to discover the properties of the physical universe as a whole? What we are asking here goes well beyond a fair assessment of Bruno's contribution to our contemporary world view: Is scientific cosmology at all possible without metaphysics?

The way chosen to address this problem is by the exploration of Giordano Bruno's cosmological thought. How was it possible for Bruno's mind to arrive at such insights about the universe that science has taken so long in proving right? What were his epistemological and ontological presuppositions? What was the logic and the dialectics of his cosmological discourse? How does his path resemble or differ from the paths taken by contemporary minds thinking about the universe as a whole? And finally, what does Bruno's fascinating intellectual journey reveal about the ability of the human mind in general to search for cosmological knowledge?

Since there are also some important metaphysical questions about the universe which Bruno asked but contemporary cosmology is not yet asking, we may also want to look at these questions and address some of the speculative problems they raise, such as the remarkable coincidence of some of the fundamental dialectical categories Hegel developed in his *Logic* with the events that are supposed to have occurred in the very first instants of the Big Bang, such as the origin and differentiation of the primordial forces and subparticles (their difference and identity, their qualitative and quantitative otherness, and so on), the unity and interrelatedness of everything in the universe; and, of course, the mind/matter problem, and the problem of God.

These questions obviously cannot be answered by science. They transcend the physical world and our empirical knowledge thereof; in short, they are metaphysical. Indeed, the more we learn about the universe the more we are compelled to ask metaphysical questions. Positivism seems no longer to be able to hold its own against the violent onslaught of metaphysics coming from all sides. Speculative reason is no longer disposed to tolerate its banishment from the realm of science. It is violently rebelling, and its rebellion has already ushered in a major new scientific revolution.

However, before addressing these questions we must first become acquainted with the precursor and founder of modern cosmology, the real protagonist of the revolution inaccurately and unfairly called Copernican. Indeed we must first try to understand the man if we really want to comprehend his thought, for the most recent misunderstandings of Bruno's philosophy arise precisely from an incapacity or an unwillingness to understand his character.

PART ONE

Bruno, The Rebel

CHAPTER TWO

The Outcast Vagabond

Filippo (known later as Giordano) Bruno was born and grew up in Nola, a small and very ancient Italian town, located in one of the most fertile valleys of the Campania, about twelve miles from Naples, with majestic Vesuvius looking down on it from the western horizon. His father, a soldier, owned a small piece of property outside the town. The boy must have enjoyed wandering about freely in that countryside, observing attentively and with growing amazement – as the young Leonardo da Vinci had done one century earlier in his Tuscan landscape – the lavish display of nature's outpouring.

Bruno loved his town so intensely that he would never refer to himself as Italian or Neapolitan, but always as 'the Nolan', despite the fact that in his time Italy and Naples were held in the highest esteem all over Europe. Any other less proud provincial would certainly have boasted of those other more honorable birthplaces when traveling and living abroad, particularly in countries where nobody had ever heard the name of his home town.

Nola, the ancient town founded by the emperor Augustus himself, lay within the boundaries of the Kingdom of Naples. Thus the young Filippo was actually the subject of the intolerant and despotic Spanish King of Naples, whom most Neapolitans regarded as a foreigner and an intruder. The Inquisition had only recently been introduced by the Spanish rulers into the Kingdom of Naples, as a result of the increasing insecurity and hostility of the Spanish Catholics vis-à-vis the Protestant Reformers and the strong encouragement to vigilance emanating from the recently concluded Council of Trent.[1] Bruno, who arrived in Naples as a student and very soon would become a Dominican novice and monk in San Domenico Maggiore, had hardly any reason to consider Naples his homeland, since there was so very little there with which he could identify intellectually or emotionally. In fact, the strong contrast, so early and keenly perceived by young Bruno, between the town of his unrestricted freedom and this subjugated realm, where foreigners reigned and Roman Catholic orthodoxy was upheld and protected with the most ruthless means, must have been a decisive factor in shaping his rebellious character and in bringing about the first manifestations of a most vigorous and uncompromising opposition to all forms of intellectual oppression at the very outset of his ecclesiastical career.

Indeed, it is already in the very first year of his admission into the Dominican Order that the young novice commits his first act of rebellion.[2] To a fellow novice who was insistently urging him to read the pious and devout *Joys of the Virgin*, the young Bruno replied that the best thing he could do was to shelve it and start reading instead the lives of the Church Fathers. The novice was shocked by this rebuff and reported Brother Giordano (the name he chose to be given in the Order) to the Master of Novices. The incident probably would not have had any further consequences had Bruno not committed very soon afterwards another even more objectionable act of rebellion. He decided to remove all the images of saints from his cell and to keep only the Crucifix. This was already going too far. The young novice was reprimanded and threatened with a *scrittura*, a written report containing concrete charges that could be presented to the local Inquisition if no immediate correction ensued.[3] Brother Giordano obliged, but he obviously still had not learned his lesson, for a few years later, while studying theology at the Studio (the free university of Naples), he became involved in a heated dispute with some fellow Dominican theologians who were passing through the city. The subjects of the discussion were the views of Arius and Sabellus – two condemned fourth century heresiarchs who allegedly rejected the orthodox dogma of the Trinity – and Bruno expressed the view that these men simply had not been correctly understood; what they really meant was not so contrary to dogma as was generally supposed.

Bruno's alarming views were, of course, immediately reported to his superiors. This time he must have felt that he was in serious trouble and that action was undoubtedly going to be taken against him, for he decided to flee. He laid down his habit and went directly to Rome, where he was confident he would persuade the

Pope to annul his religious vows on the grounds that he now was convinced that his real calling was to philosophy and science, rather than to theology and preaching. He was quite confident that the Pope would grant his request, for Gregory XIII already knew him. The young Dominican prodigy had previously been invited to demonstrate his stunning gift of memory in the Pontiff's presence. This time, however, the Pope did not show any inclination to grant the request, probably because he had already heard even more alarming rumors about Bruno. Indeed, upon his departure from Naples, Bruno's superiors had found, hidden somewhere in his cell, some books of the Church Fathers Chrysostome and Jerome containing commentaries by the great humanist scholar Erasmus of Rotterdam, who was suspected of siding with the Reformers.

Yet another accusation – this one of extreme gravity – was leveled against Bruno. Allegedly he had been involved in a brawl that resulted in the death of a fellow Dominican monk who drowned in the Tiber. Bruno decided to leave Rome immediately. Had he remained there any longer, he inevitably would have fallen into the hands of the Roman Inquisition. The rebel had crossed his Rubicon. He had broken definitively with his Order and with the Church. He would never see Rome again as a free man. When he came back seventeen years later, he was already in chains.

From the day Bruno left Rome, a free man, until he was brought back in fetters, he wandered in Europe from one city to another without rest, seeking for what he cherished most in life: freedom to think, teach, discuss privately and publicly, and publish whatever he believed was true. This incessant and passionate quest for freedom is the key to understanding all of Bruno's arrivals at the more than twenty cities he visited in seventeen years of wanderings, and all of his sudden departures from them.

In his precipitous flight from Rome, it would have seemed logical for Bruno to go to Florence, which was on his way. There he would have found the best opportunities to earn a living, and his freedom would have been safeguarded by the independence and proud autonomy of the Tuscan Duchy. But the ducal Florence of 1577 was no longer the republican Florence of the Quattrocento (fifteenth century). The Grand Duke of Tuscany, Francesco I, had married Archduchess Joanna of Austria, who 'imposed on her court and public life the strict, cold and elaborate etiquette which were the custom at the court of Spain'.[4] The Grand Duke himself was totally absorbed in his amateur chemistry. He even spent most of his time in his private laboratory where 'he soon started receiving his ministers . . . and discussed the affairs of state without having to interrupt his surveillance of his oven, test tubes, and flasks'. Thus, it is understandable that Bruno was not willing to try his fortune and to begin a new life in a city where he had so little chance of getting through to those who, although they may have had the power to protect him from his Roman persecutors, almost certainly had not the slightest interest in so doing.

It is somewhat intriguing that the very first city on the list of Bruno's sojourns in Italy after his departure from Rome is Noli, a very small town almost identical in name to his own beloved home town. One wonders how Bruno got there from Rome in the first place, for Noli is a small port located on the Italian Riviera. Genoa, the busy port of the great Republic, is the first city we are told he reached after leaving Rome. Thus, it is almost certain that he got there by boat, for there is no recorded evidence of his stopping at the intervening cities. This sea voyage underscores his haste to get out as soon as possible from the Papal States, which at that time covered almost half of central Italy.

Despite the obvious advantages of Genoa for his immediate plans, Bruno did not stay there long, probably because the plague was already taking a heavy toll from the city dwellers.[5] Noli, the little port located only fifty miles south-west from Genoa, seemed a safer choice.

After spending four months in Noli (earning enough money to survive by teaching astronomy to the local and Genoese nobility, and grammar to their children), Bruno headed north-east along the coast to Savona, a larger town almost halfway between Noli and Genoa. After only two weeks there, he headed north, this time to Turin, once more avoiding plague-stricken Genoa. Since he did not find satisfactory living conditions there either, he decided to take a boat along the Po to Venice. It is not certain whether his decision to go to Venice was due to his hopes of still finding in Italy the safe place he needed to speak and publish freely, or rather to find in the wealthy republic the financial resources he needed to go abroad. In any case, it was there, in Venice, where Bruno had his first work published. It was a booklet titled *De' segni de' tempi*

(On the Signs of the Times), and he tells us that he had it printed in order to get some money to sustain himself.[6] However, in spite of his initial success in Venice, Bruno was much more interested in the nearby university city of Padua, for Padua was, in fact, at that time, one of the most prestigious universities of Europe, and one particularly enticing for Bruno, since Copernicus had studied medicine and learnt Greek there (1501–03), and Padua had been for many years the center of violent confrontations between Humanists and Aristotelians.

So, after a sojourn of eight weeks in Venice, Bruno decided to move to Padua, but he did not stay there long either. We do not know the reasons for his decision to leave the city so soon after his arrival, but there are reasons to suspect that his decision was influenced by the strong presence and influence of the Dominican Order in Padua. In his testimony before the Venetian Inquisition the only information Bruno gave about his stay in Padua was that some Dominican friars of his acquaintance, whom he encountered there, urged him to start wearing again the Dominican habit, even if he had no intention of going back to the Order again, 'for reasons of convenience'. Bruno followed their advice. It had now become perfectly clear to him that Italy offered no safe haven to a defrocked monk and priest running around in civilian clothes.

Now, fully determined to leave Italy as soon as possible, Bruno left Padua for Bergamo and purchased there a cheap white robe over which he started wearing the Dominican scapulary he had kept all along. The advantages of wearing the prestigious Dominican habit in Italy were obvious. Bruno desperately needed money for survival, and the habit served well the purpose of facilitating gratuitous accommodation, of procuring alms from affluent benefactors, and of commending him for teaching assignments similar to those he had performed at Noli. Bruno had already broken definitively with his religious order and was determined never again to ask for readmission. Consequently, his decision to wear the Dominican habit again cannot be construed as a sign of repentance or even of hesitation; it was clearly a matter of expediency, a means to an end, and indeed a very understandable one. And the stratagem did work stupendously, for on his way to Lyon, the most prosperous city in the south of France, he stopped at Chambéry, the capital of Savoy. There he lodged, during the entire harsh winter of 1578–79, in the Dominican convent!

Despite the considerable benefits Bruno derived from the generous hospitality of the Savoyan Dominicans during his long sojourn in the convent, Bruno was surprised and hurt by the cold and very reserved treatment he received in Savoy. The animosity he sensed there was, as he was told by a fellow Italian priest, not at all personal, but due rather to a widespread and deep antipathy towards Italians. As a matter of fact, his friend told him, 'the farther you travel inland, the worse the hostility gets, so you'd better forget about Lyon and go to Switzerland instead . . . to Geneva, I would suggest'. Now Geneva was the bastion of Calvinism, so that Bruno's decision to follow his friend's advice and go there to live and study reveals a lot about his new stance towards the Catholic Church and of his readiness to defy it. In fact, the entire Geneva experience will reveal to us for the first time, clearly and fully, the nature, extent, and intensity of Bruno's rebellion.

If the Dominican habit and scapulary had been quite useful for Bruno in Catholic Italy and Savoy, in Calvinist Geneva not only were they totally useless, but they could easily become a liability. So Bruno put the habit away and started to wear cape, hat, and sword, which he received from generous Italian benefactors who had formed an Evangelical community there. He was of course asked by them if he, too, had come to Geneva to become a Calvinist, but he prudently answered them that this was not really his motive, since he knew very little about the new religion. His main purpose had been to be there to 'live in freedom and be secure'[7].

Unfortunately for him, Bruno discovered very soon how illusory his high hopes had been. Geneva was anything but the haven of freedom. Religious fanaticism and intolerance reigned there unabated and even more unchallenged than in Naples and Rome, and, because he dared to challenge it, he ended up in the very place he had tried so desperately to avoid all along in Italy: jail, for the crime of exercising a non-existent freedom of speech.

This is how it happened: Bruno started to attend lectures at the Academy of Geneva. In one of these lectures, held by De la Faye, a highly respected and authoritative Calvinist professor, Bruno had no trouble in counting at least twenty errors in the man's discourse. Totally unable to keep his mouth shut, Bruno decided to publish a pamphlet publicly exposing the professor's blunders – a crime so unforgivable for Calvinist academicians that Bruno

was immediately arrested and summoned to recant. Quite familiar with what the Calvinists were capable of doing, and ready to
do, with dissenters – thirty-five years before they had burnt right
there the Spaniard Miguel Servet, the discoverer of the circulation
of the blood, on the grounds that he challenged the Calvinist
dogma of the Trinity – Bruno recanted, apologized, and left Geneva for good. His flirtations with Calvinism were definitively
over[8]; and now, despite the alleged aloofness and coldness of the
French towards the Italians, Bruno had no choice but to try his
luck in France and to look for a place there where he could live in
freedom and feel secure. Fortunately for him, he found a place. It
was Toulouse.

Bruno was well received and well treated in Toulouse. The
university was held in high esteem and the intellectual climate
was tolerant, due in part to the strong Huguenot (French Protestant) presence in that south-western region of France. At first, he
was invited to give astronomy lessons ('the Sphere') to some
scholars there, but what he really wanted was to become a regular
philosophy professor at the university. However, for that position,
his doctoral degree in theology was not sufficient. He needed to
become a 'Master of Arts'. He promptly succeeded in this, for
when the position of ordinary lector in philosophy became vacant,
he applied for it and easily won his appointment in a public
defense.

Bruno had achieved his goal. He was now authorized to teach
philosophy at university level. For two years he taught Aristotle's
treatise *De anima* and 'other subjects' as well. We do not know
exactly what these other subjects were, but from later references
by Bruno to some highly controversial lectures he held at
Toulouse, it is safe to assume that they were polemics against
Aristotle and the mathematicians, the favorite targets of his
intellectual invectives.

When the religious civil wars broke out in Toulouse, Bruno had
to abandon the city and his position at the university. However,
after that initial successful experience as a regular philosophy
professor, Bruno was ready for the supreme challenge: Paris and
its university, Europe's most prestigious center of learning. Only
his uncompromising honesty and rebelliousness prevented him
from becoming there an ordinary professor of philosophy. All
university professors at the Sorbonne were required to attend

Mass. Bruno, however, who had been excommunicated for apostasy, refused to submit to this requirement. This automatically barred him from becoming a regular professor in Paris, despite the fact that he was considered highly qualified to become one.

Bruno did not give up. After the Toulousian experience, he was now more determined than ever to wage a total war against the Aristotelians. Since the university of Paris was the inexpugnable fortress of Aristotelianism in Europe, if he succeeded in discrediting it there, he would have won a far-reaching and decisive victory.

Bruno's weapons in his war against Aristotelianism were formidable. He was naturally endowed with a stunning memory, which he had drilled to perfection using the mnemonic techniques he had learned from an assiduous study of Ramon Lull[9]. Bruno's most diligent research and attentive examination of Lull's work started in Toulouse, where the great Catalonian philosopher was well known and admired. Immediately after earning his professorial chair at that university, Bruno started lecturing on Lull's art of memory; and as soon as he arrived in Paris, the very first extraordinary lecture he gave was about the thirty divine attributes, also inspired by Lull's 'Art'.

In addition to his prodigious memory, Bruno spoke and wrote Latin fluently and elegantly; he was a skillful polemicist; he had a thorough knowledge of Thomas Aquinas, Aristotle and his commentators, and was widely read in the Church Fathers. He was conversant in theology, mathematics, alchemy, and magic. Above all, he had discovered the Achilles' heel of Aristotelianism: its geocentric cosmology, as well as the most effective weapon to bring it down – Copernicus' heliocentric theory. Sure of his victory, Bruno had only to wait for a favorable opportunity to launch his attack. Nevertheless, first he had to secure and consolidate his position in Paris.

Despite his obvious advantages, Bruno still had serious obstacles to overcome. First of all, he was practically alone not only against the Parisian Scholastic academicians, but also against the entire intellectual world of Christian Europe. Furthermore, he was a foreigner, an Italian who dared to denounce loudly, in the host country, what was dearest and most precious to its intellectual élite: the philosophers and theologians of their most prestigious university. And, to top it all, Bruno was known to be an apostate priest, an ex-Dominican friar who dared to challenge the theology of the most brilliant theologian who had ever taught at that very same University of Paris, his fellow Dominican, Thomas Aquinas.

It was, therefore, opportune and clever of Bruno to choose precisely Thomas as the principal author for his first lecture at the Sorbonne and, as subject matter, a theological theme: the attributes of God, for indeed there was little here to quarrel about with Aristotle. As basis for his commentary he chose the first part of Aquinas's *Summa theologiae*. Bruno himself later candidly revealed the motive for his first academic performance in Paris: to make himself known and to prove himself as a knowledgeable Thomist and a powerful thinker to the professors and students of the Parisian university.

Bruno must have performed this job to everybody's satisfaction, for after having delivered his thirty 'extraordinary' theological lectures, he was asked to give a series of 'ordinary' lectures. This he refused to do because it was required from all ordinary professors that they regularly attend Mass and the Divine Offices. He was exposed by this refusal and would, at the same time, have been blocked from advancing any further had he not received unexpected help from a most powerful patron. The King of France, Henry III, had heard of his brilliant lectures and prodigious memory. He summoned Bruno to his presence and asked him bluntly if he owed his astonishing memory to some occult powers of magic. Bruno reassured him, protesting that his exceptional mnemonic skills were not attributable to magic; what nature had given him he had perfected with the techniques of the Lullian art of memory. The King was satisfied and impressed, and Bruno knew that his great opportunity had finally arrived. He quickly published a book on memory and dedicated it to the King of France.[10] His strategy worked perfectly. King Henry appointed him promptly to the position of 'extraordinary' professor at the University of Paris. Bruno had finally reached a position from which he thought he could safely launch his attack on Aristotelianism.

Only one thing was still missing, indeed an indispensable requirement for the success of his plans. However aware Bruno was of the flaws of Aristotelianism, and however capable he was of refuting Aristotle's errors in public disputations, he still had not elaborated a cosmology coherent and compelling enough to challenge successfully and eventually supplant the Aristotelian and Ptolemaic cosmology. In any case it was clear to Bruno that a cosmology far more convincing than Copernicus' heliocentric one had to be worked out before an open confrontation with the Aristotelian forces could be risked. In this respect, he was still unprepared and hence quite vulnerable, for none of the works he had published in France dealt directly with the cosmological problem.[11]

Both the religious tensions and the intellectual climate in Paris made it very difficult for Bruno to find his way to a clear conceptualization and coherent articulation of all the ontological and cosmological ideas which he had been pondering, ever since he read Copernicus' treatise on the revolution of the heavenly bodies. It was Elizabethan England, with its more liberal outlook and its encouragement and support of thinkers, who critically challenged Roman and Spanish counter-reformationist orthodoxy that provided the environment Bruno needed to help him bring to full maturity the ideas that would successfully oppose and eventually undermine the Aristotelian positions. In any case, it had become perfectly clear to him that a cosmology, philosophically far more compelling than Copernicus' controversial heliocentric astronomy, would have to be worked out before any serious attempt could be made to launch a frontal assault on Aristotelianism.

Unexpectedly, in the spring of 1583, the opportunity presented itself for Bruno to go to England and to stay there for some time. By the time he was forced by circumstances to leave again, two years later, the foundations of his philosophical edifice had been firmly laid, and the edifice itself already showed the basic structure and many of the distinctive features of the definitive form it reached upon its completion in Germany. Only after the English sojourn and experience was Bruno ready for the confrontation with the Aristotelian camp in Paris, and, in fact, the attack was launched as soon as he returned there. However, first we have to look closely into Bruno's activity during his stay in England, mainly because his English experience proved to be crucial for the development of his philosophy, but also because recently it has been grossly misrepresented.

CHAPTER THREE

The Rebel's Cause

Bruno was most fortunate to find the ideal working conditions at the residence of the French ambassador, Michel de Castelnau, Marquis de Mauvissière, who, following the French King's orders, had invited Bruno to be his guest in London. Except for the time he spent in Oxford, Bruno lived in the French embassy until the end of his sojourn in England. There he found the peace and quiet he needed to think and write without the disturbances of the academic life. Occasionally, he accompanied the ambassador on his visits to the court where he had the opportunity of making the acquaintance of numerous influential and intellectually curious noblemen.

Once in England, Bruno's immediate objective was the same as he had set for himself in Geneva, Toulouse, and Paris, namely, to make himself known and to seek acceptance as a philosophy professor in the realm's highest institution of learning. But this was only a means to an end. His ultimate goal was to launch, from a reputable position of eminence, a devastating attack on Aristotelianism, which was the philosophy espoused and defended at practically all European universities.

In his highly controversial book on Bruno, John Bossy alleges that it is not clear to him 'why he [Bruno] was going to England'[1]. The most plausible motive for the trip, the most consistent with Bruno's goals since he left Italy, namely to become a regular faculty member of a major university and to teach his philosophy there, obviously does not square with Bossy's outlandish contention that Bruno's main activity in England was to spy on his host, the French ambassador in London. But the fact that Bruno considered Oxford the best university in the world[2] strongly suggests what his real motive was for accepting Castelnau's invitation.

Bossy's naive interpretation of Bruno's motives, namely 'that he was certainly glad to see England, and the prospect of getting time to write without having to give lectures was as welcome to him as to any other academic'[3], sounds like a rather amusing projection of what the writer's own motives would have been in similar circumstances. Bossy's blindness to Bruno's true character may be the main reason why he fancies Bruno celebrating Mass and hearing confessions at the French embassy in London as a sacrilegious cover for his spying activities. There was nothing in the world Bruno wanted more than to be allowed to teach philosophy at Oxford. It was only when he failed in his attempt to achieve this goal that he withdrew to the embassy and started writing his Italian dialogues there.

Bruno's first major open confrontation with the Aristotelian philosophers (Bruno usually referred to them as 'pedants') took place in Oxford. An overzealous, almost fanatical devotion to Aristotle was at that time nowhere more intense than at the University of Oxford. From our present perspective, it seems incredible that there was a time when, at the very institution that has become the symbol of the most open and advanced scholarship and research in the world, every bachelor and master who dared to diverge from Aristotle's *Organon*, or violate any point of it, was fined five shillings!

Such was the institution at which Bruno decided to seek acceptance as a philosophy professor. With this purpose in mind he handed to the printer some opuscles he had already prepared and sent them to the Vice-Chancellor along with a rather bizarre letter of application full of self-praise. Despite the fact that the letter, coming from a foreigner, a commoner, and a defrocked Papist priest, must have sounded intolerably arrogant and defiant to genteel English ears, Bruno was accepted and allowed to teach at the university.

At Oxford, Bruno no longer needed to prove himself as a knowledgeable theologian and a specialist in Thomas Aquinas, for he had been given license to teach precisely what he was really interested in – philosophy and cosmology. Bruno had already given university lectures on Aristotle's *De anima* and the immortality of the soul at Toulouse, but never, until now, had he taught cosmology at university level, although he had given private lessons on the 'Sphere' in Noli. In August 1583, he started a series of public lectures on cosmology: the five spheres (*quintuplici sphaera*) and the immortality of the soul. The subjects he chose to lecture on happened to be precisely the most liable to get him into a lot of trouble, since they were the two pet subjects of the Oxford Aristotelians.[4] Bruno surely must have felt he was ready for the confrontation, otherwise he would have proceeded with more caution, if indeed his main objective was to gain a secure foothold at Oxford.

In any case, Bruno's decision to teach cosmology from an anti-Aristotelian perspective is a clear indication that, already very early in his English sojourn, he had a strong interest in the cosmological model proposed by Copernicus. What he had felt so inhibited to bring up in Paris, he now felt free to teach, discuss, and publicly defend at Oxford.

As was to be expected, it was not long before Bruno's speculative audacities and virulent anti-Aristotelian tirades aroused hostility among students and professors alike, and prompted some of his colleagues to challenge him to a public debate. This turned out to be much more than a heated academic polemic over some speculative issue; it was a public declaration of war, the beginning of a life-long single-handed crusade to undermine and definitively discredit Aristotelianism, destroy its unchallenged hegemony, and eventually evict it from all higher centers of learning. Bruno describes the stormy confrontation most vividly in his *Ash Wednesday Supper*:

> These are the fruits of England; and search as much as you wish, you will find all of them to be doctors in grammar in these our days, in which there reigns in the happy fatherland a constellation of pedantic, most obstinate ignorance and presumption mixed with a boorish rudeness which would cause Job's patience to waver; and if you don't believe it, go to Oxonia [Oxford], and have them tell you the things that happened to the Nolan when he publicly disputed with those doctors in theology in the presence of the Polish prince Alasco [Laski] and others of the English nobility. Have them tell you how his arguments were answered; how that poor doctor, whom they put in front as a coriphaeus of the academy in this grave occasion, remained fifteen times through fifteen arguments like a chick in the tow. Have them tell you with how much rudeness and discourtesy that pig proceeded, and with how much patience and humanity that other one, who actually demonstrated

to be a native Neapolitan raised under a more benign sky. Have
them inform you how they made him put an end to his public
lectures, and to those on the immortality of the soul and on the five
spheres.[5]

Bruno had to interrupt his lectures and leave the university altogether. This was an extremely humiliating experience for him, for
he had also been accused of plagiarizing the famous Florentine
philosopher Marsilio Ficino in three of his lectures. However,
despite the high plausibility of some casual nonchalance on the
part of Bruno, in supporting his arguments with the appropriate
authorities, evidently the real motives for his troubles in Oxford
were of a very different nature. According to Bruno the reason
why he was forced to stop lecturing at Oxford was not his alleged
plagiarizing of Ficino, but his virulent attack on Aristotle.

Bruno's failure at Oxford, however, had one significant good
result: it gave him a lucid awareness of his mission and the most
suitable means to accomplish it. From then on, there would be no
more diplomatic compromises, no more cautious restraint in his
rebellion against the academic pedants. His enemies had now
been clearly identified – the Aristotelians and the mathematicians,
the latter because of their disdain for natural philosophy and their
responsibility in upholding Ptolemaic geocentrism for fourteen
hundred years (indeed even Copernicus' errors Bruno attributed
to his excessive reliance on mathematics). The main weapons to
combat them had also been discovered: books, rather than sterile
academic disputes with university pedants, and books written in
the vernacular for laymen to read and understand, not in the Latin
jargon of the Scholastics. Indeed, if he was to have any success at
all, he now understood he had to address an entirely different
public, the non-academic intellectual elite of England, and later
on, of continental Europe.

Thus, Bruno's Oxford experience, however painful and frus-
trating – the doors to the academic life had been definitively shut
for him in England – can now be seen as the decisive turning point
in his career. He understood the utter futility of further trying to
make himself heard and respected by the Aristotelian professors
at Oxford. On the other hand, the warm reception and the honors
he had already received in France at the court of King Henry III
convinced him of the need to change his target audience and his

prospective readers from narrow-minded academicians to the highly educated nobility at the court of Queen Elizabeth. This explains his decision to write in his native Italian, a language then highly in esteem at the Elizabethan court. The Queen herself, who spoke Italian fluently, on several occasions talked about philosophy with Bruno. He also adopted a new literary genre for his writings – the Platonic dialogue – which was more elegant and certainly more entertaining than the traditional dry philosophical treatise written in Latin.

As indicated in the Introduction, considering the possible influence that the most recent book on Bruno published in English, John Bossy's *Giordano Bruno and the Embassy Affair*, may have on its readers, it is deemed necessary to discuss in more detail some of Bossy's allegations concerning Bruno's activities during his stay at the French embassy in London.

Bossy alleges that Henri Fagot, the embassy's chaplain, whom he arbitrarily identifies with Bruno, became the confidant of the French ambassador's secretary 'as soon as he entered the house' (20) (notwithstanding the fact that Bruno was the ambassador's special guest upon the recommendation of the King of France), and that the secretary promptly declared himself willing to pass on to him all the information he could get concerning the ambassador's secret correspondence, including the most sensitive one with Mary Queen of Scots, then Queen Elizabeth's prisoner. The secretary allegedly did not stop here; he told Fagot-Bruno 'that he could arrange for Walsingham to see the contents of packets going to Mary, to put in or take out whatever he thought fit, and to see that they were resealed so that Mary would not know that they had been seen' (19–20). Perhaps the real Fagot was that lucky, but it is hard to believe that the ambassador's French secretary, Nicolas Leclerc, seigneur de Courcelles, would so readily and so soon have put his total confidence – and his head! – in the hands of a perfect stranger, an Italian defrocked priest and monk with no money to pay him for his invaluable services. Furthermore, there was no guarantee that he would keep his mouth shut in a heinous conspiracy against his host and the King of France, who had graciously recommended him to his ambassador's care and protection. Truly, this would strain even a child's gullibility.

But Bossy goes further. He even fancies that it was Fagot-Bruno

himself who recruited the seigneur de Courcelles as a mole for
Walsingham! (20). This, of course, would imply that Bruno, for no
conceivable reason at all, except perhaps money, would have
dared to risk everything he had so strenuously been striving for
all his life by imprudently making overtures to a treacherous
French aristocrat who could very well one day turn around
against him and denounce him to his master. Bossy doesn't seem
to have any qualms about making the Italian guest and protegé of
the French ambassador in London a spy for the English Crown
and a despicable traitor against his devoted friends and benefactors 'as soon as he entered the house'. For, if Bossy's allegations
were true, what a wretched and contemptible individual this
Bruno must indeed have been, and how worthy of the miserable
death to which Pope Clement VIII and his Jesuit chief theologian[6]
delivered him. Not surprisingly, Bossy's malicious epilogue to his
novel reads 'Fagot at the Stake'. Obviously, Bossy felt it was
necessary and worth his while to go into all that trouble to try once
more to exonerate the Pope and his Jesuit saint for their shameful
and unforgivable crime.

In order to prove his point and conclusively identify Bruno
with the shady priest and chaplain of the embassy, Henri Fagot,
Bossy does not shy away from having Bruno assiduously perform
in London precisely those very priestly functions he had always
scrupulously avoided after leaving his Order, namely, to celebrate
Mass and hear confessions. In his testimony to the Venetian
Inquisition, Bruno declared under oath, 'I stayed in England two
and a half years, during which time, although Mass was celebrated
in the house, I did not go to it, nor did I go outside to Mass or to
sermons, for the reason already stated [I have always avoided this,
knowing that I was excommunicate because I had left my order
and abandoned the habit]'. Nor did any witness ever testify having seen Bruno hearing confessions or celebrating Mass. However,
Bossy dismisses Bruno's testimony as a lie (79), and, totally blind
to Bruno's mettle, does not shy away from considering it possible
that Fagot-Bruno heard, in the embassy, the confession of a man
called Zubiaur, who confided that he had taken a religious vow
to assassinate the Queen (36). Bruno, then, immediately reported
to the Queen, in writing,[7] what he had heard in confession under
the seal of the sacrament (35). Even if Fagot had dared to invent
the tale only to gain favor with the Queen, as Bossy himself is

inclined to believe[8], the story could not have been believed by the Queen unless she knew that Fagot-Bruno was the embassy's chaplain who regularly heard confessions and celebrated Mass at the French embassy. However, even if Fagot-Bruno did hear Zubiaur's confession, and dared to fabricate the story of his assassination plan, as Bossy suggests, would he have been so demented as to admit, and certify by writing, to the Queen of England that he, priest and official chaplain at the French embassy, had committed the abominable crime of breaking the inviolable seal of confession? Would he not inevitably have earned, by revealing his criminal deed, rather than her favor, the Queen's certain contempt and mistrust? For, if his story was believed in Court, *ipso facto* he would have been considered a criminal and foul priest. Moreover, if Zubiaur were arrested and tortured, and found out to be innocent, Bruno's favor with the Court would have ended right then and there. On the other hand, if the story were not believed, he had to be considered either a madman or a fool. In any case, and this is what really matters, the monster Bossy created was capable of despicable treason to his friends and of inducing the arrest and execution of countless others, including fellow-priests (145). He also seems to have had no qualms in revealing to the Queen a secret heard in confession, knowing that the revelation of that secret inevitably would lead to the arrest and execution of the penitent who had put all his trust in him. Bossy's allegations are simply preposterous and completely miss the point of the true character of the historical Bruno.

After conclusively 'proving' that Bruno and the chaplain of the French embassy are one and the same person in what is undoubtedly one of the most remarkable *tours de force* recently accomplished by an historian, Bossy's detective story relaxes into an attempt to discredit Bruno's character. Everything else ever written to denigrate Bruno (and truly it has been abundant) pales in the face of all the villainies Bossy subsequently heaps over Bruno's head, particularly in the last chapter of his book, 'Bruno Recaptured' and in the Epilogue, 'Fagot at the Stake', in which he proceeds to size him up. After pages of fastidious minutiae and wild speculations, this is unquestionably the most amusing part of the otherwise tedious novel. The delightfully comical irony of Bossy's strenuous endeavor is that a modern English pedant should try so hard to get even with Bruno for bashing English

pedants three centuries ago by masterfully wielding once more
the very same weapon which Bruno then derided, pedantry. But,
before we put Mr. Bossy definitively to rest, let us quote one of the
few true and fair things he says about Bruno: 'Giordano Bruno
was one of the most creative minds of the sixteenth century, and
possibly in the history of European thought and imagination'
(138). Now this is precisely what I have set out to show in this
book, and it is a real pity that Mr. Bossy did not dedicate his efforts
and talent to proving this rather than to portraying Bruno as a
despicable scoundrel.

Let us turn our attention back to the real Bruno and the philosophical relevance of his English sojourn and experience. It was
in England where Bruno for the first time became fully aware of
his powers, of the utter originality of his philosophy, of its revolutionary potential, and of his own historical mission. By the end
of 1584, the Brunian philosophy – or as he preferred to call it, the
philosophy of the Nolan – was virtually complete. In an amazingly
short period, of time extending from the late summer of 1583 to
the end of the next year, Bruno had written three major cosmological dialogues, and his most important ethical dialogue, *The Expulsion of the Triumphant Beast*. The choice of the language, as well as
the literary genre of his writings, signaled a decisive turnabout in
Bruno's life and career.

Bruno became aware of his own new philosophy, in London,
some time between the first and second drafting of *La cena* (The
Ash Wednesday Supper), his first cosmological dialogue. Although his basic insights had been inspired and stimulated by
the study and favorable reception of Copernican astronomy (in
particular of the Polish astronomer's verification of the movement of the Earth), very soon they became independent and
original precisely because of Bruno's strong disagreement with
Copernicus' heliocentrism. He saw the cause, for Copernicus'
inability to develop a cosmology in harmony with his otherwise
revolutionary astronomical insights about the solar system, in
his uncritical acceptance of the principles of the 'common and
vulgar philosophy, or rather blindness' (an obvious reference to
Aristotelianism and the cosmology it was inextricably associated
with). He was also convinced that Copernicus' inability to
undertake a fundamental criticism of the Aristotelian
cosmological tenets was due to his predominantly mathematical,

rather than physical, approach ('physical' in the sense of natural philosophy).

Thus the 'Nolan philosophy' which had come to full maturity in England was the first new philosophical system elaborated in Europe after the publication of the Copernican astronomical hypothesis; it was also the first one to build upon Copernican heliocentrism, only to quickly overcome it with an even more revolutionary image of the universe. However, Bruno's cosmology had been germinating in his spirit at least since the composition of *De umbris idearum* (On the Shadows of Ideas) in Paris. In this Latin treatise Bruno explains in detail his concept of the soul of the world (*anima mundi*), which is central to his philosophy:

> Hence in order for you to acquire a consummate and absolute art, it behooves you to copulate with the soul of the world, and once you have copulated with it, to act, for it is teeming with rational forms, and it generates a world full of similar rational forms. And these forms (Plotinus would agree) shape and form in seed everything that exists, like tiny worlds. Hence since the soul is everywhere present, all of it in the whole and in every part of it as well, you may be able to behold, as the condition of matter will allow, in every thing, no matter how small and cut off, the world, not to speak of the semblance of the world, so that we may without fear say with Anaxagoras that everything is in everything.[9]

Although Bruno was perfectly aware of the originality and novelty of his philosophy, he preferred to view it as a 'recovery' or 'rebirth' (renaissance) of the old and true philosophy of the Pre-Socratics – Parmenides, Heracleitus, Anaxagoras, and Democritus – as well as of Epicurus, Lucretius, Plotinus, and Hermes Trismegistos.

Bruno's cosmology was only a part of his new philosophy, which actually embraced all the traditional fields and disciplines of philosophy: ontology, natural theology, cosmology, psychology, and ethics; but not only was this cosmology part of the new philosophy, it was also its foundation and justification, its *raison d'être*. Just as the 'common and vulgar philosophical systems' were intimately associated with their particular cosmologies, so too Bruno's new philosophy was intimately connected and utterly dependent upon his new vision of the universe. This philosophy – a totally new cosmovision – was meant and bound to replace the old one. Accordingly, Bruno saw himself as the herald and evangelist of this new philosophy, for he understood he had a mission, not only to convince the world of its truth, but to initiate and propel the profound upheaval in human society that it made absolutely necessary, and to prepare the coming and establishment of a totally new ethical and socio-political world order. But this, of course, implied a total revaluation, a radical overturn of the prevailing values.

Thus, Bruno was fully aware of the unlimited revolutionary potential of his philosophy. A sweeping revolutionary project matured in his mind. The new cosmovision made indispensable not only an entirely new philosophy, but a totally new world as well. This, of course, implied a new ethical system, a new socio-political order, even a new religion, capable of being universally accepted and one which would no longer be the cause of religious wars and religious intolerance and persecution. The fact is generally overlooked that the ethical revolution, which Bruno contemplated, is one of the most radical projects of revaluation undertaken by any Western thinker before Nietzsche.[10]

Bruno's sudden awareness of his mission is reflected in the highly self-confident, overbearing, almost ecstatic tone of his self-praise: 'Behold the one who has traversed the air, penetrated the sky, cruised the stars . . .' and who,

> . . . in the face of every sense and reason, opened, with the key of the most diligent research, such cloisters of truth that can be opened by us; cloaked and veiled nature bared at last: he has given eyes to the moles, illumined the blind who could not fix their eyes and look at their images in so many mirrors held up to them; loosened the tongues of the mute who could not and dared not explain their intricate feelings. Restored the lame who could not make with their spirit that progress which the ignoble and dissoluble composite is incapable of making.

This exalted self-praise, couched in unmistakable evangelical imagery and so reminiscent of Kepler's jubilant self-panegyric upon discovering the laws of planetary motion, rather than the alarming onset of paranoia, reveals a lucid awareness of a momentous discovery and a pressing mission to reveal it to the world.

When the French ambassador, Castelnau, was summoned back

to France, Bruno went back to Paris with him. He was now ready, after the fecund English experience, to confront the French Aristotelians openly. In fact, in a most defiant way which seemed deliberately to emulate the arrogant challenges of Pico della Mirandola in Rome and of Luther in Wittenberg, Bruno published his *One Hundred and Twenty Articles on Nature and the World Against the Peripatetics* [Aristotelians]. He then invited the royal lecturers and challenged the professors, and anyone who wished to oppose him, to an open disputation in the famous Collège de Cambrai. Bruno felt confident of his victory now that he had fully developed his own cosmology in the Italian dialogues published in England. After his lecture, raising his voice, he challenged each and everyone in the audience to refute him and defend Aristotle. Since nobody stirred, almost sure now of his victory, he raised his voice even higher. But then the unexpected happened. A young lawyer, Rodolphus Calerius, stood up and with great serenity said that everybody had kept quiet simply because they thought Bruno unworthy of a response. He then started to defend Aristotle refuting one by one what he called Bruno's calumnies against the great philosopher. When he finished, there was a roar of approval. The young lawyer then challenged Bruno to respond to his arguments and to defend himself. Bruno must have then realized that his cause was lost, for he remained silent and left the Collège in a hurry.

Anybody who reads the Italian dialogues very soon becomes aware of Bruno's unshakeable conviction about Aristotle's gross errors in physical and cosmological matters and the overwhelming superiority of Copernicus' heliocentric hypothesis, and of the irresistible force of Bruno's arguments to refute those errors. We also know about Bruno's courage in facing adversaries. Therefore, his decision to keep quiet and leave can hardly be attributed to anything other than the clear awareness of the total futility of any attempt to challenge Aristotle at the University of Paris. Here the loyalty of the students to their Aristotelian professors was unconditional. Thus, when Bruno was about to leave the lecture hall of the Collège de Cambrai, the students grabbed him and would not let him go unless he responded or took back the calumnies he had hurled against Aristotle. Bruno managed to escape from their hands, and he never returned, for his mind was now made up. If he was ever to find freedom, publishers for his books, and a curious and benevolent audience, he had to leave Paris, not only Paris, but France also, indeed every Catholic land as well, for in all of them it was considered a serious crime to challenge the views of Aristotle and Ptolemy about the Earth and the universe. Lutheran Germany was the only place left where he could go. 'I left Paris because of the tumults,' he later told the Inquisitors in Venice, 'and I went to Germany.'[11]

As a rule, Bruno was well received and treated there. In Germany, he found the sustenance and leisure he needed to write there he published his most important works, and above all, found eager and friendly ears for his ideas.

Bruno stayed six years in Germany, from 1586 to 1592, and in that period he wrote and published profusely under the protection of Lutheran tolerance. In Wittenberg, the great Lutheran bastion, Bruno published four works, two on Ramon Lull's art of memory,[12] a new edition of his theses attacking the Aristotelians in Paris,[13] and his farewell address to the faculty and students of the Lutheran university.[14] In Prague, the imperial residence, he published another book on Lull's art of memory,[15] and resumed his attack on the mathematicians and Aristotelians, this time launching one hundred and sixty articles against them (forty more than in Paris).[16] Bruno dedicated this book, against Euclidean geometry, to the Emperor Rudolph II, for which he received three hundred talers.

But it was in Frankfurt, the great publishing center and the site of the famed international fair, where Bruno published, in 1591, his major cosmological and ontological works: the three lengthy Latin didactical poems in imitation of Lucretius' didactical cosmological poem *De natura rerum* (On the Nature of Things), *De triplice minimo et mensura* (On the Three Kinds of Minute Entities and Measure), *De monade, numero et figura* (On the Monad, Number, and Figure), and finally, the last and most important work for the understanding of Bruno's mature cosmology, *De immenso et innumerabilibus* (On the Immense and the Innumerable). While still in Germany, Bruno wrote nine other minor works which were not published until three hundred years later, in 1891.

All these works were written in Latin. Bruno, who did not speak German, had to write in a language which was not only the language of academics and churchmen, but also of the lay intellectual elite. On the other hand, Italian was not as popular in

Germany as it was in England, because of the century-old animosity of the Germans towards Rome, which had been exacerbated further by the Lutherans' rejection of Roman Catholicism and Renaissance culture in general.

Bruno's vigorous literary activity during his sojourn in Germany is evidence of the highly stimulating cultural environment of Wittenberg and the warm welcome the Lutherans gave him there. But did he go as far as becoming a Lutheran himself as he had before, in Geneva, given half-hearted allegiance to Calvinism? Bruno's promiscuous flirtations with the official churches of the countries and cities in which he happened to be residing do not necessarily betray any vacillation in his religious beliefs, but rather a clever and, under the circumstances, necessary opportunism in the service of his great passion – philosophy. Good evidence of his life-long preference for Catholicism over Protestantism is the fact that he made efforts, while still in Paris, to obtain absolution from the Pope for his apostasy.[17] This should not be construed (as the Catholic priest Cicuttini suggests in his otherwise excellent study of Bruno's philosophy[18]) as a contrite and rueful longing to return to the bosom of the Church, which allegedly by then he was already feeling very sorry for having forsaken, but should rather be understood as a clever maneuver to gain access to the philosophy chair at the University of Paris, to which he could not be appointed as long as he remained excommunicated.

Still in Germany, after a brief sojourn in Catholic Mainz and Wiesbaden – where Bruno says he did not find the treatment and sustenance that suited him (*trattenimento a mio modo*) – he went to Marburg and applied again for a philosophy chair in that Lutheran university. The faculty denied his request, probably because they considered him a Roman papist theologian, rather than a philosopher. Bruno was furious. The Rector attested in the university records that Bruno came to his house and insulted him impudently. Bruno had told him to his face that he was acting against international law (*ius gentium*), against the common practice of all German universities, and against every disposition towards good manners and humane treatment (*contra studium humanitatis*).[19] This rather amusing incident throws light, not only on Bruno's pride and rebelliousness, but also on his ardent desire to be allowed to teach philosophy, his philosophy, in a university, any university, whether Catholic, Anglican, Calvinist, or

Lutheran, and on his willingness to comply with whatever formal requirements had been established as a necessary condition to be appointed to the desired position.

After his disappointment with Calvinism in Geneva, Bruno never again gave his allegiance to any Protestant denomination, nor did he prefer any particular one over his native Catholicism, for the simple reason that he had already found a new religion in a philosophy that he believed transcended them all. His uncompromising monism (generally understood as impious pantheism) was in fact totally incompatible with any form of Christianity. Thus, rather than any strong conviction for or against any of the conflicting doctrines, it is rather Bruno's indifference to dogmatic theology which is the key to understanding his apparent denominational versatility.

It was in Lutheran Wittenberg that Bruno had finally found the climate of freedom he had been looking for and had never found elsewhere. Thus, when the less tolerant Calvinists took away from the Lutherans the control of ecclesiastical affairs in that city, Bruno, remembering his ordeal with the Calvinists in Geneva, decided to leave Wittenberg. In his *oratio valedictoria*, the farewell address to the university, he praises Luther, along with the other great Germans he admired – Albert the Great, Nicholas of Cusa, Paracelsus, and Copernicus.[20]

From Saxony, Bruno went to Prague, where he got some money from the Emperor for the book he had dedicated to him. This allowed him to return to Lutheran Germany, to the city of Helmstedt in Braunschweig, where there was another reputable university, the Julian Academy, of whose philosophical faculty he became a member. His stay in Helmstedt, which lasted a year and a half, was of enormous importance for the development and maturation of Bruno's cosmology, for it was here that he wrote his three cosmological and ontological Latin poems, which he published in Frankfurt two years later.

Bruno's German sojourn had completed the transformation of the impetuous but still uncertain rebel into a self-assured and purposeful revolutionary. When Rome got wind of his doings and dealings in Germany, it resolved to stop him at all costs. Something that looked very much like a trap was set, and Bruno fell unsuspectingly into it.

CHAPTER FOUR

The Venetian Trap

It is very likely that Bruno had already met the Jesuit, Robert Bellarmine (soon to be made Cardinal by Clement VIII) in Germany. We have no details of this encounter, but it is almost certain that, on that occasion, the Jesuit got a first-hand knowledge of Bruno's virulent anti-Aristotelianism and unorthodox views about the Earth and the universe. He was also aware of the intense publishing activity Bruno was conducting in Germany. It is only natural that, on his return to Rome, Bellarmine hastened to warn the Pope and the Holy Office of the danger this man's books represented for the cause of the Counter-Reformation in Germany, where Lutheranism had already spread over almost half of the country.

We will probably never know whether it was of his own accord that the young Venetian patrician Zuane (Gioanne) Mocenigo extended an invitation to Bruno in Frankfurt to come to Venice and be his guest. Allegedly, he was interested in learning from Bruno the secrets of his art of memory. The interest of Henry III in mnemonics is not surprising; after all, the French king had frequently heard from the Sorbonne professors high praises of Bruno's astonishing memory, and power-thirsty sovereigns obviously cannot but profit from whatever memory improvements they can achieve. However, the young Venetian nobleman's sudden curiosity and willingness to become Bruno's disciple in the art of memory is very strange. He had his guest come all the way from Frankfurt to Venice, lodged him in a spacious room in his palace and provided him with everything he needed. The situation is rendered even more suspicious by the fact that it was Mocenigo's confessor[1] who later urged him to deliver Bruno to the Venetian Inquisition, and who denied him absolution until he had done so.

We also do not know, and probably will never know, why Zuane Mocenigo one fine morning decided to go to precisely that bookstore in Venice which happened to have in display one of the books that Bruno had just published in Frankfurt, and why he picked up precisely the book which had nothing to do with the art of memory, but rather with geometry and physics, namely *De triplici minimo et mensura* (On the Three Kinds of Minute Entities and Measure). Above all, we will never know why he asked the bookstore owner whether he happened to know the author of that book, something rather unusual for a bookstore visitor to ask a bookstore owner unless he already had some reasons to suspect the acquaintance. If he didn't, it certainly must have been an agreeable surprise for Mocenigo to hear from Ciotto, the Venetian bookstore owner, that, in fact, he did know the author of the book in which Mocenigo had suddenly become so interested. Moreover, Ciotto added, he had met Bruno in Frankfurt and had held long conversations with him there, for the publisher he was doing business with happened to be also the publisher of Bruno's books. (Complying with a venerable tradition, the publishers who attended the Frankfurt fair were under the obligation of procuring decent lodgings for foreign authors as well as for their wholesale book buyers.) So, for several weeks, both Bruno and Ciotto had lived in the Convent of the Carmelites in Frankfurt. If all this was pure coincidence, then Mocenigo's request to Ciotto to forward his letter of invitation to Bruno in Frankfurt can hardly be construed as a well-premeditated trap finally to catch the evasive heretic and apostate. It was rather an edifying example of candid and disinterested intellectual curiosity for, in that letter, Mocenigo asked Bruno to accept his invitation to come to Venice and to live in his palace as his special guest in order to satisfy his ardent desire to become his disciple in that marvelous art of memory in which Bruno was the unrivaled master.

However, if it was not a coincidence, and Mocenigo knew beforehand who Bruno really was and of his contacts in Frankfurt with the bookstore owner, then it is not easy to avoid the suspicion that Mocenigo was nothing but an instrument of those who were most interested in delivering Bruno to the Inquisition, and who had seen in the well-to-do patrician the ideal lure to entice Bruno to return to Italy. In that case, then, Mocenigo's walk to the bookstore that fatal morning was part of a well-premeditated plan, and his feigned curiosity about mnemonics merely a clever stratagem to mask his real intentions.

It is, in fact, difficult to believe that such a good and devout Catholic as Mocenigo, who regularly confessed his sins with a confessor whose advice he was so prompt to follow, would, out of sheer curiosity about the art of memory, burden for many months his scrupulous conscience with what his religion considered a most serious mortal sin, to wit, lodging, feeding, and providing clothes and books to a notorious renegade apostate priest known to have lived, taught, and published heterodox and blasphemous books in Anglican England and Lutheran Germany. And all this precisely in that period of Church history – the zenith of the Counter-Reformation – in which religious intolerance had been driven to a frenzy in Spain and all of Italy, the Index of Forbidden Books had just been established, and the Inquisition tribunals, including the Venetian one, wielded unlimited power over all issues that related to the orthodoxy of the Catholic faith.

Bruno made the fatal mistake of accepting Mocenigo's invitation. It is not easy to understand why he so innocently accepted it. Since his precipitous escape from Rome fifteen years earlier, Bruno had carefully avoided setting foot again in Italy. He knew that the danger of falling into the hands of the Inquisition was considerable, particularly now that he had published his most controversial books, and was known to have entertained friendly relations with the heretical rulers of Geneva, England, and Germany. But Mocenigo's offer seemed sincere and guileless; in his letter there was no mention at all of any interest on his part in Bruno's philosophy or cosmology. He was requesting his services merely as a tutor of mnemonics and geometry. Besides, Venice was not Rome, nor was the Most Serene Republic under Papal jurisdiction. Indeed, Venice was known for its proud autonomy, independence, and freedom. With such an affluent and influential patron there, Bruno could be sure of his protection as well as of his generous hospitality. And, of course, Bruno also had a craving to see his beloved Italy again after so many years of disheartening exile.

Upon his arrival in Italy, however, Bruno did not go directly to live in Mocenigo's palace. He may have decided to first reconnoitre the terrain before moving in, since from August to December, 1591, he stayed in Padua, where he tutored some German students and managed to get two new books published. From there, he visited nearby Venice frequently, where he met and conversed regularly with men of nobility and learning. Finally, at the beginning of the winter, he moved into Mocenigo's palazzo, where he stayed for five months, until 20 May 1592. During that time he instructed his host in the principles of the art of memory and geometry as had been agreed.

We know that Mocenigo already had the intention of delivering Bruno to the Venetian Inquisition shortly after Easter of 1592, for, suspecting he was not a man of God, he had sent Ciotto, the bookstore owner, to the Frankfurt fair with the special request to find out what kind of person Bruno really was. Upon his return, Ciotto told Mocenigo that he had talked in Frankfurt with some people who knew Bruno. They said they did not understand how Bruno was in Venice, for he was a man who had no religion. When Mocenigo heard this, he told Ciotto that he already had made up his mind to report Bruno to the Inquisition, but that he still wanted to get his money's worth in as much instruction as he could get from Bruno before he turned him in.[2]

Mocenigo accordingly started to show a growing interest in the 'other things' (cosmology for certain, and perhaps also magic) that he had heard Bruno knew so much about. For obvious reasons, Bruno had always been reluctant to talk about those subjects with his host and had carefully avoided discussions with him about them; but Mocenigo had now become so insistent that Bruno became suspicious of his real intentions and decided to leave Venice as soon as possible and return to safe territory in Germany.

It was too late. When he informed Mocenigo of his desire to leave for Frankfurt, for a couple of weeks, to take care of some business regarding the publication of his books, Mocenigo reproached him for withholding from him knowledge he felt he had a right to receive after all the generosity he had showered upon his guest and all the expenses he had incurred on his behalf. Bruno reminded him that he had agreed only to teach him the art of memory and geometry, and insisted that he had fulfilled his obligation conscientiously and thoroughly. Mocenigo disagreed and continued pressuring him. Finally, that very evening, after Bruno had completed his preparations to leave anyway and was already lying in bed, Mocenigo came to his room with a servant and six gondoliers of the neighborhood to force him to stay and teach him those other subjects or face the consequences. When Bruno refused and complained about the rude and unfair treatment he was receiving, Mocenigo ordered his servant to lock him up in his quarters. The next day he denounced Bruno and turned him over to the Venetian Inquisition. Later on, in one of his depositions to the Inquisition's tribunal, Mocenigo declared under oath that he had done this in compliance with the conscience-binding injunction he had received from his confessor. He had done his duty as a loyal son of the Holy Mother Church and consequently could no longer be denied absolution in confession for the grave sin of lodging and supporting a heretic.

In his three depositions to the five Venetian Inquisitors in May 1592, Mocenigo testified under oath that he had heard from Bruno the following heretical propositions and blasphemous utterances: that it was a big blasphemy on the part of the Catholics to affirm that bread is transubstantiated into flesh; that he was an enemy of the Mass; that no religion pleased him; that Christ was a rogue, for if he was capable of seducing people, he could just as well predict that he would be crucified; that there is no distinction of persons in God, for this would imply imperfection in God; that the world is eternal, that there are infinite worlds, and that God is continually creating them, for God necessarily wills all He can do; that Christ performed only apparent miracles, and that he was a magician, and so were the apostles, (and this led him to think that he, Bruno, could do just as much and even more than they did); that it was apparent that Christ did not want to die, and that he shunned death as much as he could; that there is no punishment of sins, and that souls created by the power of nature pass from one animal to another; that human beings are born from corruption just as animals are when they are reborn after deluges; that the Virgin could not have given birth and that the entire Catholic faith was full of blasphemies against God. Mocenigo also attested that he had heard Bruno express his intention of founding a new sect under the name of philosophy, and that he said it was necessary to take away from the monks their right to preach and their income, for they pollute the world; that there is no proof that the Catholic religion has any merit before God; that not to do to others what we don't want others to do to us is enough for the good life, and that he laughs at all other sins.[3]

This is certainly a long and grievous list. Most of the propositions are clearly heretical, some even outright blasphemous, but if Bruno did indeed talk to Mocenigo openly about these matters before Easter of 1592, then why did Mocenigo still need to find out through Ciotto, from people in Frankfurt, whether they thought Bruno was a man of God? Was not any single one of these propositions, let alone the entire long list, sufficient to convince Mocenigo beyond any reasonable doubt that Bruno was a most wicked and pernicious heretic? If not before Easter, is it credible that Bruno waited until after Easter, and hence after Mocenigo had already been informed by his spy, Ciotto, of the negative opinions the people he had interviewed in Frankfurt had of Bruno, to start revealing to his inquisitive host such grossly heretical and blasphemous views? And is it not utterly beyond comprehension that, the very night before turning his guest in to the Venetian Inquisition, the good and pious Catholic Mocenigo would still insist that the blasphemous heretic stay with him under dire threats if he refused? What Mocenigo did clearly reveal by his insistent entreaties that night were his real motives for his demands (and they totally coincided with what he had previously told Ciotto), namely that he wanted to hear from Bruno's mouth what he thought of those other subjects, besides mnemonics and geometry, in which he knew Bruno was also an expert and which he suspected his tutor was hiding from him, since he had always avoided discussing them with him, let alone giving him regular lessons on them. Nor are we inclined to believe that this increasingly avid curiosity of Mocenigo's was due to the fact that he felt he had been short-changed by his tutor, and was simply trying to get his money's worth by requesting some additional esoteric instruction in addition to what already had been delivered to him, in compliance with the initial agreement to a tutorial in mnemonics and geometry.

If Bruno had indeed always been suspicious of Mocenigo and had carefully avoided talking to him about his cosmological views, is it credible, then, that he would confide to him clearly blasphemous and heretical views about those fundamental Christian dogmas that only recently had been clearly redefined by the Council of Trent, knowing, as he did, that his young and devout host entertained the most cordial relations with the Venetian clergy?

A much more relevant question than the one concerning

Mocenigo's real motives for inviting and betraying Bruno is: Why did Bruno accept Mocenigo's invitation in the first place, being aware, as he was, of the great danger his return to Catholic Italy would pose for him, particularly after having entertained most amicable relations with the arch-enemies of Catholicism, and after having published many works containing views in flagrant contradiction of the official orthodox teachings of the Catholic Church at the peak of counter-reformationist zeal and intolerance?

Before attempting to find an answer to this question, which is of the greatest importance for understanding Bruno's revolutionary agenda, we must first review the list of the heretical allegations imputed to him by Mocenigo, for some of them indeed seem to be in agreement with some of the views expounded in his writings, and others may provide some clues to his reasons for returning to Italy.

In general, Mocenigo's accusations betray a rather unsophisticated mind, one not accustomed to theological subtleties. Particularly those accusations which refer to orthodox, clearly defined, and strictly theological subjects such as transubstantiation, the Trinity, the virginity of Mary, and the divinity of Jesus Christ, are so unqualified and obtrusive that it is very unlikely that Bruno ever openly discussed with his host in those brash terms his views about these subjects. It is, however, quite probable that Bruno did internally reject some of these dogmas, for they are generally incompatible with the basic tenets of his philosophy, and Bruno himself candidly admitted to the Inquisitors in Venice that he had, in fact, had doubts about some of those dogmas since his adolescent years, particularly about the ones referring to the Trinity and the Incarnation, but that his speculative stance had always been strictly philosophical without any intention to impugn the dogmas of the faith.

Considerably more interesting, on the other hand, are those accusations of Mocenigo's that refer to philosophical, particularly cosmological, questions, and to magic. Bruno's belief in the eternity of the universe and the plurality of worlds – a belief based on the theological argument that divine omnipotence cannot suffer any self-imposed restraint – was clearly and repeatedly expressed in his published cosmological works.

On the other hand, the transmigration of souls into animal bodies is possible only if the individual souls can exist separately from the bodies they inform, which is totally incompatible with Bruno's monistic views. Hence, if Bruno was sympathetic to the unorthodox doctrine of transmigration he must have interpreted it in the sense of the immanence of the soul of the universe in all bodies, not only in the animal ones.

Finally, Mocenigo's allegation that Bruno maintained that both Christ and the apostles performed miracles by virtue of their magical powers is highly plausible, for Bruno's interest in, and extensive knowledge of 'white' magic, is amply documented in the numerous writings he dedicated to this subject. However, only in the light of Bruno's revolutionary agenda and strategy will we be able to understand the reasons, indeed the necessity, to ascribe magical powers to Jesus and his apostles. If Christianity were to be replaced by a new religion – to which Mocenigo imprecisely alludes as 'a new sect under the name of philosophy' – it was of the utmost importance to undermine its most solid foundation: the miracle of Jesus's resurrection and all the miracles Jesus and his apostles allegedly performed to prove his divinity. It is, in fact, not unreasonable to assume that Bruno's life-long intense interest in magic was ultimately motivated by his revolutionary agenda which included a sweeping religious reform. This, at first sight unwarranted, suspicion will become a plausible hypothesis when we discuss the reasons Bruno may have had for accepting Mocenigo's invitation to come to Venice.

Why did Bruno accept Mocenigo's invitation? To my knowledge no biographer of Bruno has suggested until now a plausible explanation for this. The romantic hypothesis of Bruno's home-sickness for his beloved mother country, from which he had been absent for fifteen years, is not very convincing. Bruno must have had far more compelling reasons to expose himself to the great danger a return to Italy under those particular personal and historical circumstances posed for him.

Angelo Corsano, the author of the book *Il pensiero di Giordano Bruno nel suo svolgimento storico*[4], has given us an important clue to solve this riddle. After the publication of Bruno's three great Latin poems in Frankfurt in 1591, in which he had brought to full maturity his cosmological and ontological views covering the entire physical and spiritual reality of the universe – from the minima of the microcosm to the maxima of the macrocosm – Bruno thought the time had finally arrived for action. He was now well known in Germany, France, and England; he had published extensively, and was now finally in secure possession of all the theoretical weapons he needed for the final confrontation with the powers that held Christian Europe chained to error under the yoke of dogmatic tyranny.

However, Corsano believes that Bruno's intentions were merely reformist. He merely wanted to propel a liberalizing reform from within after having been pardoned by the Pope and allowed to return to the bosom of the Holy Mother Church. Corsano's main argument for this assumption is that Bruno intended to publish and dedicate to the Pope, shortly before being delivered by Mocenigo to the Venetian Inquisition, a book titled *Delle sette arti liberali* (On the Seven Liberal Arts), a book whose innocuous contents hardly contained anything capable of arousing the anger of Clement VIII.

Corsano, intent on proving his thesis of a transition in Bruno's thought from the radical to the moderate in his later years, misunderstands Bruno's real intentions, his plans, and his strategy for carrying them out. If there was an evolution in Bruno's thought and intentions, it was from the unfocused to the lucid, from the compromising to the radical, from the reformist to the revolutionary. This contention, I believe, will not be very difficult to substantiate.

First of all, by 1591 Bruno had become totally convinced of the falsity of Ptolemaic geocentrism as well as of Copernicus' error in still believing in a center of the universe. He had further clearly identified the principal cause of those misconceptions: too much faith in mathematics and neglect of common sense, observation, and reason. He was also aware of the fact that the two most authoritative philosophical systems of his time, on which the entire theoretical apparatus of Catholic dogma was based, namely Aristotelianism and Neoplatonism, were not only supportive of geocentrism, but also were so tightly interlocked with it, that the collapse of geocentrism would inevitably result in their own discredit, and consequently the Catholic dogmatic edifice would thereby be seriously weakened if not utterly undermined. For, if the Church had been wrong for so long in what was supremely important for mankind to know about the universe it inhabited, what trust did it deserve for the rest of its beliefs? To reform the Church from within in its basic philosophical presuppositions would have been even more illusory than to try to make it come to terms with the dogmatic adjustments and trimmings the Reformed and Lutheran Churches had been demanding from Rome with such little success, as their uncompromising rejection by the Council of Trent had clearly demonstrated. Bruno could not possibly have been so naïve as to think he could, from within, convince the leading Church theologians to defenestrate the entire philosophical foundation of the dogmas they were trying so hard to defend from the Protestant assault. Unlike the Protestant Reformers, Bruno did not want to reform the Christian religion, but rather to replace it with a loftier one, specifically with one that not just all Christians, but all of humanity could accept. Bruno had long known that this was his most urgent task, his mission, and his supreme calling. And now, after the publication of his major works in 1591, he was finally ready for action.

Thus, by 1591 Bruno had become keenly aware of the pressing need for this radical religious revolution. It had already been the supreme ideal of the greatest Renaissance thinkers, particularly of Marsilio Ficino and Pico della Mirandola, to bring to the different peoples and nations of the world, so profoundly alienated from, and hostile to, each other because of their different religious beliefs, a religion they could all accept and follow, in the hope that universal religious harmony would significantly contribute to bringing peace to the world. This grandiose project was embraced with zealous earnestness by Lorenzo il Magnifico de' Medici, who ordered Marsilio Ficino to stop translating into Latin the works of Plato, the philosopher most highly revered by the Italian Renaissance Humanists, and immediately to start translating the *Corpus Hermeticum* attributed to Hermes Trismegistos, which recently had been brought to Florence from Constantinople. Lorenzo and his Florentine academicians were convinced that it was there where the most solid and promising foundation for the much needed universal religion could be found, for they firmly believed that Hermes, the great Egyptian sage and priest, had been a contemporary of Moses, and were ecstatic about the fact that some of the doctrines expounded in Hermes' sacred books remarkably coincided not only with the monotheistic beliefs of Judaism and Neoplatonism, but also with the loftiest thoughts of Plato himself about the origin of the universe and the immortality of the soul. Hermes'

doctrines and authority were thus considered of crucial importance for the establishment of a religion which Christians, Jews,
and Muslims alike could accept, and which finally could be
instrumental in bringing peace and harmony to the leading
nations of the civilized world.

This ideal Bruno wholeheartedly shared with the great Florentine Renaissance thinkers. Also, his own long experience in France
and Germany, ravaged by religious wars between Catholics and
Protestants, and the cruel intolerance and persecution of religious
dissenters he had witnessed wherever either Calvinism or Roman
Catholicism were politically dominant, had made for him the
pursuit of this ideal even more pressing. It was perfectly clear to
Bruno that this ideal could never be realized as long as the acceptance of Christian dogma by all nations of the world continued to
be the non-negotiable condition and goal of Roman Catholic
proselytism. A new religion based on reason and a realistic vision
of the world had to be founded if it was to have any hopes of being
universally accepted. Bruno's cosmological model and the new
philosophy with which it was intimately interlocked finally provided the foundation indispensable for a universally acceptable
new religion.

Bruno knew only too well that he could never be successful
with this ambitious project in Germany. Despite the respect and
esteem that both colleagues and students at the Lutheran
universities of Wittenberg and Helmstedt showed him, Bruno
remained severely handicapped in any attempt to win over to
his cause the powerful German nobility whose support was
indispensable for his success, and this was mainly for two
reasons. First of all, he was a foreigner, an Italian who did not
master their language and who could communicate with most
of them only in Latin. (The fact that Bruno was an apostate
monk, on the other hand, did not much harm his credibility and
ability to impress the Germans, for this trait he had in common
with Luther.) Secondly, the Lutheran Germans were so en-
thralled by their newly acquired religious freedom and so
carried away by the new forms of intense emotional piety
Luther's Bible had made possible for them, that they would have
hardly been inclined to lend benevolent ears to an Italian who
proposed to them the rejection of their newly discovered Evangelical Christianity in favor of a philosophical religion based on

that very wretched 'whore of reason' Luther was so fond of disparaging.

Italy was Bruno's only possibility. There he could display the full range of his rhetorical powers in his native tongue, and there again he could hope to gain for his cause the open-minded, highly educated, wealthy and politically influential laymen, as well as the flower of the Italian intellectual élite at the prestigious Italian universities. And of all of Italy, the places where he could most easily muster both kinds of valuable helpers were unquestionably Venice and Padua.

Venice was an independent republic, not subject to the jurisdiction of the Papacy, proud of its autonomy, prosperous, and more open to the culture of the transalpine countries than the rest of Italy. And, not far away from Venice, there was Padua, with one of the most prestigious universities of Europe, particularly famous for its chairs of mathematics and astronomy, where Copernicus himself had studied, and Galileo would soon be granted the very chair in mathematics Bruno unsuccessfully applied for. Mocenigo's invitation could not but have appeared to Bruno as a unique opportunity to carry out his designs in the most favorable possible cultural environment. Also, the fact that Mocenigo was a wealthy and influential Venetian patrician promised to provide not only ample and very comfortable sustenance, but also protection against the local Inquisition, should it ever be needed. Finally, Mocenigo's young age led credibility to his motives for the invitation, namely his curiosity and desire to become Bruno's disciple in both geometry and the art of memory, once he heard from their common acquaintance, the bookstore owner, that Bruno was in Frankfurt and would probably welcome his generous invitation.

The fact that Bruno was most interested in procuring the support both of the Venetian nobility and the academicians of Padua is amply demonstrated, on the one hand, by the fact that Bruno, upon his return to Italy, did not immediately take up his lodgings in Mocenigo's palace, but cautiously chose to dwell for a while in Padua. There he hastened to establish contacts with several professors and provided for his sustenance with the fees he received from private German students he agreed to tutor. On the other hand, to befriend and secure the support of the wealthy and influential Venetian nobility – and perhaps also to feel out, on the spot, the sincerity and reliability of his future host – Bruno would regularly spend the weekends in Venice, where he would frequent the favorite meeting spots of the intellectual circles of the nobility, namely the bookstores and the spice-and-drug stores. Only three months after his arrival in Padua, in the winter of 1591, Bruno was ready to move into Mocenigo's palace. It was a decision he would always regret having made.

Thus, it appears that Bruno's decision to accept Mocenigo's invitation was motivated, not by a desire to procure from the Pope his pardon, the lifting of his excommunication, and his readmittance to the Church, with the hope of promoting from within a reform of the Catholic Church, as Corsano suggests, but rather by the hope of carrying out, in the only country where he had any chance of success, his plans for a radical religious and cultural revolution. It was only after realizing he was not making much progress in Venice towards this objective that he thought of gaining the favor of the Pope, most probably because he had experienced in Venice the reluctance of the Venetians to follow him as long as he had not accomplished his reconciliation with the Church. The dedication of the book *On the Seven Liberal Arts* to Clement VIII was therefore not evidence of his conversion from an extreme radical to a more conformist stance, but rather the necessary move of a clever strategist upon encountering a formidable obstacle to the realization of his plans.

Bruno's plans were, in fact, definitively dashed when he was delivered by Mocenigo to the Venetian Inquisition. However, he still made a last attempt to carry them out by trying to escape from the grip of the Inquisition, leaving Italy, and waiting abroad for more propitious circumstances. The only way out of this extremely dangerous situation was to recant. It was the extremely humiliating but necessary price he had to pay if he wanted ever to be able to fulfill his mission. He was forced to kneel down in front of his judges, recant all his beliefs – not only the theological, but also the cosmological ones of which he was totally convinced – ask humbly for forgiveness, and even request a more rigorous punishment than what the judges might think he deserved. He submitted himself to this humiliation only because he knew it was his only chance to save his life and possibly to get another opportunity to carry out his plans, or at least to keep on publishing abroad, in the hope that others, if not himself, would succeed in what he personally could no longer achieve in his native country.

CHAPTER FIVE

The Rebel's Punishment

To fight against this lack of
understanding, against this world of non-
understanding, was impossible.
KAFKA, *The Hunger Artist*

In spite of Mocenigo's onerous accusations, the Venetian Inquisition failed to convict Bruno, mainly because the other witnesses
called to testify did not confirm those accusations. It was, however, the duty of the Venetian Inquisition to report the more
serious cases to the Congregation of the Holy Office in Rome. As
soon as Rome heard of Bruno's Venetian trial, the Pope instructed
the Papal Nuntius in Venice, himself a member of the Inquisitorial
Tribunal, to convince the Signoria to surrender the culprit to
Rome. The Doge and the Venetian Senate were initially most
reluctant to surrender to Rome their jurisdictional rights over
Bruno; but the insistence and relentless pressure of the Pope
finally moved the Senate to deliver Bruno to Rome. Bruno was,
after all, not a Venetian citizen. Furthermore, the Inquisition had
long since indicted him in Naples and Rome, and there were
several precedents for Venice delivering to Rome other culprits
charged with the crime of heresy. Above all, the Pope was entitled
to this special favor from the Doge in a matter of such gravity and
importance to all Christendom, as was the case of such a notorious
heretic and heresiarch.[1] Bruno was thereupon brought to Rome
and confined to the dungeons in the Palace of the Holy Office.
There he stayed for seven years, subject to numerous interrogations and most probably even torture.

Whereas the detailed proceedings of Bruno's short trial by
the Venetian Inquisition have been preserved in their entirety,
those of his protracted trial by the Roman Inquisition have

mysteriously vanished. Most scholars now believe they will never be found.

The vicissitudes of the original acts of the Roman trial are indeed very mysterious. After the trial, the acts were kept in the secret archives of the Holy Office. There they remained until Napoleon I conquered the Papal States and made Pope Pius VII his prisoner. Because he had conceived the grandiose plan of making Paris the cultural center of the civilized world, Napoleon plundered the Archives of the Holy Office and ordered them to be transported to Paris. After Waterloo and the recovery of the Papal States, Pius VII reclaimed the Holy Office archives from Louis XVIII. However, the coach that was carrying the acts of Bruno's Roman trial from Paris never arrived in Rome. The acts have never been found, and it is not likely that they ever will. Consequently the only information we have of Bruno's trial by the Roman Inquisition is the one contained in the *Sommario*.[2]

The summary of Bruno's trial by the Roman Inquisition was published for the first time three hundred and forty-one years after Bruno's execution. Allegedly it was composed not very long after the event by an anonymous editor of the original minutes of the proceedings. The manuscript was discovered by Monsignor Angelo Mercati, a member of the Papal Curia, in the private library of Pope Pius XI. Previously the manuscript had been in the private library of Pope Leo XIII, but nobody knows how it got there nor anything about its wanderings since its composition. It is true, however, that neither one of these Popes thought it fit to allow the manuscript to be published in order to clarify the position of the Church in Bruno's case and to allow the public to better understand the reasons the Church had to condemn Bruno, despite the fact – or is it rather because of the fact? – that Bruno had recently been made a national hero and a symbol of the rebellion against religious intolerance by all the radical anticlerical and antipapal movements of the recently unified Italian state. It was only in 1941, when the whole world was worrying about another, by far more vicious kind of intolerance and oppression, that Monsignor Mercati, with the authorization of Pius XII, decided to publish the *Sommario*. However, that belated and long overdue publication was not intended as an apology to the world for the injustice done to Bruno. Monsignor's introduction to the *Sommario* reveals the true motives for declassifying the document, namely to exonerate the Pope and the Roman Inquisition from blame in the trial and execution of Giordano Bruno.

Mercati's introduction clearly reveals the tactics used to achieve the intended result, namely, character assassination, only this time slightly more subtle than the traditional one. The main contentions are that Bruno was a dissolute man and a blasphemous heretic; that he was condemned for his theological, not his cosmological errors; and that he refused to recant because he was mentally ill. Thus, Bruno was posthumously robbed of what was perhaps his greatest title to glory: remarkable courage, a most lucid and determined resistance against intolerable tyranny, and the attempt to abolish by coercion the inalienable right of the human mind to search for truth.

While Bruno's process in Rome was moving very slowly, an unexpected event occurred which precipitated things. A new witness was found who seriously incriminated Bruno. It was one of his jail companions in Venice, a Cappuccine monk who viscerally detested the defrocked Dominican, and who, after having been convicted of contumacious heresy, was burnt in the same Roman public market place where Bruno was to be executed only three years later. His testimony was devastating for Bruno's cause. But since it came from a criminal – as well as most of all other testimonies, except those from Mocenigo – the Inquisitors could not base their condemnation exclusively on such questionable testimony. Consequently, a thorough examination of Bruno's works was ordered and entrusted to the Jesuit theologian Robert Bellarmine.

Bellarmine eventually came up with a list of errors gleaned out of Bruno's works and submitted it to the prisoner for recantation. Bruno was again willing to recant his theological errors in Rome as he had previously done in Venice, but only until September 1599, when something very strange must have taken place in Bruno's mind. Although totally convinced that he would be burnt alive if he did not recant, Bruno surprisingly changed his mind and told his judges he had nothing to recant, for he could not find anything in his writings that contradicted the dogmas of the Church. He claimed further that he had merely been grossly misunderstood and misinterpreted by the theologians and the Inquisitors.

He was given forty days to reconsider. The forty days passed and Bruno remained adamant in his intransigent position. He then sent a letter to the Pope pleading his case and protesting his innocence. The Pope opened the letter but refused to read it. He instead instructed the Inquisitors to proceed with the condemnation and to surrender Bruno to the secular arm. This they did, and Bruno was taken to the Roman public square called Campo di Fiori, a rag tied around his tongue, degraded of all his orders, and stripped of all his clothes. He was then burnt alive on the stake. Before the pyre was lit, a monk approached Bruno holding a crucifix in his hand; he moved it towards Bruno's lips, but Bruno turned his head away.

This gesture has been interpreted as the most convincing proof of Bruno's godlessness and utter wickedness, but it is also possible to interpret it as a refusal to provide even the slightest sign of capitulation to the powers he had so vigorously fought all his life. It may also be true what some witnesses say, that they noticed a smile on Bruno's face while he was walking to the scaffold. If this is true, we may conjecture that that smile arose from his lucid awareness of being then the only human being in the entire universe who knew the basic truth about it, and that only the fools who condemned him could believe they were the center of the universe.

The real reason why the Pope and the Inquisitors condemned and executed Bruno was that they found it intolerable that he conceded authority only to reason – his reason – rather than to their own firm convictions, the weight of millenary tradition, and universal consensus. The rest was only pretext. Bruno had repeatedly declared he was willing to recant those eight heretical propositions for which he was condemned as far as they had anything to do with orthodox dogma. Even the fact that he had entertained friendly relations with the representatives of three great reformist movements (the Calvinists in Geneva, the Anglicans in London and Oxford, and the Lutherans in Marburg, Helmstedt, and above all Wittenberg, the bastion of Lutheranism) did not damage him much, for he assured the Inquisitors that the Reformers had never succeeded in persuading him to abandon his orthodox Catholic faith. Instead, Bruno's refusal to recant his convictions on cosmological matters to the ecclesiastical authorities who examined and judged him, despite the efforts of Bruno's detractors to prove the contrary, appears to be the decisive reason for his condemnation.

For Robert Bellarmine, the theologian in charge of examining and judging Bruno's cosmology, could not but fully realize the disastrous impact on dogma that the Brunian idea of the infinite, acentric universe, and hence of the utter cosmic insignificance of mankind that inevitably resulted from it, would have. It was this most unsettling view that posed the real danger to Christianity, not those other heretical, purely theological propositions that Bruno repeatedly declared he was willing to recant if he had ever held them.

However, due to the fact that the original proceedings of Bruno's Roman trial have mysteriously disappeared from the secret Vatican archives and almost certainly, as Monsignor Mercati has indicated, have been definitively lost, we will most probably never know with certainty what the real reasons for Bruno's condemnation were. However, we do know that Bruno repeatedly declared his readiness to recant any errors he could have incurred regarding dogma. He also admitted he had had doubts about certain dogmas of the Church since his novitiate days. However, he vigorously protested that he was only thinking as a philosopher, not a theologian, and that everything he had written or publicly defended in any way related to dogma was done from the point of view of the philosopher.

The Roman Inquisition justified its condemnation of Bruno's cosmological views – which were indeed subversive not so much to Catholic dogma as to the philosophical systems that supported it – by alleging that they were contrary, if not to dogma, at least certainly to the received and authoritative opinions of the Church Fathers (which are not absolutely binding as the dogmatic pronouncements are). By contradicting these opinions one could at most be accused of temerity, never, however, could one be condemned to be burnt alive at the stake for heresy.

It is therefore Bruno's defiance of the erroneous opinions of the Pope, Inquisitors, and theologians of the Holy Office concerning the Earth and the universe which most probably was the real reason for his condemnation, first because he established reason, and not tradition or faith, as the ultimate criterion for knowledge in cosmological matters, and second because he rejected the cosmology wherewith the two main philosophical systems which were supporting the Catholic dogma were inextricably linked.

Of all the accusations leveled against Bruno, one in particular gives us a clue as to where his real threat to the Church was perceived to lie. It was the accusation Mocenigo brought against him in Venice, namely that he intended to found a new sect based on his philosophy. This made Bruno not only a heretic, but a leader of heretics, a heresiarch. This accusation, in fact, reveals a sensitivity to the supreme danger of allowing Bruno to continue writing and teaching, and helps us to understand why the Church had no choice but to stop him from doing so. The accusation was based on the following indisputable facts. First, Bruno had produced a revolutionary cosmology proposing a totally new vision of the universe and of man's place in it. Secondly, he intimated a concept of God which, in sharp contrast to the orthodox Christian idea of the Trinity, could be easily understood and universally accepted. Thirdly, he opposed and intended to put an end to the disastrous wars, the persecutions, and the intolerance which invariably resulted from conflicting religious doctrines. Finally, he believed that the only way to deliver Europe and the world from those chronic calamities was to realize the lofty Renaissance ideal of one universal religion, which no longer would be based on a particular divine revelation, but on reason, so that all rational human beings of all nations could accept it.

I contend that Bruno, after publishing his last three ontological and cosmological works in Frankfurt, was ready to take action in this direction. He devised a plan and a strategy to carry it out, and he needed the understanding, acceptance, and allegiance of powerful followers, which could only be gained by persuasion. His native Italy was the only country where he could expect to get the indispensable help he needed to carry out his plans effectively, and inside Italy the Venice-Padua axis was the ideal area in which to recruit his followers and initiate his campaign.

The allegation, of the Church apologists of the Inquisition in their handling of Bruno's case, that he was not condemned because of his philosophical, particularly cosmological opinions, but because of specific heretical views regarding certain dogmatic propositions, is highly questionable in view of the otherwise incomprehensible insistence of the tribunal on interrogating Bruno repeatedly on strictly cosmological and philosophical matters. In fact, two of the eighteen lengthy interrogatories Bruno was submitted to during his trial in Rome (the twelfth and the fourteenth) were dedicated exclusively to the questions concerning the infinity and eternity of the universe and the multiplicity of worlds in it[3]; and the eighteenth and last dealt exclusively with philosophical questions concerning the soul.[4] Of everything Bruno had written in his books it was clearly his cosmology that worried the Church theologians most, for it contradicted and undermined the philosophical foundations of the Catholic dogma established by the Aristotelian Aquinas in his *Summa Theologiae*, and above all, because Bruno's cosmology provided a solid basis for the revolutionary world view and religion he was suspected to be planning.

This is unequivocally demonstrated by the fact that on 24 March 1597, Bruno was summoned to appear in front of the entire Congregation of dignitaries of the Holy Office and was there invited to abandon one single thing: 'such vanities of the multiple worlds', after which the peremptory order was given '*quod interrogetur stricte, postea detur ei censura*', that he be interrogated rigorously, and then be censured (the Latin adverb *stricte* was the usual technical euphemism for torture). The order given by the Congregation, after their injunction to Bruno to abandon, explicitly and directly, his cosmological views, was that he be tortured with the *corda* (the cord), and that afterwards the final sentence should be pronounced over him.[5] Finally, in the seventeenth interrogatory, after asking Bruno about the Trinity and the Incarnation, his judges went back to the same old question about the plurality of worlds. And in the eighteenth and last interrogatory session, dedicated to censuring his published works, Bruno was requested to respond to strictly cosmological and ontological propositions drawn from them, one of which was, again, his doctrine of the infinite universe.[6] It therefore appears clearly from this procedure of the Congregation of Cardinals that Bruno's cosmological views, and not his alleged theological errors, were his judges' main preoccupation. Firpo arrives at a similar conclusion: 'From then on, the sore spot in Bruno's trial centered on the Brunian doctrine of universal animation, whether in the aspect of the world soul, identified in some way with the Holy Spirit, or in the definition of the individual soul' (author's translation).[7]

Several witnesses, who had been in jail with Bruno in Venice, alleged having heard him refer to the great prestige that his philosophy had already gained in Germany; he boasted that his, in fact, was the only philosophy the Germans respected; he had also revealed his intention of going to Germany to found there a sect. There were even rumors already about some of his followers there, who were known as the 'Giordanists'. Another witness testified that Bruno once told him that, should he ever be forced to go back to a Dominican monastery, he would set it on fire and escape to Germany where he could be free to live and think as he pleased.[8]

All of these accusations were obviously most unsettling for the Catholic theologians. What worried them most of all were not the heretical views and the vulgar blasphemies that were attributed to him, but rather Bruno's books, his prestige and friends in Germany, and the plans he was suspected of secretly brooding on, and scheming to carry out, should he ever be set free and allowed to return to Germany. Above all, it was his cosmology which was rightfully perceived as the greatest threat, particularly in a time when the Reformation was spreading all over Europe, for Bruno had written and published his books in Germany, in impeccable Latin style, for educated readers all over Europe.

Most dangerous was the fact that Bruno had developed a comprehensive philosophy of nature and the universe based on, and at the same time transcending, the heliocentric model suggested by Copernicus (whom the Germans claimed as their own), which was quickly becoming more and more plausible and acceptable to an increasing number of independent minds. Should Bruno be set free and allowed to return to Germany with that deadly weapon in his hand, he undoubtedly would be in a position to launch a formidable attack on the antiquated ontology and cosmology of the Roman Catholic Church, and hence indirectly on its entire magisterial authority.

Bruno had subjected himself in Venice to the humiliation of begging on his knees for forgiveness only to save what was most precious for him – his freedom and the possibility to launch his attack, at a more favorable occasion and from a more advantageous position, against the obsolete philosophical system (Aristotelianism) which the most powerful religious institution in Europe had hailed as its most reliable philosophical foundation. In Rome, however, the situation had radically changed; he was no longer ready to plead on his knees for forgiveness. Thus, by December 1599, after he had heard that one of his most vicious and damaging accusers, the Cappuccine monk Celestino di Verona, who had shared the Venetian prison cell with him, had been burnt alive for his heresies in the Campo di Fiori, it became perfectly clear to him that he could no longer save what until then he had thought could be saved, and that a solemn recantation would only irreparably damage his project and seriously blunt the force of his rebellion. He also knew that after seven years of confinement in a noxious dungeon, and after his submission to innumerable interrogations and tortures, his physical strength was so weakened, and above all, his reputation in Italy so seriously damaged, that his original plans of winning support from the learned Italian nobility and university professors had no possibility of ever being realized. Probably the most decisive motive for Bruno to refuse to recant his philosophical errors was the certitude he had now reached that, even in the most favorable outcome of his trial, his judges would condemn him to a very long punitive imprisonment.[9] Under those circumstances, the only power he had left, which needed to be saved at all costs if his struggle was to be carried on by others after his death, was the power to rebel to the end, and to say no to those who so badly wanted him to recant. He knew his books would be burnt in Rome and forbidden in all of Catholic Europe, but they could not be destroyed or sequestered from potential readers elsewhere. His books would survive him, and his ideas would speak for him after his death; they were to carry on the revolution he had planned and was prevented from accomplishing. He expressed the single power he still retained, the power to say no, through that terrible gesture of rebellion that would speak more eloquently than all other verbal negations: the refusal to kiss, in sign of submission and repentance and as the unequivocal token of his total renunciation of all his convictions, the crucifix that the monk brought to his lips before the pyre was set ablaze. This was Bruno's final victory and his way of depriving the defeated of their most coveted trophy.

Three other interpretations have been proposed to explain why Bruno refused to recant, and why he accepted the horrible death he could otherwise easily have averted. The first one, represented by Berti, Tocco, and Mondolfo, is the traditional one of the late-nineteenth-century, mostly Italian, free-thinkers: Bruno died as a victim of religious intolerance and sacrificed his life for the sake of freedom of thought. This romantic interpretation fabricates the myth of the heroic and indomitable Bruno, a Promethean titan crushed by the illegitimate power and devious methods of a tyrannical Papacy, intent on preventing humanity from receiving from him the gift of enlightenment. This explanation becomes implausible in the face of Bruno's repeated recantations, abjurations, solemn protestations of faith, and humble prostrations before his judges, both in Venice and in Rome.

The second interpretation, represented by Mercati and other Catholic apologists of the Church, explain Bruno's final refusal to recant as a stubborn obduration of his spiteful pride brought about by a progressive deterioration of his mental powers. Bruno, they contend, during his lengthy trial gave repeated signs of repentance and of an ardent desire to return to the fold of the Mother Church, until suddenly he changed completely and was overcome by heinous hatred and satanic pride. This could only be attributed to some secret mental disorder which finally overpowered him. Considering the violent attacks of rage Bruno had experienced against some of his fellow inmates, and the blasphemies they had allegedly heard him utter against Christ and the saints, it was legitimate to assume that a serious mental deterioration was the reason for his refusal to recant.[10] Should this interpretation be true, however, rather than absolving the Pope and the Inquisitors from the terrible injustice the propounders of the anticlerical interpretation accuse them of for having victimized a champion of free thought, it would clearly burden them with the even greater injustice of condemning a poor demented person to such a horrible death, something which was clearly and explicitly forbidden by their own Canon Law.

The third interpretation – or rather type of interpretation, for there are several varieties – tries to avoid the excesses of both romantic hero-worship and apologetic demonization. On the one hand, it acknowledges Bruno's human weaknesses and the enormous complexity of human motivation, and on the other, it recognizes the full legitimacy of the Inquisition's trial. Among these, the one submitted by Corsano is plausible, although not altogether convincing: Bruno's request to be readmitted to the Church was prompted by his sincere wishes to reform it; this is why he was so submissive in Venice; in Rome, however, after his hopes had completely vanished, his dignity forbade him to betray his convictions, specifically his philosophical ones; he accepted death, not as the heroic champion of free thought, but out of loyalty to himself and to his own principles. This interpretation presents a more complex image of Bruno: in spite of his weaknesses, hesitations, and indecision, in the end he proved to be a man of character and integrity, for he was willing to die for what he believed in, and refused to save his life at the price of a cowardly self-denial.

Unlike Galileo, who did save himself at the price of a gutless self-denial, Bruno did not have Galileo's possible excuse: that the world would profit more by his remaining alive than by his noble death, for he would eventually give the world, as he actually did, a knowledge of the laws of nature that would immensely benefit mankind. Bruno had already told the world all he thought it needed to know to completely change things around. For Bruno the time for action had already arrived in 1592, but, by December 1599, he also knew that he was henceforth irreparably blocked from taking any significant action to forward his revolutionary project.

The interpretation that sharply disagrees with Corsano's contention that Bruno had merely reformist and conciliatory plans with regard to the Catholic Church seems more plausible. Bruno does not show in any of his writings any desire whatsoever to save the Church, its dogma, its philosophical foundations, its hierarchy, its morality, or its power structure. He wanted instead an entirely new order for the world, a transvaluation of values similar to the one Nietzsche would propose three centuries later.[11] As theoretical foundation and justification for that total revolution, Bruno had proposed a new philosophy based on a totally new vision of the world and the universe, a philosophy which could, in turn, serve as basis for an utterly new undogmatic religion acceptable to all rational men and which would thereby put an end to the senseless religious wars which were ruining European civilization. From this new philosophy and religion a new type of morality would also inevitably emerge, in which virtues, hitherto regarded as vices, would regain their old ascendancy. These include intellectual curiosity; freedom of thought, religion, and speech; intellectual honesty; free and in-depth education of the minds of the young; critical thinking; rebelliousness to despotic authority, and tolerance and respect to the views and rights of all even if, and precisely when, they happen to disagree with ours.

This was Bruno's revolutionary program, an Utopia no doubt, but still the ultimate goal towards which all his actions and publications were directed. To consider them merely as an intent to reform the Catholic Church from within, as Corsano does, is totally unwarranted.

This interpretation of a revolutionary, rather than a merely reformist Bruno, has recently received substantial support from two Italian Bruno scholars, Luigi Firpo and Michele Ciliberto. Firpo, a historian, discovered a hitherto unpublished manuscript of considerable importance for detecting the real reasons for Bruno's condemnation by the tribunal of the Roman Inquisition. The document, dated 9 September 1599, contains the minutes of what was supposed to be the final hearing of the Congregation of Cardinals of the Holy Office. Therein are recorded, with bureaucratic accuracy, the individual votes of the Cardinals on the final sentence, for this last hearing was to result in the definitive sentence to be presented to the Pope for ratification at the end of the session over which he was to preside. The document well deserves being translated from the original Latin into English; it is presented here for the first time in its entirety to the English readership:

Congregation . . . September 9, Thursday, 1599.

[The cause] of Brother Giordano Bruno of Nola, of the Order of Preaching Friars, doctor in Sacred Theology, imprisoned in the jails of the aforementioned Holy Office, interrogated and tried for and about heretical depravity and other things more extensively explicated in the acts, after the process regarding these things instituted against him was recorded, in which the following votes were given:

R[everendus]. D[ominus]. Iulius Monterentius, procurator of the prosecution, voted that, with regard to the first part of the trial he has not been convicted for the propositions brought up against him; with regard to the other propositions, that he be tortured.

R. D. Marcellus Filonardus, assessor of the Holy Office, voted that Brother Giordano should not be regarded as convicted; nevertheless that he be tortured severely [*graviter*], and that a term to change his mind over the other articles should be fixed.

R. P[ater]. Albertus de Florentiola, General Commissary of the Holy Office: considering the infamy of this man, and considering that he cannot have other witnesses than criminal prisoners, according to the added confession at hand, he has indeed been convicted on many counts, just as on many others he will not be convicted, and with regard to those on which he has not been convicted let him be tortured severely, and with regard to those on which he has been convicted, let a term be fixed for him to change his mind.

R. P. D. Petrus Millinus voted that the said Brother Giordano Bruno be tortured with regard to those counts on which he has not been convicted, and with regard to those articles on which he has been convicted let a term be fixed for him to change his mind.

R. P. [Ippolytus Beccaria] voted he should be tortured neither just once nor twice: and that he be judged on what he shall declare.

R. P. D. Anselmus [Dandinus]: with regard to those articles of which he has been convicted let a term be fixed for him to change his mind; concerning the chief point of the Trinity let him be tortured; and if he does not give proper satisfaction, let him be delivered to the secular curia.

His Holiness Our Lord Clement Pope VIII, after having heard the votes of the aforementioned Reverend Lord Prelates and Fathers, doctors in theology and in both Laws, consultants of the said Holy Inquisition, decreed and ordained that a term be fixed for him to change his mind in everything he has confessed, and that, in the meantime, the allegations of the witnesses as well as his confessions be well examined, and that the cause be reinstituted.[12]

The importance of this document lies in the fact that it clearly attests to the fact that the allegations of all of Bruno's accusers, including those of Mocenigo and Bruno's fellow inmates, were found to be inadequate for a conviction, mainly because they were made, except in the case of Mocenigo, by characters of ill repute, fellow convicts, and even heretics already punished by the Inquisition. The conviction therefore had to be based exclusively on Bruno's own writings or on his confessions to the judges. This is where the role of the Jesuit, Robert Bellarmine, by far the intellectually most powerful theologian of the Inquisition, becomes decisive. He had been instructed to study carefully Bruno's writings and to excerpt from them all the propositions that he thought deserved censure. After months of examination, Bellarmine succeeded in compiling a list of eight censurable propositions, two of which were of a cosmological nature. They were presented to the accused for his response – recantation or defense – and he did so to Bellarmine's almost complete satisfaction. There were still one or two points, he said, that remained somewhat obscure. This evidence, contends Firpo, clearly proves that Bruno was not condemned for his theological, but rather for his cosmological 'errors'.

Bruno's final adamant and defying position obviously irritated his judges. The fact that they were incapable of refuting his views only contributed to increase the tension between them. Thus, Bruno, after seeing the collapse of the first part of the trial because the accusations of all his detractors were considered by the judges themselves to be invalid for a conviction, began to see his process as a personal duel with his judges, a sort of power match with extremely powerful yet dismally ignorant (in astronomical and cosmological matters) and conceited pedants, united in a conspiracy to crush him morally and physically with the sole purpose of debunking his threatening philosophy. Consequently, when Bruno was repeatedly subjected to severe torture with the sole purpose of extracting from him a confession of heresy regarding purely disciplinary or dogmatic issues (such as the one regarding three distinct persons in the one God) about which he had already several times confessed his doubts and expressed his readiness to accept the orthodox doctrines of the Church, he was outraged by the grave injustice done to him. His profound indignation was probably the principal reason for his refusal to surrender to the unfair demands of his judges. For, if a tortured man yielded – so ran the ordinances of the Holy Office – he would automatically become a convict, whereas if he did not break down, his steadfastness would, *ipso facto*, acquit him from all the charges of heresy brought against him.

In all fairness to the Pope it must be said that when the sentences of the Cardinals were presented to him, he did not explicitly approve the torture they had voted for (in this point he showed more humanity than the Cardinals, who unanimously voted for torture, two of them for severe torture, another for repeated torture), nor did he reject it. He simply ignored it, recommended that a conviction be sought by examining further the witnesses and

Bruno's writings, and that only after the conclusion of that further examination a final session of the Congregation be convened to pass sentence over the accused. We do not know for certain whether the unanimous vote of the Cardinals in favor of torture was actually carried out before that last session. We do know, however, that the only two ways left to get a legal conviction, after the testimony of the witnesses had been declared invalid, was the admission of guilt under torture or the voluntary obstinacy of the accused to recant a proposition considered heretical.

The dilemma for the Cardinal judges was clear. If they tortured the accused and he did not break down, he would have to be acquitted of all accusations leveled against him, and, if they chose not to torture him, they would have to condemn him because of his philosophical and cosmological views, since he had repeatedly expressed his willingness to recant all his theological errors. We also know that Bruno never admitted under torture being guilty of the crime of heresy, for that would have given his judges the legal justification for the conviction they were looking for. We also know that he refused to admit that his philosophical and cosmological views were heretical. The inevitable conclusion is that Bruno, if he was actually tortured and never broke down, should have been acquitted, since, according to the very rules set up by the Inquisition, his steadfastness under extreme duress acquitted him of all charges of heresy. On the other hand, if he was not tortured, then the conviction would have had to follow on grounds of obstinacy on heretical propositions. Consequently, Bruno had to be convicted of obstinate refusal to change his mind on purely ontological and cosmological issues. In both cases he was unlawfully and unjustly condemned by the Congregation of the Holy Office, and we must disagree with Corsano and even Firpo, who refuse to openly condemn the highest authority of the Church for this crime by acknowledging the legitimacy of the conviction. It is therefore not certain, but quite probable, that Bruno was actually tortured; this had been, after all, the unanimous recommendation of the Cardinals as the easiest way out of the dilemma. (An eye-witness of his walk to the stake said his body looked utterly emaciated and broken down by torture.) If he was indeed tortured, why then did the Inquisitors not let him go free? We know for certain that he never admitted his guilt. Consequently he should have been acquitted of all charges.

Because they would not let him go after all accusations had been declared invalid, Bruno could not but conclude that his judges were bent on destroying him at all costs. Perfectly aware, as indeed he was, of the inevitable consequences of his decision, he calmly responded to the peremptory injunction that he recant his errors (in the final twenty-second interrogatory session before the plenum of the Congregation presided over by the Pope) that he had nothing to recant, for he knew of nothing he should recant, but that he was willing to prove his innocence to any theologian they would appoint for a fair and open discussion. Consequently, he would not accept the guilt laid on him by his judges, especially now that they were judging him exclusively on the basis of his own writings and confessions. He would yield only to the Pope, as an impartial judge in a debate between equal contenders. He nonetheless remained ready, as he had always been, to change his mind if proven wrong, and to accept the final judgment of the Pope.

Upon this defiant declaration, the dice were cast and Bruno's fate was definitively sealed. Clement VIII refused even to read Bruno's last letter of appeal, on the basis that the time allowed for him to change his mind had already elapsed. When his judges, in presence of the Pope, pronounced over him the dreadful sentence, Bruno rose from his knees and uttered the famous words: 'With greater fear do you pass sentence over me than I feel on receiving it.'[13] He surely must have felt at that terrible moment that if justice was denied to him by the supreme authorities of a Church which claimed to be founded and guided by God incarnate, there was no point in trying to save his life, particularly if there was no longer any realistic possibility of carrying out the radical revolution that would definitively put an end to such intolerance and injustice. He had no choice left but to seek refuge in the only God he could believe in – the cosmic mind animating his eternal, infinite, acentric universe.

What the judges, who condemned Bruno to death, dreaded most was a cosmology that dealt the finishing stroke to their anthropocentric universe. However, there was something just as intolerable for them: Bruno's irrepressible intellectual aggressiveness. It was precisely this aggressiveness – the result of a remarkable conjunction of Bruno's rebelliousness and the creative imagination of his powerful intellect – that posed the greatest threat to the established religious edifice and its underlying philosophical foundation. To counter this threat, Bruno's challenge had to be demonized into satanic pride, and it had to be unconditionally suppressed, for his judges could not understand and would never accept that 'no great science was discovered in the spirit of humility'.[14]

Bruno was, above anything else, a true philosopher, in the sense that Socrates understood and realized this extremely rare type of human being, one who dedicated his life to the uncompromising pursuit of truth. Bruno, too, sought the truth relentlessly, and in order to find it he questioned everything. To question with radical intellectual honesty implies a resolute refusal to be rocked in the slumber of illusions, and the courage to relish the bitterness of unwelcome discoveries. In order to undertake this self-imposed task of questioning everything Bruno had first to be convinced of one indispensable requirement – his ability to find the truth all by himself. He could not trust anybody else's opinion, no matter how authoritative, and, in fact, he distrusted not only Aristotle and his followers, but even his much admired Copernicus as well. This self-reliance and universal distrust anticipated Descartes's radical philosophical stance and was the main reason for Bruno's violent clash with the Church authorities. For his was a time of faith and dogma, a time in which the monopoly of truth, all truth, not only religious, was believed to belong exclusively to the Church, whereas Bruno's dauntless questioning rendered everything questionable; it challenged the establishment and threatened to topple the pillars of religion; it therefore ultimately undermined the security of existence and the solidity of the state. Allegedly, this new corruptor of youth already even had loyal followers, the so-called Giordanisti! Can we then blame the defenders of the faith and protectors of the establishment for doing everything in their power to silence and destroy this menace?

Thus, Zuane Mocenigo thwarted Bruno's plans, and the Inquisition succeeded in eliminating for centuries to come the threat of the radical religious and ethical revolution that a successful intellectual movement inspired by Bruno's new ontology and cosmology had the potential of bringing about. That revolution obviously failed. However, the other revolution, the cosmological one, could not be stopped. Bruno had laid its foundations, and the flames that consumed his body were incapable of destroying them.

PART TWO

The Brunian Revolution

CHAPTER SIX

Copernicus Overrun

The revolution that prompted the transition from the medieval to the modern world was the most radical upheaval in the history of Western civilization, for it destroyed a frame of reference that had provided meaning and security to the entire population of Europe, North Africa, and the Near East for almost two thousand years, and abruptly replaced it with a most upsetting new world view. Professor Alexandre Koyré most accurately delineates the basic characteristics of this revolution:

> This scientific and philosophical revolution – it is indeed impossible to separate the philosophical from the purely scientific aspects of this process: they are interdependent and closely linked together – can be described roughly as bringing forth the destruction of the Cosmos, that is, the disappearance, from philosophically and scientifically valid concepts, of the conception of the world as a finite, closed, and hierarchically ordered whole (a whole in which the hierarchy of value determined the hierarchy and structure of being, rising from the dark, heavy and imperfect earth to the higher and higher perfection of the stars and heavenly spheres), and its replacement by an indefinite universe which is bound together by the identity of its fundamental components and laws, and in which all these components are placed on the same level of being. This, in turn, implies the discarding by scientific thought of all considerations based upon value-concepts, such as perfection, harmony, meaning and aim, and finally the utter devalorization of being, the divorce of the world of value from the world of facts.[1]

This was a bloodless revolution of ideas and values. It brought about, among other things, the supremacy of reason, the birth of skepticism and free thinking, and the complete devalorization of being (or what amounts to the same thing, the irrevocable divorce of ethics from cosmology). The so-called Copernican Revolution threw the European population out of whack; not only did it jumble its bearings, it also blew away its center. The irony is that, as it sometimes happens with great discoveries, this one, too, was attributed to the wrong person.

The only reason for calling this revolution Copernican is that in 1543 the Polish astronomer Nicholas Copernicus proposed, somewhat timidly, that the revolutions of the planets could be more elegantly explained by assuming that the Sun, rather than the Earth, was located at the center of the universe.[2] This conjecture was undoubtedly revolutionary, for it contradicted a world view that had prevailed unchallenged in the West for fifteen hundred years. But Copernicus' heliocentric hypothesis alone, however revolutionary, did not have the demolition power needed to bring down a world order that was so firmly established. For this to happen a great deal more was required than just swapping centers. Copernicus unquestionably had dealt a very serious blow to humankind's insatiable need for centers, for now people were told that their home planet was not the center of the universe. But Copernicus assuaged some of their frustration by assuring them that even if the Earth was not the center of the universe, at least the Sun was. Somewhat displaced from its central position in the universe, humanity could still feel secure: it was still pretty near the center.

The decisive blow to mankind's desperate need for security was in fact delivered in the sixteenth century, but not by Copernicus. For indeed the crucial cosmological insight of the misnamed Copernican Revolution was not that the Earth is not the center of the universe, but rather that the universe has no center at all. Also, if it had no center, then it had no boundaries either; and if it was boundless, it was legitimate to conclude it was also infinite, and then it would not be long before mankind realized, with dismay, that it had been banished forever from the cozy center it had hitherto thought it securely possessed and cast out into a desolate infinite, centerless universe. Reduced to a speck of dust drifting aimlessly in an infinite cosmos, it was impossible for mankind to continue considering itself the ultimate reason for the universe and the sole purpose of Creation; lost in a boundless acentric labyrinth, it felt doomed to inevitable extinction and destined to vanish without leaving behind the slightest trace of its fleeting existence.

The first man in European post-medieval history to formulate explicitly and clearly that the universe has no center[3] was not Copernicus (who died without ever realizing it), but the Italian Renaissance cosmologist Giordano Bruno. This single insight provided the scientific and philosophical revolution of the seventeenth century with the demolition power it needed to shatter the old world view. This was a major turning point in history, and the beginning of a value crisis that has lasted until our days. In Nietzsche's words, 'Since Copernicus man is rolling out of the center unto X.' On a historical worldwide scale, this revolution, the Brunian Revolution, signaled the beginning of the substitution of one paradigm of civilization by another. It was the dawn of Modernity.

The enormous resistance that Bruno's unsettling new world view would encounter among the defenders of the old is not difficult to understand. Very few thinkers in the two centuries that followed Bruno's death dared to hold it, and even less to defend it publicly. This is how the German philosopher Ernst Bloch describes what had happened:

> Perhaps it is still possible for you to relive what this meant: the roof of the heavens was pulled off, the world-onion with the seven skins exploded, along with the remote lanterns that shone on us through the stars; burst wide open was the confining jail of shells and spheres; an infinity of the cosmic Maximum dawned on the world, or so it seemed, as it had never been experienced before, except by mystics, when they immersed themselves in the infinity of God.[4]

Thus Bruno not only frustrated our instinctive craving for centers, but he also burst the bubble of our grandiose and highly comforting illusion of being the center of the universe. Humanity suddenly had become intolerably absurd, for what absurdity could be more unbearable to humanity than that of its utter cosmic insignificance?

Actually, Bruno achieved much more than definitively blowing away an obsolete cosmological model. His most significant contribution to the development of Western thought was his success in liberating both philosophical and scientific thought from the shackles that had hampered them for centuries. He unseated basic principles and presuppositions which had been considered, until then, sacred and inviolable by both science and philosophy, and set out to develop new ones in agreement with a few basic insights of Copernican astronomy, but only after driving them to their ultimate consequences. Thus, Leonardo da Vinci and Giordano Bruno were probably the first post-medieval thinkers to be convinced of the power of the human mind to fully comprehend the universe without the aid of revelation, and Bruno was certainly the first one to attempt such a purely rational explanation.

However, if Bruno is to be regarded as the true initiator of Modernity and the decisive intellectual inspirer of the scientific and philosophical revolution of the seventeenth century, he must have accomplished what Koyré pinpointed as the essential characteristic of that revolution: the 'devalorization of being, the divorce of the world of value and the world of facts', that is, 'the discarding by scientific thought of all considerations based upon value-concepts, such as perfection, harmony, meaning and aim'.

Consequently, from Koyré's point of view we would have to consider as Bruno's most revolutionary insight – a consequence of his discovery of cosmic acentricity and infinity – the view that the properties of matter are identical everywhere and in all directions (homogeneity), and that the universe would look more or less the same to a potential observer from whatever heavenly body he would happen to be looking at it, what is now known as 'isotropy'. Hence, for Bruno, there are neither hierarchies nor topographical privileges exclusively reserved for certain classes of heavenly bodies. He thereby becomes the first modern thinker to hit upon the basic cosmological laws of homogeneity and isotropy.

Cosmic isotropy and homogeneity are so fundamental to contemporary cosmology that they are generally referred to as the 'cosmological principle'. Having been the first man in European post-medieval history to discover them, Bruno already rightfully deserves to be recognized as the father of modern cosmology.

Thus, Giordano Bruno was not only the founder of modern cosmology, but also the initiator of true Modernity, for he destroyed the cosmos of the ancients and replaced it with the infinite, acentric, labyrinthian universe. He thereby totally 'devalorized being', as Koyré specified, for he banished forever from cosmological thought the ideas of perfection, harmony, meaning, and aim. This devalorization of being became so radical and comprehensive in Bruno's thought that he stretched it beyond the cosmological to the ontological realm. Thus, matter is no longer regarded by him as vile and inferior to mind and spirit, but rather as their equally noble and indispensable companion. Bruno's rehabilitation of matter[5] signals the culmination of that devalorization of being which Koyré considered the unmistakable sign of the beginning of Modernity.

It was not until the beginning of the nineteenth century that Bruno was called back from his long exile of oblivion. The one who rediscovered him was no other than the man who, for many years, was considered by many to be the greatest German philosopher, until his friend and rival Hegel deprived him of that honor. Between 1797 and 1800, Friedrich Schelling developed his philosophy of nature and published several works to expound it. One of these bore the title *On the World Soul, a Hypothesis of Advanced Physics for the Interpretation of the General Organism*. Here, Schelling acknowledged his indebtedness to both Bruno and Spinoza, the two philosophers whose revolutionary ideas about God and nature played a decisive role in fashioning Schelling's central concept of the Absolute. Finally, in April of 1802, Schelling published a dialogue considered by many the watershed of German idealism. He could not find a more appropriate title for it than . . . *Bruno*.

Thus it was mainly through Schelling that the greatest minds of nineteenth-century Europe – philosophers, Romantic poets, and scientists – began to direct their attention once again to Bruno's ideas about God and nature, and about the relationship between mind and matter. From then on, Bruno's popularity grew incessantly, not only for speculative and scholarly, but also for political, reasons.

However, Bruno's place in the history of Western thought needs to be reassessed mainly on the basis of the cosmological model he proposed for the first time to the intellectual elite of sixteenth- and seventeenth-century Europe. Copernicus' Sun-centered, closed universe superseded Ptolemy's Earth-centered one; later Descartes' and Newton's Sun-centered, open universe replaced Copernicus'; but Bruno's acentric, open, and infinite universe superseded them all. Contemporary cosmology, despite the astounding astronomical discoveries made in the twentieth century, has hardly improved on this basic model ever since it was first proposed by Bruno. The two most important corrections made to it are that this acentric, open, boundless universe had a beginning and is still expanding. Although Bruno did not believe that the eternal universe had a beginning, he did assert that it was not static but undergoing constant transformations.

Bruno viewed his revolutionary cosmology as a rebirth of the forgotten cosmology of the Pre-Socratic philosophers. While the Humanist Renaissance was mainly a rediscovery and revival of Classical Greek language, literature, sculpture, architecture, and philosophy, especially Platonic philosophy, what Bruno was determined to bring back was something that the Renaissance Humanists had totally neglected: the philosophy of nature and the discourse on the cosmos that the Pre-Socratic philosophers had initiated and vigorously conducted until Plato and Aristotle put an end to it with their model of a closed, finite, centered, hierarchical, and geometrically perfect universe. And, the main reason for the Renaissance Humanists' lack of interest in the natural philosophy and cosmology of the Pre-Socratics, was precisely their ardent admiration for Plato and the Neoplatonists.

Awakened from his dogmatic slumber by Copernicus, Bruno realized the falsity of the established cosmology and saw clearly the reason why it had held mankind in ignorance about the most elementary facts about the universe for more than fifteen hundred years: the Ptolemaic world view was intimately and inextricably interlocked with the two philosophical systems that sustained the whole edifice of Western civilization: Aristotelianism and Neoplatonism. Ptolemy's cosmological model was firmly established and stood like an inexpugnable fortress defended by the only intellectual army that existed in Europe – the hosts of Aristotelians and Neoplatonists quartered in its universities. The almost complete impregnability of the fortress had been secured by the invaluable service that the Ptolemaic cosmology had provided to the ingenious architects of that imposing edifice of Christian, particularly Catholic, dogmatic theology.

It is not difficult to see how congruous a geocentric universe was with the fundamental Christian dogmas of Creation, Incarnation, Original Sin, Ascension, Heaven, and Hell, and how useful it was for the agencies of Christian apologetics. It made a lot of sense that God had decided to become man and to dwell among men, if humanity had been placed at the center of the universe, for in that case it was evident that humankind was regarded by its Creator as supremely important, to the point of creating an entire universe exclusively for its sake (although the complementary belief that humankind's final destiny will be to be removed as far as possible from that center was always felt to necessitate additional, non-geocentric, explanations).

It is in the Frankfurt poems that Bruno's most mature cosmology and natural philosophy are contained. In them he undertook the revival of Pre-Socratic speculations about matter and the universe – the infinitesimally small and the infinitely large – most congruous with Copernicus' novel heliocentric world view, and succeeded in constructing a cosmological model of his own, which has perhaps very few totally original 'first' insights, but which, as a whole, represents one of the most astonishingly modern cosmological models ever conceived by a pre-twentieth-century cosmologist.

Bruno was one of the very few men in Europe who, in the relatively long period of eighty years that elapsed after the publication of Copernicus' *Commentariolus* of 1514 (where he exposes his heliocentric views for the first time), took Copernicus' views seriously and lectured widely on them in several European universities, once he had become aware of the enormous revolutionary potential the heliocentric hypothesis contained. However, what is really amazing about Bruno's Copernicanism is that long before Europe had taken notice of Copernicus and accepted his views, Bruno was already criticizing him sharply for not having gone far enough in his thinking. Thus, instead of becoming Copernicus' over-enthusiastic and uncritical epigone, Bruno became his severest critic.

Bruno had, in fact, become aware of the fact that Copernicus had failed to take full advantage of his fundamental insight – the movement of the Earth on its axis and around the Sun – to propose a radical new model of the universe which would capture and integrate all the consequences of that crucial discovery and fully exploit its enormous potential. Bruno then decided to work out his own cosmological model, based on reason, vivid imagination, and careful observation of astronomical phenomena. Its main features had already been established as early as 1584 when Bruno published in England his *Ash Wednesday Supper*; but the model was successively corrected, improved, developed, and described in detail in the works Bruno wrote between 1584 and 1591, particularly in the three Latin didactical poems he published in Frankfurt in 1591. In order to understand Bruno's place in the history of ideas and to assess his contribution to the foundation and development of modern cosmology it is therefore indispensable that we become fully acquainted with this model.

Copernicus' 'revolution' was certainly not a philosophical one; as a matter of fact, it wasn't even a scientific revolution properly speaking (as Kepler's, Galileo's and Newton's manifestly were). Copernicus simply revived the ancient heliocentrism and provided it with compelling mathematical and astronomical support. If Copernicus did initiate the sixteenth-century astronomical debate, Bruno is the man who gave it real depth by raising it to the philosophical level. It was on this terrain that the decisive battle of the Brunian Revolution had to be fought.

CHAPTER SEVEN

Bruno's Cosmological Model

Not only did almost all cosmological models of Antiquity and the Middle Ages harmonize with the doctrines of the philosophical systems that supported them, but these cosmologies were so essential to these systems and so inextricably intertwined with them that if a particular cosmological model was forced to yield to a model more in conformity with reality, the entire philosophical edifice became precarious. So is the demise in the seventeenth and eighteenth centuries of Aristotelianism and Neoplatonism (which had prevailed unchallenged for almost fifteen hundred years until Copernicus' model of the universe replaced the Aristotelian-Ptolemaic) an inevitable consequence of the rejection of the cosmological model with which they were inextricably interlocked?

Bruno became fully aware of the extreme vulnerability of both Aristotelianism and Neoplatonism after realizing the superior conformity to reality of the new cosmological model proposed by Copernicus, in comparison with the Ptolemaic model which those philosophical systems supported. He became so keenly aware of the intimacy of this dependency that he very soon regarded Copernicus' system as the most formidable weapon at his disposal for his planned all-out assault against Aristotelianism.

In order to assess the originality of Bruno's cosmological model, it may be useful to recall the principal features of the three models which, in the sixteenth century, claimed most appropriately to describe the structure, size, and shape of the universe. These were the Aristotelian-Ptolemaic, the Copernican, and Tycho Brahe's model.

The first one, certainly the most authoritative among philosophers as well as astronomers, was the Aristotelian-Ptolemaic model. It placed the fixed and immobile Earth in the center of the

universe, allowing all other heavenly bodies to rotate in regular
and perfect circular orbits around it. These heavenly bodies did
not move by themselves nor were they moved by others, but
needed to be held in their orbits and impelled around the Earth
by huge transparent transporting spheres, which in turn were
ultimately moved by the *primum mobile*, (first movable) the last
and most outlying sphere that enclosed them all. These transporting spheres were concentric and hierarchically ordered according
to the increasing immateriality of the bodies they carried. Since
the Moon was considered to be closest to the Earth and its aspect
showed marked luminous irregularities, it was assigned to the
first sphere. The second and third spheres were those of Mercury
and Venus respectively, whereas the Sun was transported by the
fourth sphere. The more distant planets, Mars, Jupiter and Saturn,
were carried around their orbits by the fifth, sixth, and seventh
spheres. Finally, the fixed stars, the most remote from Earth of all
the heavenly bodies, were all equidistant from the Earth, since
they were riveted to the eighth sphere, which was also called the
firmament. This sphere was believed to rotate at enormous speed
around the Earth once every twenty-four hours. The ninth sphere,
the *primum mobile* (for some the tenth, the ninth being a purely
crystalline heaven), although invisible, was the most important,
since it imparted motion to all the underlying spheres after receiving it from the *causa prima* (first cause) or supreme motor, God
himself. This *primum mobile* was also the ultimate boundary and
edge of the closed, finite world, for beyond it was the empyrean
heaven, the abode of God and the elect.

The universe was conceived as a perfect continuum, in which
empty space – the void – simply did not exist. This was a
mechanical and perfectly geometrical model, for all movements
were perfectly regular and due to the friction of contiguous
bodies.

The four elements – earth, water, air, and fire – existed only on
Earth and its immediate atmospheric surroundings, but were not
to be found in the superlunar bodies. Instead, they were made of a
fifth element called ether, or the quintessence, for the Aristotelian-
Ptolemaic model established that in the finite closed universe, the
Earth, which was made up of the heaviest of all four elements, was
located at the center, and that above the Earth was water, on top
of water, air, above the air, fire, and finally above all inferior four

elements was the quintessence, ether, of which all heavenly bodies were made.

This model was based on mythical Pythagorean and Platonic views about the mathematical perfection of cosmic topography, once the physical properties of density and weight had been selected as the ultimate criteria for the topographical order. Thus, the densest and heaviest element occupied the lowest place, whereas the lightest and most subtle had the highest. Then, in virtue of the 'valorization of being', the merely topographical 'lowest' was transformed into the ethical 'basest' and 'vilest'. This was, of course, the element earth, whereas the most noble and sublime was the element that came closest to the immaterial and purely spiritual, namely the ether. After all, one could hardly deny that the suns and stars were fiery, and that they were above the Earth, nor that the subtle air occupied the regions above both earth and water. Thus, the concepts of density and weight ended up generating, after their ethical transformation, the entire topography of the perfect cosmos.

Not only was this model accepted almost unanimously by scholars in all European universities throughout the sixteenth century, but it was sanctioned and zealously defended by the supreme doctrinal authorities of both Catholic and Protestant churches. In Nietzsche's words, this was the 'theological astronomy' which Copernicus defeated.[1]

As is well known, it was Copernicus who challenged the validity of the Ptolemaic model, and proposed instead his heliocentric model as early (or late!) as 1514, in a manuscript with very limited impact entitled *Commentariolus*. Almost thirty years later, in the year of his death, Copernicus published his major work, *De revolutionibus orbium coelestium* (On the Revolutions of the Heavenly Bodies), and dedicated it to Pope Paul III. In it, the heliocentric model was presented and mathematically demonstrated, however not as an original one, but as the model held by several ancient astronomers and philosophers as well. Copernicus' model, however, was different from the Aristotelian-Ptolemaic, mainly in that it placed the Sun in the center of the universe. Most of the features of the traditional geocentric model were left intact: the spheres, the firmament, the ether, the center, the edges, and the absence of the void. Copernicus had merely replaced one center by another, and let the rest continue revolving around the new center as it had done around the old one.

No professional astronomer took Copernicus seriously until the great comet of 1577 made its appearance. Then Tycho Brahe, the great Danish astronomer, started to pay attention to Copernicus, and very soon changed his mind and introduced a new cosmological model. The planets and comets, he admitted, do not revolve around the Earth, but rather around the Sun, as Copernicus asserted. But it was not easy, not even for the greatest astronomer of his time, to get rid of the sacrosanct theological astronomy that all the churches and university professors of Europe were upholding, and Brahe allowed the Sun to continue revolving around the Earth! Thus, in Brahe's model, the Earth continued to be the center of the universe.

These were then the three most authoritative cosmological models of the sixteenth century against which we now have to set Bruno's model in order to assess its originality and revolutionary potential.

Bruno's arguments against all these models were not based on new empirical evidence or more accurate mathematical calculations, but only on reason, good common sense, and a vivid imagination. The cosmological model which Bruno first and foremost needed to attack and undermine was obviously the Pythagorean-Platonic, which had been blended with the Aristotelian-Ptolemaic mechanistic model. It postulated perfectly regular motion in all heavenly bodies and a topographical hierarchy of increasing perfection. Thus, it was based on geometry and the Platonic view of ideal perfection obtaining only in the superlunar world, as well as on the Aristotelian concept of weight.

Bruno's cosmological model rests on an entirely different ontological basis, the *antica filosofia*, or ancient philosophy of Heracleitus, Anaxagoras, Epicurus, Lucretius, and the Stoics. From Heracleitus, Bruno borrowed the concept of eternal flow and becoming of all forms and entities in the universe. Also, from Heracleitus, as well as from Anaxagoras and the Stoics, he adopted the concept of a universal *logos* or *nous* (mind) immanent in the universe. From Epicurus and Lucretius, he took the idea of an infinite, eternal universe whose ultimate building blocks are elementary indivisible particles called atoms. (However, unlike Classical Greek atomism, Bruno maintained that the elementary particles were automotive and self-steering, rather than minute, utterly compact, dented pellets haphazardly colliding with each other and sticking together once a viable form was reached.) It is here that the Stoic concept of the soul of the universe furnished Bruno with a key concept for the metaphysical foundation of motion. Movement, he argued, does not come to bodies from outside; they have it in themselves, for every body is animated by its own internal principle of motion, its 'soul', the cosmic soul present in everything without suffering division or fragmentation. Not only is this soul in every single body, but it animates all the elementary particles of matter as well.

The Nolan elaborated his cosmological model in a relatively short time[2], but only after a strenuous process of speculation and private and public discussions and criticism of the other models. It reached its final and most mature form only months before Bruno's arrest and incarceration by the Venetian Inquisition (May 1592), in his last great cosmological treatise, the didactical poem in Latin *De immenso et innumerabilibus* (On the Immense and the Innumerables) written in Helmstedt and published in Frankfurt in 1591.

Bruno's cosmology is ultimately based on two principles: the infinitude and acentricity of the universe and its homogeneity and isotropy.[3] With them, Bruno not only 'devalorized being', but he also completely dehumanized the universe by removing the last vestiges of cosmic anthropocentrism.

Full and precise comprehension of Bruno's mature cosmological model is essential for a fair assessment of Bruno's contribution to the evolution of cosmology and science as well as to the history of ideas. It can only be attained, upon close examination of its development and coherence, by tracing the successive steps its author took and highlighting his most relevant insights.[4]

Bruno's first move was to challenge the traditional essential difference between terrestrial and celestial elements and bodies, a distinction which may be appropriately referred to as cosmological dualism. He denounced the glaring contradiction of the traditional Aristotelian-Ptolemaic world-view which asserted, on the one hand, that the Earth is the vilest of all heavenly bodies (since it is the heaviest and darkest), while, on the other hand, it placed it in the supremely privileged position of center of the universe, however not as its powerful center of gravity and universal attraction, but as the inert and motionless hub of a system of perfectly circular, concentric, and transparent transporting spheres.

Such spheres were conceived by Aristotelians, Platonists, Neoaristotelian Scholastics, and Neoplatonists as carriers and movers of all celestial bodies. Copernicus initiated the dismantling process of this elaborate cosmic structure. He removed one sphere – the solar one, but he did not dare to go further, and left the other spheres in place. Bruno went all the way: he abolished all the spheres, including the last one, the sphere of the fixed stars equidistant from the Earth, the so-called firmament or celestial vault. The decisive step had been taken: the universe was unbound, its hierarchies were abolished, the walls of the firmament thrown down, and all heavenly bodies set free. The open, infinite, acentric universe was born.

Once the spheres were abolished, the question arose: if there are no spheres, what was it then that kept the heavenly bodies at apparently constant distances from each other and prevented them from falling? Above all, what caused them to move? Indeed, the greatest obstacle to overcoming the traditional view was the difficulty in explaining the motion of celestial bodies. What caused the regular, circular, apparently perfect movements of the Moon, the Sun, and the planets? Certainly not gods or angels or demons, as some ancients had fancied, but still they seemed to need to be pushed or pulled by something, for it was extremely difficult to conceive of heavenly bodies moving themselves.

But, if the heavenly bodies don't need spheres to transport them, Bruno argued, why should they need to be carried, pushed, or pulled by anything at all in order to move? Why not assume that they are able to move themselves freely in space? Convinced that action at a distance is impossible, and not disposing as yet either of the notion of inertia (which Galileo was very soon to discover) or of Newton's gravitational force, Bruno attributed the movement of heavenly bodies to an intrinsic principle of motion. Aristotle had called the principle of motion in self-moving bodies (as most living organisms are) *psyche*, that is, soul. Celestial bodies, Bruno concluded, must also have souls; like all animals they, too, are capable of moving themselves.

This conclusion apparently makes Bruno an animist and a vitalist. However, if, according to Newton, bodies are capable of moving other bodies instantaneously and at a distance just by being present to each other, then either the bodies are really moving themselves spontaneously towards other bodies, or they are attracting other bodies to themselves. Actually, they are doing both, according to the third law of Newton. However, is this not attributing to the bodies themselves their own immanent principle of motion? The only difference is that, instead of a soul, Newton postulated a mysterious internal force – the force of universal gravitation – whose nature and reason for existence he never could, or even tried, to explain. Why should two bodies, by merely being in the presence of each other, mutually attract? To allege that there is a 'force' that causes this mutual attraction (a view which eventually was proved by Einstein to be incorrect) is just as gratuitous as to assert that the bodies have in themselves their own principle of motion. An utterly unexplainable fact of nature had merely been given a different name.

Still, if bodies do move about freely and spontaneously, what prevents their collision? For Newton the answer was simple: nothing at all. Bodies do collide, provided they are massive enough and near enough to each other. The conclusion then was inescapable (in a universe that is not expanding): the only reason for the universe not to have already collapsed on itself was that it had not had enough time to do so, but eventually it would, unless it were actually infinite and eternal. Newton could not bring himself to accept the actual infinity and eternity of the universe, although he did postulate the infinity of the space that contained the universe. Absolute space, he contended, is infinite.

In order to avoid the chaos that would inevitably result from self-moving celestial bodies in infinite space, Bruno attributed to them self-steering power as well. However, self-steering implies cognition and choice, and whatever is capable of cognition and choice displays the characteristics of what traditionally has been called 'mind' or 'intelligence'. The conclusion was inescapable: bodies not only have in themselves their own principle of movement, soul, but also the principle of cognition and choice, that is, mind. Everything, then, in the universe is moved by the cosmic soul and steered by the cosmic mind.

Bruno, however, insisted that the heavenly bodies are part of ordinary, imperfect physical reality which is constantly undergoing transformations. This implied that the properties that Plato attributed to forms, namely immutability, permanence, and perfection, do not apply to the heavenly bodies; they are totally absent from physical reality. Bruno adhered to Heraclitus' view that physical reality is in constant flux, and agreed with both his and Plato's view that all concrete physical reality is imperfect and mutable; but he differed from Plato in rejecting two separate realms of reality: the world of perfection, immutability, and permanence, the world of pure forms, and the world of physical reality, mutable and imperfect. According to Bruno, there is only one world, that of unstable, mutable, and imperfect physical reality. The Platonic world of forms, to be sure, does not totally disappear from Bruno's ontology, but physical objects are no longer conceived by Bruno as mere copies and participations of separate and autonomous pure forms; the only forms he still retains in his ontology are more like Aristotelian forms, immanent to physical bodies and atoms as the inseparable principles that animate, move, and steer them.

By identifying the Earth as a celestial body similar to all other opaque bodies in the universe and by eliminating the transporting spheres, Bruno freed the Earth, as well as all other celestial bodies, from all external constraints. They were all free to move about in the ether or infinite space, not randomly for sure, but following the autonomous commands of their own internal principles of motion. And since these injunctions imparted by the cosmic mind to the bodies it informs cannot be conceived as totally arbitrary and whimsical, but rather as highly rational, they may quite legitimately be interpreted as a vague anticipation and a rudimentary form of what later came to be known as the 'laws of nature'. However, the Newtonian concept of physical laws, with rigorous universal validity, laid the foundations for an utterly deterministic conception of the universe, in which the principle of causality reigned supreme. In Bruno's world, however, there is room for indeterminacy and spontaneity.[5]

In any case, one fundamental and inviolable cosmological premise underlying Bruno's thesis that bodies are capable of moving themselves is that, despite their apparently unrestrained automotive power, order in the universe must be maintained at all costs. Thus, if all bodies are bent on avoiding chaos, this must be attributed to an innate tendency to conserve themselves, that is, to maintain their integrity and avoid disintegration, not unlike inertia, the basic law of physics discovered by Galileo and Newton, which is the likewise inexplicable innate tendency of bodies to conserve their present state, whatever it may happen to be, either movement or repose.

In the absence of a sound physical theory of dynamics (which Galileo started to develop very soon after Bruno's death), it is not surprising that Bruno resorted to animistic principles to explain cosmic movement, for even long after the foundation and development of dynamics by Galileo, the nature and cause of cosmic motion remained a mystery for Bruno's successors.

Bruno's speculations about the movement of heavenly bodies led him to a totally new concept of weight in harmony with his basic cosmological insights. Aristotle was wrong in explaining the movement of the heavenly bodies by a transcendent, incorporeal, first cause and a series of subordinated movable transporting spheres. He was, however, no less mistaken in explaining weight as the tendency of heavy bodies to go back to their natural place if they happened to have been unnaturally removed from it, so that the more compact and earthy a body was, the more readily it tended to come back to where it belonged, the center of the Earth.

Thus, consistent with his explanation of the movement of heavenly bodies and with his rejection of privileged cosmic centers, Bruno proposed his theory of weight. Bodies tend to fall not because they are seeking to regain the original position they had violently lost, as close as possible to their natural center, but because, endowed as they are with their own principle of movement and self-steering, they somehow 'sense' their separation from the whole they were originally a part of, and move to restore their wholeness. In other words, weight for Bruno is the innate tendency of parts to restore the whole, of which they are parts, but this again, arguably, is nothing but the principle of conservation driven to its ultimate consequences. Just as inertia is the tendency of bodies to conserve their physical state, weight, for Bruno, is the body's tendency to preserve its integrity. And this again is a necessary consequence of the basic cosmological presupposition of the conservation of order in the cosmos. Despite its obvious animistic flavor, Bruno's new concept is remarkable because it succeeds in totally universalizing weight; it is a property henceforth applicable, not only to bodies situated on the planet Earth, but also to those on all other heavenly bodies as well, indeed to the heavenly bodies themselves if originally they happened to be a part of a larger whole. Bruno's new concept of universal weight, therefore, paves the way for Newton's theory of universal gravitation, which obviously implies that all heavenly bodies are heavy. However, this keen ontological insight of Bruno's, admittedly faulty and rudimentary, has been regarded by his shallower critics as an irrefutable proof of his irrational magical animism.

With regard to certain astronomical issues such as the size, composition, movement, and distance from the Earth of the heavenly bodies, Bruno arrived at conclusions that none of his contemporaries, and only very few of his successors prior to Newton, ever reached. Thus, he clearly established the difference between stars and planets existing beyond our solar system.[6] He also asserted the irregularity of their speeds and trajectories, whereas all his contemporaries and immediate successors adhered to the Aristotelian ascription of uniform circular (or elliptical) motion to all heavenly bodies. Bruno also predicted that there were other planets in our solar system, not yet discovered due to their distance and size, and that they may be 'larger and smaller than our own'. He correctly indicated that the farther away from the Sun these planets are, the larger is their orbit around it, and 'the greater their orbit the more slowly they accomplish their journeys around the Sun'. He also predicted that, the farther away from the Sun a planet is, the more quickly it spins around its center[7], which is a remarkable prediction considering the fact that the larger planets Neptune, Jupiter, Saturn, and Uranus all revolve on their axes at speeds faster than that of the Earth's rotation. In fact, the largest of all, Jupiter, revolves on its axis in only ten hours!

With regard to the Sun, besides insisting that it is not, as Copernicus believed, the center of the universe, Bruno arrived at another correct insight. The Sun, he contended, is not totally immobile; it, too, revolves around its center.[8] The conclusive proof for this remarkable anticipation came twenty years later, when Galileo discovered that the sunspots were on the Sun's surface, and that they consistently moved in the same direction.

Along with these correct insights, Bruno also had some erroneous astronomical views. For example, he denied that the Moon had any impact at all on the regular fluctuations of the tides (Galileo, by the way, agreed with him). The reason for this error was Bruno's reluctance to explain motion by any pulls or pushes coming from external agents, and particularly his conviction that action at a distance (without a medium of transmission) is impossible. But was Bruno really so wrong about this after all? Did not Einstein's general theory of relativity put definitively to rest Newton's assumption of a universal gravitational force that explained the tides by the pull that the Moon exerted over larger masses of water and the transmission of this pull through an ether which Einstein proved to be utterly superfluous?

Bruno also erroneously believed that the Moon, like the planets of the solar system, revolved directly around the Sun, and that it had water, clouds and air, and, consequently, that it could also very well support extraterrestrial life and even lodge intelligent inhabitants. Bruno again was mistaken in his assumption that not only other planets, but also other incandescent stars like the Sun could be inhabited by living creatures.

With regard to the Earth, Bruno thought that there was water in its center, or perhaps the fluid of some molten metal, but this, rather than an error, is a remarkable anticipation of what is actually the case.[9]

Bruno also admitted the possibility that the Sun and some of the other stars of the universe were fixed and immobile.[10] This seems inconsistent with some of his other theories and predictions. However, by attributing some stability to the Sun and the other suns Bruno did not contradict his basic conviction that the Sun rotates. He may have been referring to relative, rather than absolute, fixation, in the sense that the suns would act as centers to their own planetary systems, and thus appear as fixed, although in reality they, too, rotated and had other movements as well, and thus were not exempt from the universal motion and the transformations which Bruno claimed to be an essential characteristic of all heavenly bodies. Bruno, however, explicitly stated his insecurity about this, since 'none has observed them'.

Most of these misconceptions, far from being the product of a wild imagination, are the result of some basically correct cosmological insight. Thus, Bruno refused to believe that the Sun – or any other heavenly body for that matter – was made exclusively of fire or any other special single element, such as ether or the Aristotelian quintessence. It was by far more reasonable to assume that all and the same elements that were found on the Earth – fire, air, water, and earth – were also present in all heavenly bodies; in sum, that there was nothing extraordinary about them, a view which was indeed a long way from considering them divine, as many Aristotelians and Neoplatonists did. The root of their error was, according to Bruno, their inability to distinguish between physical reality and mathematical conceptions in their speculations about heavenly bodies; thus, it was Plato's idealism and Aristotle's own residual Platonism that led them astray when they speculated about the heavens. It is here that Bruno's empiricism and radical opposition to idealism come most clearly to the fore. It was precisely this strong empirical turn of Bruno's mind that led him to the crucial conviction that both the elementary constitution of the heavenly bodies, as well as their movements, are irregular and therefore utterly incapable of being adequately represented by any mathematical equation.

In view of this, it would be unfair to highlight Bruno's manifest astronomical errors (which resulted mainly from the rudimentary development of astronomical science and technology in his time, since he did not even have a telescope at his disposal) in order to present them as clear evidence of the unscientific bent of his mind. Instead, closer attention should be paid to the basic point he was trying to make when he was arguing in favor of a particular misconception, for Bruno's astronomical errors must be interpreted and judged within the frame of his entire cosmological model. Thus, when Bruno affirms the probability of life on the surface of the Sun and other 'fiery' bodies, the point that he was trying to make is that the very same conditions that make possible life on Earth also exist on other heavenly bodies despite their incandescent appearance. Indeed, if the same elements that are found on Earth are also to be found on those fiery heavenly bodies, there was reason to believe that similar living beings could exist there as well.

Only the rudimentary state of astronomy and chemistry in Bruno's time made it impossible for him to be more precise about the properties and elementary composition of the heavenly bodies. The really amazing fact is that this rudimentary state of science did not prevent him from reaching his most crucial and revolutionary cosmological insight, namely the similarity of structure, composition, and movements of all heavenly bodies, independently of their distance from the Earth – an insight whose validity has remained unchallenged until this day, and is the fundamental theoretical presupposition of contemporary astronomy and cosmology, particularly of that science indispensable and precious to astrophysics, namely spectography, which made possible the revival of cosmology by providing indisputable proof of the expansion of the universe. The astronomical errors Bruno incurred while driving his basic cosmological insights to their ultimate consequences, like the existence of air, water, and life on the Sun and the Moon, are of relatively little importance compared to the paramount relevance of those insights. Indeed, as happens all too often with Bruno's unsympathetic critics, they entirely miss the forest by riveting their eyes on some misshapen peripheral tree.

When Bruno expressed the opinion, again not entirely correct, that the movement of heavenly bodies is circular rather than rectilinear, the point he was trying to make is that circular motion could only be natural to heavenly bodies, since rectilinear motion is proper only to parts violently separated from the whole when they are striving to regain their wholeness, as stones lifted from the surface of the Earth do when they fall back. Physical science had not yet come up with a plausible rational explanation of why heavenly bodies moved in circular (or quasi-circular) orbits in space. Kepler would soon attribute the elliptical orbits of the planets to magnetic forces only recently discovered by Gilbert, and later on Newton explained them by the universal force of gravitation. Both of these explanations were eventually proved to be not entirely correct. On the other hand, Bruno's view that rectilinear motion was totally foreign to heavenly bodies was not off the mark, if we accept Einstein's view that bodies in spacetime naturally move along the geodesics created by the warping of the fabric of spacetime by mass/energy. Thus, according to Einstein, rectilinear motion is impossible for bodies in curved spacetime.

In any case, it is important to note that Bruno's insight into the homogeneity of all heavenly bodies paved the way for Newton's insight into the universality of physical laws, since Bruno asserted the homogeneity, not only of the stuff all heavenly bodies are made of, but of their properties and movements as well.

In his arguments against both Platonists and Aristotelians, Bruno revealed himself as a highly independent and critical thinker, opposed to idealism, determined to rely exclusively on observation and reason (hence leaning decisively towards an empiricist position), opposed to all forms of dogmatism, and most willing to correct his own views, if compelled to do so, by either reason or empirical observation. His constant plea is to reject all entities fabricated by the mind (such as transporting spheres, cosmic hierarchies, the quintessence, and so on) which are neither observable in nature nor postulated by reason as necessary for the explanation of physical reality. Bruno does strongly favor intuition and reasoning in cosmology, but only under the strict supervision of empirical observation. Thus, far from blocking the advance of science (as the philosophical systems which he so vigorously fought obviously did), Bruno showed the right way to it by establishing reason and empirical observation as the most reliable means to acquire knowledge of the universe.

Probably none of the particular insights that make up Bruno's cosmological model was totally original. Whether it was the infinity of the universe, or its acentricity and boundlessness, or cosmic homogeneity, or the plurality of worlds, or the transmutation of everything into everything, there is almost always someone else, either Nicholas of Cusa, or Lucretius, or one of the Pre-Socratics, who must be given credit for the first recorded formulation of those insights. However, the originality of Bruno's model does not consist in the unprecedented novelty of each and every one of its features, not even of the crucial ones (as was the case with Kepler's, Newton's and Einstein's models), but rather in the predominantly correct selection, among the many other incorrect insights of his numerous precursors, of a considerable number of correct ones, for all those insights were known in his time and had been known to many for many centuries before him, and yet it was only Bruno who took them seriously and blended them into a coherent whole. As Paul Henri Michel pointedly remarks,

> The great merit of Bruno is that he tried to speak in the name of a science that was still mute (the heliocentric cosmos of Copernicus differs little in its structure and limits from the geocentric cosmos of Ptolemy). Without being an astronomer, he clearly saw the scientific nature of the problem of the infinite. It was no longer enough for him to assert the existence of other universes, simply assumed or conjectured, beyond a universe that remains closed. In order to enter upon unexplored paths, he claims to throw down what he calls 'the walls of the firmament'; and he pursues this purpose with such boldness that we may be permitted to smile, but in the history of science it marks nevertheless a new period – a

subsequently completed period in which stand out the fear of Pascal, the peaceful serenity of a Spinoza or a Fontenelle, the proud assurance, already impaired, of the nineteenth century.[11]

Bruno unquestionably did see 'the scientific nature of the problem of the infinite', and his 'boldness' certainly 'marks . . . a new period . . . in which stand(s) out . . . the proud assurance of the nineteenth century'. This is precisely the crucial point that continues to be overlooked by those unsympathetic scholarly critics of Bruno who, profoundly disturbed by his alleged monistic pantheism, cannot see in his cosmology anything but Hermetism, animism, and haughty disdain for mathematics.

CHAPTER EIGHT

The Infinite Universe

Natur hat weder Kern noch Schale,
Alles ist sie auf einem Male.[1]
GOETHE

The insights that are most fundamental to Bruno's cosmology, and which, at the same time, seem to have had few if any precursors, namely the infinity, homogeneity, and acentricity of the universe had already been proposed by the Ancients, probably by some of the Pre-Socratics, and certainly by Lucretius, whose book *De natura rerum* (On the Nature of Things) profoundly influenced Bruno's thinking.[2]

Also, among Bruno's contemporaries there seem to have been a few who shared his views about the infinity of the universe. Some critics claim that the first modern astronomer to explicitly maintain the thesis of an infinite universe was Thomas Digges.[3] Professor Alexandre Koyré disagrees:

> In spite of the very able defence of the priority rights of Digges made by Professor Johnson in his excellent book, *Astronomical Thought in Renaissance England,* I still believe it was Bruno who, for the first time, presented to us the sketch, or the outline, of the cosmology that became dominant in the last two centuries.[4]

Thus, Koyré totally agrees with Professor Lovejoy, who in his classical *Great Chain of Being* wrote:

> Though the elements of the new cosmography had, then, found earlier expression in several quarters, it is Giordano Bruno who must be regarded as the principal representative of the doctrine of the decentralized, infinite, and infinitely populous universe; for he

not only preached it throughout Western Europe with the fervor of an evangelist, but also first gave a thorough statement of the grounds on which it was to gain acceptance from the general public.[5]

Whereas it is not certain that Bruno had read Digges or knew of his views on the infinity of the universe[6], we do know that he had read Cusanus' (Nicholas of Cusa's) *De docta ignorantia* (On Learned Ignorance) and that he was most familiar with the Cardinal's thoughts. The merit of having been the first philosopher of the dying Middle Ages to assert the infinity of the universe has often been ascribed to Cusanus.[7] Koyré, however, contests this. While admitting that the Cardinal did deny the finitude of the universe and its enclosure by the walls of the heavenly spheres, Koyré points out that Nicholas of Cusa

> ... avoids as carefully and consistently as Descartes himself the attribution to the universe of the qualification of 'infinite', which he reserves for God and for God alone. His universe is not infinite (*infinitum*) but 'interminate' (*interminatum*) ... It never reaches the 'limit'; it is, in the full sense of the word, indetermined ... It cannot, therefore, be the object of total and precise knowledge, but only that of a partial and conjectural one.[8]

Koyré is categorical in his assessment of Cusanus: 'Nicholas of Cusa, though it has often been so claimed, is not a forerunner of Nicholas Copernicus'; but he adds 'and yet his conception ... goes far beyond anything Copernicus dared to think of'.[9] Now this is precisely what Bruno grasped, and what allowed him to go not only far beyond Copernicus, but beyond Cusanus as well. For, according to Bruno, the universe is not just indetermined, but downright infinite. And this infinity is an attribute, first of all, of space:

> There is a single general space, a single vast immensity which one may freely call Void: in it are innumerable globes like this in which we live and grow; this space we declare to be infinite, since neither reason, convenience, sense-perception nor nature assign to it a limit.

Bruno goes further. To make sure that no ambiguity remains, he clearly and explicitly proclaims the infinity, not only of space, but also of the heavenly bodies contained in it:

> It is certain that . . . it will never be possible to find an even half-probable reason, why there should be a limit to this corporeal universe, and, consequently, why the stars, which are contained in its space, should be finite in number.[10]

Not only is the universe, *de facto*, infinite, it necessarily has to be so, Bruno argues, using now a theological argument: the universe is God's creation, and the infinite cause cannot but produce an infinite effect, since no reason can be given why it would restrain itself, having the power to create an infinite universe. Such an infinity would still be an imperfect one, since it implies multiplicity and discreteness. This infinite creation, argues Bruno, is not incompatible with God's divinity and omnipotence; in fact, it is what most suitably reveals them.

Even the idea of the acentricity of the universe, a necessary consequence of its infinity, was not totally original. Bruno may have got the idea from Lucretius, or perhaps from Nicholas of Cusa. However, here, once more, it is not clear whether Cusanus, when writing about the circumference that has no center and the center that is everywhere, was really referring to the universe, not to God. Cusanus himself almost certainly had borrowed the famous saying '*sphaera cuius centrum ubique, circumferentia nullibi*' (the sphere whose center is everywhere, its circumference nowhere) from the Pseudo-Hermetic *Book of the XXIV Philosophers*, an anonymous compilation of the twelfth century, where it was used unambiguously to denote God[11], but he went a bit further. Cusanus did apply the saying to the universe, however not literally, and made God its figurative rather than its geometrical center. For the universe, according to Cusanus, has neither a geometrical center nor a circular boundary, for this would imply geometrical perfection and absolute regularity, and the whole point of *De docta ignorantia* was to drive home the Platonic notion that there is no absolute perfection and regularity in sensorial reality. Hence, knowledge of all physical reality could only be approximate and conjectural. Consequently, only God could be viewed as the figurative center of the universe, and Cusanus explicitly said so: 'God is the center and the circumference of all stellar regions.'[12] What Cusanus meant was this: There is no perfection in the physical universe; if the universe had a geometrical center and a circular boundary, it would be a sphere; but a sphere is the most perfect geometrical solid; so if we still insist on ascribing a center and a circumference to the universe, only God qualifies, for He is the identity of these two opposites.

It was Bruno, finally, who, inspired by Lucretius[13], resolutely applied the famous saying straightforwardly to the universe – the universe resembles the (impossible) infinite sphere whose center is everywhere and its circumference nowhere – thus taking good care not to assign to God any topographical role, neither as center nor as enclosing boundary; in fact, Bruno left God totally out of the cosmological picture.[14] Thus Bruno unambiguously proclaimed that 'the world is infinite and therefore, there is no body in it to which it would pertain *simpliciter* [without restrictions] to be in the center, or on the center, or on the periphery, or between these two extremes.'[15]

Yet another basic feature of Bruno's cosmological model, the absence of hierarchical structure in the universe, was previously stated by Cusanus. The gist of the Cardinal's argument was to disagree with the utterly inconsistent Aristotelian view that the Earth, in spite of being the center of the universe, had to be regarded as the vilest and most imperfect of all the heavenly bodies, indeed as the natural home of all imperfection. A learned ignorance could not uncritically agree with cosmic hierarchies so elaborately contrived, for imperfection and change, even decay and corruption, were to be found also in the Moon and the Sun, indeed in all of the heavenly bodies, since they were all part of physical reality and, as Plato taught, absolute perfection cannot be found in any physical entity perceptible by the senses. Thus, Nicholas of Cusa, antedating Bruno, rejected a cosmic hierarchical order by attributing imperfection equally to all heavenly bodies. However, he did not go far enough, for he retained the entire traditional array of heavenly spheres, including the eighth one, of fixed stars that moved most rapidly, the firmament that was supposed to enclose the whole universe. Thus, although Cusanus refused to respect the universe's ancestral privilege of being a perfectly regular sphere, he continued to honor the firmament as the wrapper of an otherwise imperfect, irregular, and acentric universe.

In contrast, Bruno's rejection of a cosmic hierarchical order was radical and absolute. First he abolished all the spheres, and then he explicitly asserted that all the elements that are found on Earth are also to be found in all heavenly bodies. He argued that these have movements similar to the terrestrial ones (agreeing with Cusanus in that this movement is naturally circular, but, unlike Cusanus, already attributing rotary motion to the Earth and even to the Sun and the rest of the stars and planets of the universe), and finally he agreed with Cusanus' most original and bold intuition that life and intelligent beings of a different nature from ours are very likely to exist on many other heavenly bodies as well. With these sweeping assertions Bruno had firmly established the fundamental cosmological principle of universal homogeneity and isotropy.

Koyré sums up his assessment of Cusanus' contribution to modern cosmology: 'As we see, a new spirit, the spirit of the Renaissance breathes in the work of Cardinal Nicholas de Cusa. His world is no longer the medieval cosmos. But it is not yet, by any means, the infinite universe of the moderns.'[16]

This is certainly not true of Bruno's world. Not only is his world no longer the medieval cosmos, but neither is it any more the cosmos of the Neoplatonic Renaissance. His view of the universe is the first truly modern one in the history of Western civilization.

In order to understand this, we must bear in mind what both Koyré and Lovejoy indicate, namely that the novelty and revolutionary potential of Bruno's thought does not lie so much in this or that particular cosmological insight, but rather in the coherence and completeness of his entire cosmological model – the 'sketch' or 'outline', as Koyré calls it – and, as Lovejoy specifies, in his clear and compelling statement of the grounds on which this model was based. If Bruno borrowed from his predecessors most of his cosmological insights, and there is no doubt that he did, he certainly must be given credit for the good taste and judgment he showed in choosing, most of the time, precisely the correct ones, and in discarding the wrong ones, and in combining the former into a most coherent and compelling model.

Furthermore, the fact that Bruno preached his cosmological model 'throughout Western Europe with the fervor of an evangelist' places him on a level very different from that on which all of his precursors stood. It is indeed a very different matter occasionally to express a view about the universe in writing, however pointedly, than to make it the core of a doctrine a man is willing to dedicate his entire life to, preaching it to the world like a gospel.[17] Since this was done rationally, through rigorous argumentation in open discussion, not fanatically or demagogically, his doctrine not only betrays a remarkably unshakeable conviction, but also takes on the character of a most urgent and enlightened mission. This preacher, rather than as an evangelist of joyous tidings, appears as an awe-inspiring prophet announcing the destruction of the old world and the imminent advent of a new one.

Bruno's concept of an infinite universe is intimately related to his idea of infinite space, which, however, rather than being a total void or absolute vacuum, was conceived by him as filled with ether, a supremely tenuous medium which offered no resistance to the movements of celestial bodies. Whereas the idea of the void, and hence of a totally empty space, was rejected by Aristotle and the Peripatetics, Bruno postulated absolute space, that is, the vacuum or void, (which he identified with a non-substantial ether no longer considered a fifth 'element') as a necessary assumption for explaining the free motion of cosmic bodies in the absence of transporting spheres. 'All motion is accomplished either starting from a void, or towards a void, or in a void.'[18]

Bruno's 'affirmation of an infinite space, a general place, homogeneous, three-dimensional, having neither up nor down, neither center nor periphery, the affirmation, in short, of a space independent of the body of the universe'[19] irresistibly led him further to the affirmation of an infinite universe.

The hypothesis of a finite world in infinite space was inadmissible for Bruno. If absolute space existed, Bruno argued, it had to be filled with infinite worlds. Otherwise, a single finite world located in that infinite space had to be conceived as an insignificant point, a nothingness unworthy of God's omnipotent creative power.

In sum, with regard to the infinity of the universe, this is what Bruno explicitly states: there is infinite space, which he calls ether, a sort of extremely rare cosmic air[20] totally different from the quintessence which Aristotle imagined. This 'air' becomes 'the common and universal space, the infinitely spacious bosom which holds and embraces the whole infinite universe'. In this infinite space there are innumerable, in fact, an infinite number of celestial bodies. These celestial bodies are either suns (hot and fiery) or planets (cold).

Thus, Bruno not only asserts the infinity of the receptacle, space or ether, but he further explicitly affirms the infinity of the celestial bodies that move within this infinite space. To the objection that there can be no finite parts of an infinite, Bruno answers that they are not parts of the infinite but parts within the infinite.[21]

Thus, the Brunian universe has no enclosing boundaries, edges or surfaces; hence it is infinite, acentric, and shapeless. As a whole, it is totally immobile, like Parmenides' One, but the parts within it, numerically infinite although individually limited in many ways, are constantly moving, changing their shape, and even transforming themselves into different entities.

Bruno's argument for an infinite universe is compelling, even theologically: infinite perfection, he argues, must express itself in an infinite creation. For if God decided to create the universe, why would He have limited Himself to the creation of this single visible closed world that, despite its obvious immensity, cannot but appear as utterly insignificant in comparison with all He could create? Truly, it was difficult to accept that an omnipotent God should have chosen to manifest Himself in such a limited way and so drastically to have restrained Himself in His work of creation, particularly considering that His intention in creating, as many theologians insisted, was precisely to manifest His infinite great- ness, wisdom, and power to all possible intelligent observers of his creation.[22]

To reinforce this theological argument, Bruno advanced the philosophical consideration that there must be an infinite passive power in nature corresponding to the infinite active power of God; otherwise, if we assume that the passive power of nature is finite, we would have to conclude that the finite imposes limits on the infinite. We would thereby claim 'with supreme inconvenience that the prime and highest principle is similar to a man who wants to play a guitar, but does not learn because he has no guitar; or to someone who is able to do something but does not do it, because the thing that he can do cannot be done by him, which is an obvious contradiction'.[23] A finite universe would then be, as Paul

Henri Michel suggests, a 'kind of divine reticence'.[24] God, Bruno argues, could not be miserly: 'Why do you wish that this center of divinity which can amplify itself infinitely into an infinite sphere should remain sterile and envious [*invidioso*] . . . ?'[25]

Bruno could not accept the idea of a finite universe on the grounds that, whether it was an infinite external cause or an infinite internal immanent principle that brought it to existence, in either case the result had to be infinite as well. Consequently, if the universe were finite, it could not have an infinite external cause but had to have in itself the finite principle of its finitude and, since it holds the totality of being, it nonetheless had to be regarded as the Absolute. We would then end up with a finite Absolute, a sort of finite God. Bruno, in spite of his stark monism, was still too much of a Platonist and a Christian to countenance this view. Phrasing Bruno's thought with the words that we just quoted, if the 'center of divinity' decided to 'amplify itself infinitely into a . . . sphere', the sphere had to be infinite as well.[26]

Thus, Bruno attributes infinity to both God and the universe. However, he scrupulously distinguishes between the infinity of God and the infinity of the universe. The infinity of God, Bruno explains, is totally comprehensive, that is, it is absolute, since there are no limits or boundaries in God. On the other hand, although the universe has no edge, limit, bound, or surface, in a sense it does contain boundaries and limits because it is composed of infinite finite parts, which are themselves bounded and limited. Nonetheless, the universe is truly infinite because it actually realizes endless divine possibilities, not once and for all, for sure, but successively, along the eternal duration of the evolving universe.

But can an infinite series of finite elements actually exist? Is this Brunian concept of a whole, consisting of an infinite number of finite parts, mathematically sound? Does it not conflict with Kant's and Cantor's view that a set of infinite elements cannot actually exist? However, even if the amount of matter in the universe were finite, that is, even if the number of heavenly bodies and particles, although immense, were finite (as the conventional Big Bang theory seems to postulate), absolute certainty about the finitude of the universe could be attained only if a measurement of the quantity of matter in the universe could be taken by an ideal observer who would compute, at one particular point in space-time, the total amount of matter that, at that precise instant, actually exists in the universe. This, of course, would be impossible for many reasons, among them because the observer would not only have to be able to compute, but also to coexist simultaneously with all the mass and the energy of the universe. Hence, the assertion that the amount of matter in the universe is finite, despite its high plausibility and the impressive estimates that have already been made of the total amount of particles and sub-particles in the universe, can never reach absolute certainty. Kant was probably right in asserting that we will never know for sure whether the universe is finite or infinite, temporal or eternal.

But even if the total amount of matter of the universe, at any given time, were indeed finite, at least one kind of cosmic infinity is certainly still possible, namely one that would be realized gradually and successively throughout the eternal duration and evolution of the universe. Actual infinity in the form of a simultaneous coexistence of infinite parts is certainly not a necessary implication of Bruno's model, but it does support this other kind of infinity, for Bruno conceived the universe as constantly and eternally evolving. Thus, in the first dialogue of his treatise *De infinito universo et mundis* (On the Infinite Universe and Worlds), Elpidio asks, 'What is this spreading forth?'[27] and also, in that other quotation we just cited, Bruno asserted that the divinity must 'amplify itself into an infinite sphere'. Thus, an infinite set of finite parts actually could exist, if not simultaneously at least successively. In this case, the infinite variety and complexity of forms and species that would successively emerge in the infinite eternal worlds would give even more credibility to the idea of divine omnipotence in an ongoing process of creation. In fact, it is precisely in this way that real omnipotence would be most effectively deployed. Thus, even if the innumerable elements of the universe are actually finite at a certain instant, it is still conceivable that the successive transformations they undergo never end, and consequently, that they appear and vanish indefinitely, thereby giving rise to endless new forms and combinations.

This, of course, is particularly plausible if the hypothesis of an oscillating universe is true; but even if it is not, even if our universe is irreversibly expanding and will never again collapse upon itself into another singularity, successive infinity is still conceivable, for, if one Big Bang were possible there is no reason to suppose that other Big Bangs, within or without our universe, are not just as possible. Why should there be only one Big Bang? Here, too, Bruno's theological argument would make sense: if the omnipotence of God made one Big Bang possible, why should it not make innumerable Big Bangs possible as well? Why this thrift in Him who is overbounteous and who allegedly creates observers precisely for them to admire his omnipotence?

One of Bruno's most astonishing anticipations of contemporary cosmology is his view of a fluid, supremely energetic, and constantly evolving universe. The stubborn resistance to this view, now unanimously held by the entire scientific community, lasted until the second quarter of this century. Almost all ancient and modern cosmological models (except, perhaps, the Heracleitan and some ancient atomistic models) subscribed to the idea of a static universe, in which no expansion, no contraction, and, above all, no evolution ever occurred. Even Einstein clung to the idea of the static universe so tenaciously that he even went as far as tampering with his equations of general relativity to support his erroneous belief by means of a contrived cosmological constant. Only the conclusive evidence provided by Hubble in 1929 forced Einstein to change his mind.

More than three hundred years before Hubble's discovery, Bruno was the first modern cosmologist to challenge the static model, and he did so, reasoning most cogently from the theoretical basis of his revolutionary concept of a fecund and energetic matter.[28] Thus, upon integrating the ideas of an infinite, dynamic, and evolving universe, Bruno presented a model of the universe not matched, in its remarkable affinity and congruence with numerous contemporary ones, by any other model developed before Hubble's momentous discovery.

In one point, however, Bruno's cosmological views are in sharp disagreement with contemporary cosmology's most widely accepted theory of the origin of the universe. According to Bruno, the universe not only has no boundaries and edges in space, it also has no boundaries in time. The universe had always existed and would always continue to exist; it was eternal. If creation still had to be upheld (mainly for reasons of Catholic dogmatic theology), Bruno disagreed with the common doctrine that it had taken place at the beginning of finite time, a time that could be measured back to time-point zero. If there had been a creation, and Christian dogma was most unequivocal about that, then the universe had to be coeval with the Creator, for it was meaningless to conceive a 'time' when only God existed without the universe. If God has the power to create the universe, Bruno argued, it is ridiculous to fancy that he would have 'waited' for the right time to use that power. (This was by no means an heretical opinion; St. Augustine had held it long before Bruno.) Thus, for Bruno, there was no beginning of time, and hence also no beginning of the universe. Space, time, and everything that is in space and time, were conceived by Bruno as being infinite.

Although the most generally accepted contemporary cosmological models sharply disagree with Bruno with regard to the question of whether or not the universe is infinite, in one point they do agree, namely that neither finitude nor infinity can be attributed to just one or two of the elements of the problem. Thus finitude cannot be attributed to just one or two of the four terms of Einstein's 'quaternity' (space-time-mass-energy) and denied of the rest. All four are finite. Likewise, according to Bruno, space and time and all the bodies contained in them are infinite. Neither position has succeeded as yet in proving its point, and consequently Kant's first antinomy – the world had a beginning in time, and is also spatially bounded – remains unsolved and, very likely, is insoluble as well.

It is not impossible that, in the end, Bruno's conception of the eternity of the universe will turn out to be more in conformity with reality than the most authoritative cosmological theories of contemporary science. An increasing number of new scientific many-universes theories are being proposed that support Bruno's view that the universe had no beginning in time. Bruno's model of an infinite evolving universe, that has always existed and will always exist, is in remarkable conformity with some revised and updated Big Bang models. Such a universe would be a truly infinite universe in the most rigorous sense of the word. The case is still open.

In any case, Bruno's view that the universe is infinite and acentric and has no beginning and will have no end was awesome and intolerable for his contemporaries. One cannot but wonder how the first modern man who conceived this terrible thought and drew the necessary consequences could bear its awesomeness without going insane. Bruno's alleged joyous serenity, in the face of an impending unavoidable and most excruciating torment and death, could not have come from just the satanic hubris of knowing that he was the only human being on Earth to be in possession of the key to the riddle of the universe. On the other hand, he was still too much of a religious mystic and idealist philosopher to believe that a mind endowed with such comprehensive power would completely vanish into total nothingness after death. It is, in fact, possible that the main source of that joyous serenity was precisely the fundamental insight of the philosophy he could not be persuaded to part with. Perhaps he was certain of his near-at-hand reunion with, and definitive immersion into, Parmenides' One, Heraclitus' river of fire, the *logos* of the Stoics, and Anaxagoras' *nous* – the cosmic mind that pervades, contains, and regulates everything.

PART THREE

Bruno's Metaphysics and Epistemology

CHAPTER NINE

Mater-Materia

Despite Bruno's remarkable insights in the field of cosmology, his most significant contributions to philosophy are to be found in his ontology. First, he laid the groundwork, long before Galileo and Gassendi, for modern atomism; then he developed an entirely new concept of matter; and finally he proposed the first comprehensive ontological system of post-medieval Western philosophy to reject Platonic dualism in favor of a monistic conception of reality. Even if Bruno was not entirely successful in his speculations about the relationship between physics and mathematics, here, too, Bruno deserves recognition for having initiated a debate that continues to engage the most powerful contemporary minds.

It was Pythagoras who first detected an intimate relationship between the physical world and the mental world of mathematics. Upon discovering the mathematical properties of music and the movements of heavenly bodies he concluded that the essence of reality – all reality, both sublunar and supralunar – is number. It was the first outright identification of the physical with the mental world.

Plato agreed with Pythagoras' insight that the essence of the physical is the ideal, but he objected that ideal mathematical perfection is never fully realized in the sublunar world. Every single concrete being of the physical terrestrial world is flawed and imperfect. The degree of perfection and hence also of beauty of all material bodies depends on their success in imitating their ideal form; but the ideal forms themselves are nowhere to be found in the physical world. They exist in a purely metaphysical realm sometimes referred to as 'Plato's heaven'. Plato went as far as to assert that only the ideal forms really exist and, quite paradoxically, that the ideal world is the only truly real world. This doctrine is the cornerstone of Platonic dualism, for it postulates two separate, essentially different and hierarchical worlds: the imperfect physical and the perfect metaphysical world. Thus, Plato's ontological dualism effectively put an end to the prevalence of the monistic ontologies of the Pre-Socratics and set the pattern for almost every philosophy that achieved any ascendancy in the following nineteen hundred years.

Plato's disciple, Aristotle, sharply disagreed with his teacher's radical dualism. Plato's heaven is an illusion, he declared, the ideal is an essential part of the physical, and forms are inseparable from matter. He did, however, agree with Plato in the view that, although perfection does not exist in the sublunar world, it does in the supralunar world, for neither the composition nor the movements of the heavenly bodies showed any imperfection. This led him to the view that these two physical worlds, the sublunar and the supralunar, were essentially different. Aristotle, therefore, remained a physical dualist, for he divided the physical world into two essentially different subworlds. However, unlike Plato, he was rather a metaphysical monist, for although he did postulate two different metaphysical principles of reality, namely matter and form, he insisted that they could not exist separately and independently from each other, neither in the purely metaphysical world, since Plato's heaven did not exist, nor in the physical, because there matter and form were inextricable. Thus, the monistic ontology of the Pre-Socratics was only partially restored by Aristotle.

The decisive step towards the restoration of Pre-Socratic monism was taken by Bruno. Paradoxically, despite Bruno's staunch opposition to Aristotle's physics and cosmology, he accepted Aristotle's metaphysical model of the inextricable union of matter and form in physical reality. Bruno, therefore, agreed with Aristotle's view that Plato's heaven is an illusion, but strongly disagreed with his belief that perfection existed in the supralunar world. Imperfection, Bruno argued, siding with Cusanus, is universal. The Sun, the Moon, and the stars have imperfections in movement, shape, structure, and composition not much different from those found on the Earth. Thus, Bruno's own cosmological insight of universal cosmic homogeneity together with Aristotelian hylemorphism (the metaphysical doctrine of matter and form as inseparable constituent principles of physical reality) led him to the most revolutionary insight of his new philosophy, strict physical and metaphysical monism.

From this perspective we can better understand Bruno's quarrel with the mathematicians. He refused to side with them in the Pythagorean view that number is the essence of reality. Although numbers are necessary for measuring physical phenomena, they can neither accurately represent nor fully explain them, let alone constitute their essence. Natural philosophy, on the other hand, has at its disposal a language capable of much more adequately describing and explaining the phenomena of physical reality, a conceptual language derived mainly from visual images.

The philosophical doctrine which contributed most decisively to form Bruno's conviction that imperfection is universal and consequently that Aristotle's cosmology was flawed was atomism. Inspired by Democritus, Epicurus, and Lucretius, Bruno developed a philosophy of matter totally based on atomistic principles. He, too, regarded the indivisible physical minimum, the atom, as the ultimate unit of matter, but the atomistic doctrine he developed differed in many respects from ancient classical atomism.

Whereas Galileo and Gassendi are generally celebrated as the founders of modern atomism, the fact that Bruno developed the first modern coherent atomistic model to explain phenomena of physical reality remains widely ignored. In fact, it is almost certain that Galileo found inspiration for his atomistic theory not only in Democritus, Lucretius and Hero of Alexandria, but also in Bruno, whose influence, however, he carefully avoided acknowledging in his books and correspondence probably for fear of provoking further the Roman Inquisition.

Bruno's atomism was the result of hard philosophical reasoning.[1] Whereas Galileo, in the final stage of his own speculations, viewed the atom as an unextended geometrical point, Bruno conceived the atom as a three-dimensional physical particle capable of spontaneously moving itself.[2] Thus, his atomism turned out to be more in conformity with physical reality than Galileo's, for contemporary nuclear physics informs us that the ultimate particles of matter are quanta, that is, extended and measurable packets of mass/energy in spacetime.

But how did Bruno try to solve the serious problems surrounding an atomistic conception of matter and to answer the objections that its numerous adversaries were always quick to present against it? In particular, what were his ideas about the void and the nature of light?

The most serious objection leveled by the Aristotelians against an atomistic conception of matter was the fact that atoms, in order to move, seemed to necessitate empty spaces between them. On the other hand, it was a crucial tenet of Aristotelian physics that a void could not possibly exist: action and interaction through a total void, in the absence of a medium, was considered impossible (*'actio in distans repugnat'*). Furthermore, if voids between atoms existed, the internal cohesion of solids, as well as the phenomena of condensation and rarefaction, became very difficult to explain unless special forces acting between the atoms were postulated. Galileo did in effect once, in remarkable anticipation, rather timidly suggest the possibility of such interatomic forces, but he never developed this insight any further.

Bruno, on the other hand, also subscribing to an atomistic conception of matter, solved the difficulties posed by the problem of the void by identifying it with ether, to which he sometimes referred simply as 'the void', thereby providing the necessary medium in which actions between atoms as well as between macroscopic bodies could take place.[3]

However, Bruno still needed to explain the stable combinations which resulted from the unions between the atoms in a theory that was, for sure, eminently kinetic, but pitifully un-dynamic. Bruno, of course, could not anticipate the existence of either gravitational or electromagnetic forces that account for the attractions and repulsions which obtain between the smallest particles as well as between the heavenly bodies. But this is hardly an excuse, for he never developed, nor even countenanced, the existence of forces between bodies. However, it must be said to his credit that he also refused to suscribe to the idea of merely mechanical random collisions between the atoms, indeed, more generally, even to a merely mechanistic and deterministic picture of the universe like the one his immediate successor, the eminent mathematician René Descartes, developed and succeeded in imposing on the greatest European minds for the next three centuries. As a consequence, Bruno resorted to the only alternative available to him, at that time, to explain both atomic and interstellar motion, namely a rather naïve metaphysical animism. He contended that it was the intelligent soul of the universe, immanent in every atom as well as in every heavenly body, that effected and directed their movements. However, we must bear in mind that Bruno was almost compelled to resort to this animistic explanation as a result of an atomistic conception of matter in which, on the one hand, Democritan random was emphatically excluded and, on the other, no rôle whatsoever was assigned to the action of interatomic or intermolecular forces. Only a few years after Bruno's death, experimental physics would be put on the right track by Gilbert's discovery of magnetic forces, which in turn would eventually lead to Leibniz's introduction of force into the philosophical discourse and to Newton's discovery of the gravitational force.

Unlike Galileo, Bruno has the merit of never having confused physics with mathematics in his conception of the atom. Whereas Galileo maintained in the *Discourses*[4] that the minimum corpuscle of matter was an unextended, dimensionless point, Bruno regarded it as a concrete physical entity. Indeed, the main reason for the absence of perfection in the physical universe was precisely the spontaneity and high motility of the atoms; purely geometrical points could hardly be conceived as having such properties. Thus, Bruno's conviction about the essential difference between the mathematical and the physical regarded not only the larger physical bodies, but extended to the atoms that constituted them as well. Atoms were not purely geometrical entities, but the ultimate concrete indivisible particles of physical reality, and the primordial, permanent, and unalterable concretizations of the indeterminate prime matter (the *materia prima* of Aristotle). Whereas Galileo hypothesized that the matter of the minutest particles in heat, light, and the elements was diverse (a hypothesis obviously incompatible with the notion that the atom was a geometrical point!), here again Bruno insisted on the homogeneity of matter, even in the atoms. The diversity of forms that resulted from the unions of atoms was due only to the variety of arrangements and combinations of an infinite number of atoms, all of which had the same spherical form and size.[5]

Bruno, therefore, conceives matter as being ultimately discrete, made up of substantially homogeneous atoms which have in themselves their own principle of movement, and hence their own internal source of kinetic energy, and which move, not in a vacuum, but inside an extremely subtle medium which he called ether.[6] Despite its evident shortcomings, Bruno's atomism remains a valuable contribution to early modern physical theory, and a remarkable anticipation of contemporary atomic physics. For, unquestionably, Bruno's atomistic conception of matter is the closest one[7] to contemporary atomistic theory ever developed before the late nineteenth century, with the exception, perhaps, of Leibniz's, whose 'monads' are much more similar to Planck's quanta than Bruno's solid atoms. Leibniz, in fact, produced a model of the atom even more congruous with the findings of contemporary physics than Bruno's, by conceiving, for the first time in the history of Western thought, the ultimate physical minimum (which, borrowing the term from Bruno, he called the monad) as pure force and energy, rather than as a compact, solid corpuscle. Still, Bruno, too, regarded as internal the main source of activity of his minute homogeneous pellets, for he was just as opposed as Leibniz to a purely mechanist concept of matter (like the one Descartes proposed) according to which motion resulted merely from mechanical pulls and pushes. Only the names for this principle and source of atomic activity were different: Bruno called it 'soul', whereas Leibniz dubbed it 'force'.

Notwithstanding the novelty of Bruno's atomism, the most revolutionary aspect of his ontology is unquestionably its radical monism. Order, particularly complex organization, is regarded in rigorous monism as an essential property of matter. Thus, matter does not require an external cause nor even an internal principle for order to emerge; matter is already naturally and essentially disposed and prone to order and organization. Order, organization, and structure are matter's own peculiar forms of existence, intrinsic features of its facticity. In strict monism, the Aristotelian notion of the indissoluble interconnectedness of matter and form is paramount; matter and form are not two different and separate entities as they were in Platonic dualism, but two aspects or modes of one and the same physical reality.

The conceivably most extreme form of monism would demand the total disappearance of metaphysical causes 'behind' or 'beyond' the perceptible totality of reality (in contemporary jargon, self-organizing mass/energy in spacetime). In this conception, mass/energy would contain in itself the 'seeds' as well as the 'trees', the virtuality and the actuality of everything that is or ever will be. Traditional dualism, on the other hand, does not tire of postulating a cause of organized complexity ('behind' or 'beyond', and therefore essentially different from, and 'more spiritual' than, self-organizing mass/energy) underlying the phenomena and bestowing upon them their orderliness and complex organization.[8]

Bruno starts by rejecting both the Aristotelian and the Democritan concepts of matter. In Aristotle's view matter, is a powerless, merely receptive substratum, bare of every qualitative and quantitative determination. Thus, Aristotle could define matter only negatively: *'neque quid, neque quale, neque quantum, neque aliud quid ex quo res determinatur'* (neither a thing, nor a quality, nor a quantity, nor any other thing by which anything can be determined). For Democritus (as well as for Epicurus and Lucretius), on the other hand, in agreement with his atomistic theory, matter is just the inert and compact stuff common to all atoms.

In sharp contrast to these conceptions, matter has, according to Bruno, the intrinsic power to generate all possible forms, and the immanent intelligence to direct and govern all organized complex forms that issue from it. To forge his own concept, Bruno borrowed from Aristotle's concept of matter merely the aspect of real possibility, while rejecting the notion that matter was merely an empty receptacle of forms. Instead, he fancied matter as the perpetually pregnant mother of all forms. The Aristotelian form, still conceived somewhat dualistically by Aristotle as the active principle supervening on utterly passive and barren matter, is transformed by Bruno into the principle of matter's native fecundity. Matter thus becomes for him 'matrix' and 'mater', the fecund womb of all forms.

Late medieval scholastic philosophy had blocked the way to such a concept by clinging to Aristotle's understanding of matter as a continuum, whereas modern philosophy, since Descartes, preferred the atomistic concept that has prevailed until recently.[9] Common to both of them is the total passivity and barrenness of matter.

As is well known, dualism had its greatest moment (after Plato and Plotinus) in the philosophy of Descartes. The cornerstone of the Cartesian ontological model is its utterly mechanist concept of matter. Matter was conceived by Descartes and his followers as totally passive, static and inert, devoid of every quality, except of the strictly quantitative property of three-dimensional extension in space. Consequently, bodies were thought to be totally incapable of spontaneous and autonomous motion, even in Newton's strongly dynamic universe. In order to move, bodies needed to be pushed or pulled by forces induced by other bodies, and once they were in motion, they were just as powerless by themselves to stop moving, as Galileo's and Newton's laws of inertia stated. The interaction between bodies was considered to be purely mechanical and hence subject to laws capable of being formulated in rigorous mathematical equations, a circumstance which made these laws necessary and universal. Everything moved and functioned with clock-work precision. The universe was the perfect machine, indeed so perfect that Laplace believed that, if some supermind had perfect knowledge of all the laws governing the universe, as well as of the state of the universe at one particular time, it could predict indefinitely, both forward and backwards, all future and past events. This was the inescapable conclusion of the assumption that everything in the perfect machine that was the universe was causally linked with everything else.

The ascendancy of Cartesian determinism was so great that, if already in the Cartesian universe all animal movements were necessary and predictable, it did not take very long before even all human psychic phenomena received a purely mathematical, specifically geometrical, explanation. This is precisely what Spinoza undertook to demonstrate in his *Ethics*, in which he defined the effects, emotions, and sentiments of the psyche with the rigor and exactness of Euclid's geometry, *more geometrico.*

It is true that Descartes had seen to it that the human spirit was left out of his mechanistic model by conceiving the soul as a separate, autonomous, thinking substance, essentially simple and hence unextended. He declared that in the universe there were two, and only two, distinct separate and mutually irreducible substances: *substantia extensa* and *substantia cogitans*, the extended and the thinking substance, matter and mind. Only because feelings and emotions were not considered purely spiritual, but already contaminated by the matter of the body, could they be forced by Spinoza into the fetters of his sentimental geometry.

The discovery of biological evolution, by Darwin and Spencer, did not alter substantially the metaphysics of the Cartesian mechanistic and deterministic universe. Even in the hypothesis of a cosmic evolution, all the universal and necessary laws of nature and the equations that formulated them had somehow to be contained in the primordial cosmic bodies. Thus, Laplace was able to propose, without contravening his deterministic principles in the least, an evolutionary conception of the solar system. Out of the primordial solar mass eventually the rest of the system would necessarily emerge and evolve. It is true that the universe had now started to look more like an organism than like a machine, for it was capable of growth and evolution. But that was no serious setback for determinism. After all, Descartes had already concluded that all animals were nothing but machines.

Even before the discovery of general relativity and quantum mechanics, a few serious attempts were made to subvert the mechanistic concept of the universe. The most powerful impulse came from the German idealists, especially from Schelling's *Philosophy of Nature*, and from Hegel's *Logic* and *Phenomenology of the Spirit*. The main target of their attack was the Cartesian ontological dualism with its irreconcilable difference and unbridgeable gap between mind and matter. The gap was indeed closed by the idealist philosophers, but only at the price of totally sacrificing matter to mind; all the phenomena of the universe were but the visible manifestations of the Absolute Spirit. Consequently, the laws that linked natural phenomena with one another were no longer purely mathematical, but logical as well, and dialectics provided the dynamics of this new logic. Thus, both biological and cosmic evolution received a strong theoretical support, and the commonly held concept of an inert and utterly passive matter was denounced by Hegel as a total misconception. However, even in Hegel's system, determinism still held its own, since every natural phenomenon remained connected to logical necessity with all the rest.

However, after Hegel's death, a group of his disciples, known as the Hegelian Left, was very critical of his solution of the mind-matter problem. They viewed it as the result of a typically aristocratic and idealistic disregard of, and even contempt for, matter which could easily be traced back to its Christian-gnostic roots. But the material world was too overwhelmingly real, particularly for the destitute proletariat and lumpenproletariat of the industrial societies of nineteenth-century Europe, to be so unconscionably devalued. As a result, another resolute and vigorous attempt was undertaken to dismantle the dualistic-mechanistic model of the Cartesian universe. It was Marx's, Engels', and Lenin's dialectical materialism.

This time, the dialectical materialists took matter very seriously, so seriously that they even made it the cornerstone of their novel metaphysical system. They conceived matter no longer as Aristotle's and Descartes' inert, static, and utterly passive stuff, but as endowed with the very same dialectical dynamism Hegel had attributed to the universal *logos*, the Absolute Spirit. By restoring the primacy of matter, they believed they had put Hegel, who was standing on his head, back on his feet.

This dialectical-materialist concept of matter, as Ernst Bloch has pointed out, is the result of an unsuccessful attempt by its theoreticians to restore the dignity of matter by working on a concept of matter that started to take form in the speculations of some Arab medieval members of the so-called Aristotelian Left, particularly Avicenna and Averroës, and which finally was brought to its most mature and compelling form by Giordano Bruno.[10] Indeed, Bloch regards Bruno as one of the most important precursors of dialectical materialism, because of his revolutionary concept of matter as well as the utterly dialectical bent of his mind, which resulted from his appropriation of the Cusanian concept of the coincidence of opposites.

Bloch contends that dialectical materialism, despite its vociferous homage to matter, did not exploit the enormous potential contained in Bruno's concept of matter. In dialectical materialism, he argues, despite the dynamism that Hegelian dialectics injected into it, matter remains essentially unchanged, that is, inert, static, and utterly devoid of quality, for quality, according to dialectical materialism, is brought into matter only by quantitative 'jumps'. Accordingly, evolution in matter is brought about only by conflict and struggle, that is, ultimately by the clashes, pulls and pushes of the old Cartesian mechanism. True, dialectics became the internal law of that struggle, but it remained external to matter. The old dualism had not been surpassed; matter had no internal vigor, no real autonomy, no 'soul', no freedom. The disastrous consequences of this pitifully lame ontology of dialectical materialism were only to be expected.

We can very well understand Bloch's disappointment. He was a true and sincere Marxist, yet he was deeply frustrated by the Leninist and Stalinist perversions of genuine Marxist ontology. He believed there still was hope for Marxism, but its future depended largely on a thorough revision of its concept of matter. Bloch found in Bruno the inspiration he needed for undertaking the pressing reform of the ontology of dialectical materialism.

The cornerstone of Bruno's ontology is his insight: matter is intelligent and intelligence is material. The dialectical élan is within matter itself, for it is of the essence of matter to be self-propelling, to evolve, and to bring forth from within itself all the forms it is capable of adopting. Matter is self-organizing and self-metamorphosing. In order to organize into ever new forms and structures, it does not need external pushes and pulls, nor does it need a God or a demiurge to put order into its native chaos. Matter is in and by itself supremely energetic and resourceful.

One can easily understand why not only the materialist Bloch, but also even the German idealists, particularly Schelling, found inspiration in Bruno's concept of matter. According to Bruno, mind informs matter and is indeed necessary, not to create matter or to put order into it while remaining utterly alien to it, but rather to supply from within the patterns of all the forms capable of coming forth from the fecund womb of *mater-materia* (Matter, the universal Mother) in virtue of its indissoluble bond with mind. Indeed, matter is intelligent and intelligence is material – the fundamental article of Bruno's monistic credo and the prototype of all dialectical coincidences of opposites.

Despite acknowledging the superiority of Bruno's concept of matter over all the others, including that of dialectical materialism, Bloch thought that Bruno's concept was still defective, because it did not include the most important element of Marx's historical materialism, namely the work and activity of man, his capacity and his duty to transform the world and to drive it forward towards the eschatological Marxist Utopia. The reason why Bloch is critical of Bruno's matter-concept in this regard is his mistaken view that Bruno's universe was complete and perfect, that nothing needed to be done in order to perfect it, and that if it did indeed evolve, it could and would necessarily do it by itself, without the assistance of man's activity and labor. Bloch arrived at this misconception from his opinion that it was the scholastic concept of the *ens perfectissimum* (the most perfect being) that determined Bruno's image of the universe. In fact, following Cusanus' concept of God as the *possest* (the Being that is all it can be), Bruno did maintain that the universe contained all possible forms, however, not simultaneously, but successively. Therefore, it does not necessarily follow that Bruno excluded the work of man from the ongoing creative process of matter. Indeed, there are forms that only man is capable of bringing forth (those of art and technology, among others) and of transforming, through them, both nature and the world. To counter effectively Bloch's objection, we must not forget that Bruno's universe is infinite, not only spatially, but morphologically as well, and that this morphological infinity is constantly propelled by the dynamics of a relentless dialectics. Thus, cosmic perfection can never be attained.

Perfection, according to Bruno, does not exist in the universe. In fact, he did not even hold that the universe had a tendency towards perfection, a goal or a *telos* towards which it must strive. Bruno's universe, unlike Aristotle's, is not teleological. If the production of an infinity of forms may in some way still be thought of as a goal, it must be remembered that for Bruno such 'perfection' can only be achieved successively, in the course of the eternal duration of the universe, in which continuously new forms are being created. The idea that man contributes effectively to the creation of new forms and thereby also to the transformation of the world is therefore totally consistent with, and even an integral part of, Bruno's concept of matter, which is therefore very far from being reactionary, as Bloch contends. Consequently, to assert that Bruno excluded the contribution of man to the transformation of the world on the basis of his alleged presupposition of cosmic perfection is totally unwarranted.

It is possible that Bloch would not have entirely disagreed with us, for the final sentence of his brilliant book reads as follows:

> There is no way outwards and precisely towards its More [of the universe] – the eschatological depth – without Bruno and Spinoza, and without this other, not internal, conscience – against subjectivism and mechanism as well.[11]

Bruno's universe has no Seventh Day. His 'Pan' (Greek god and symbol for the All) is not complete and ready. It is rather the Heracleitan Pan, the eternally flowing river of forms incessantly impelled by the irrepressible urge of the cosmic mind. Indeed,

Bruno's *mater-materia* contains in its fecund bosom the entire future of the universe, hence man's future too, his evolution and history, with his capacity to assist and complement the work of nature in the production of its bounteous cornucopia of forms. So understood, Bruno's matter is indeed, as Bloch would have it, *'das Prinzip Hoffnung'* (the Hope-Principle). Unfortunately for Marxism, Bloch's efforts to humanize it by infusing new life into dialectical materialism's sterile concept of matter came too late. Marxism was not killed by its rigid materialist ontology, but by its disastrous economics; it was already too late for revisionist metaphysical remedies.

It is precisely in the light of the great Neo-Marxist philosopher's revisionist dreams that we can understand his disappointment at what he considered Bruno's failure to anticipate, in his philosophy, the Marxist agenda of active and vigorous world- transformation. Bloch misses in Bruno the great Marxist hope for the eschatological Utopia – the commitment to, and the universal appeal for, a classless society in which exploitation will no longer exist – and, above all, the faith in man's collective efforts to bring about the transformation of a world of oppression and hunger into a world of free individuals, where there would be abundance of material and spiritual goods for everyone. Bloch was wrong in his belief that Bruno was nothing but a contemplative for whom his philosophical speculations were the only thing that really mattered. However, there are enough traits in Bruno's character and thought that suggest that he was much more than a resigned contemplative. As we will see, when we discuss Bruno's revolutionary ethics, Bruno's philosophy, far from being merely speculative, does indeed urge humankind to action. For what more efficacious appeal for humanity's self-liberation is there than to urge it to strive to increase everywhere intellectual honesty, friendship, peace, tolerance, education, love of beauty, and respect for life, and to banish all superstition, ignorance, mental laziness, and narrow-mindedness? If Bruno's ethical and religious revolution had succeeded, and the Brunian – rather than the Marxist – Utopia had become mankind's goal, perhaps the world would now be a better place to live in. As in the Marxist ethics, all other-worldliness was banished from Bruno's ethics: it too focused on the here and now. But, unlike the Marxist and most of the other-worldly ethics, it did not need authoritarian institutions, neither parties nor churches, to achieve enthusiastic acceptance and secure successful implementation.

CHAPTER TEN

The Cosmic Mind

Awed by the superabundance and complexity of patterns in the universe, Bruno's restless mind speculated about the source of this order. He could find satisfaction neither in the traditional theistic explanation nor in that proposed by the ancient atomist natural philosophy. In fundamental disagreement with his much admired Lucretius and his atomist predecessors among the Pre-Socratic natural philosophers and Epicurus, Bruno did not accept chance as the ultimate explanation for a universe awash with patterns of complex organization. But neither could he reconcile himself with the traditional view that an omnipotent and omniscient God had created, out of nothing, in the beginning of time, a complete and perfect cosmos. He did agree, however, with the traditional view in one point, namely that only supreme intelligence could be the cause of this order. But wasn't this, after all, precisely what Plato, Aristotle, Plotinus, and the Scholastics had been arguing all along? So far, his answer to the question, where does the order of the universe come from, could hardly have been more conventional.

His disagreement with the traditional view starts with his assignation of a location for that source of order. Did it exist 'before' and 'outside' the universe, as the traditional view firmly held, or rather was it located 'inside' the universe as an integral and essential part of it? The issue was not merely topographical. What really was at stake was the Brunian concept of matter which we discussed in the previous chapter. Actually, the debate was nothing short of a frontal confrontation between two diametrically opposed views of reality: dualism – ontological, cosmological, and theological – on one side, and radical monism on the other. The universe, he proclaimed, has a mind, and this mind, the cosmic mind, is immanent to it.

Was this insight original? If not, from whom did Bruno borrow it? Who had held, before him, that the universe has a mind of its own? The unity of mind and cosmos had been propounded only by a few downright monistic or pantheistic Pre-Socratic natural philosophers, and later on also by the Stoics.

The fact that Bruno's concept of mind-in-matter is remarkably akin to Anaximander's notion of the 'unlimited' (*apeiron*) has been generally overlooked. According to Anaximander, everything owes its existence to this principle; from it proceeds everything that is new, and to it returns everything that once has been. Anaximander's incorruptible and imperishable *apeiron* is therefore the ultimate principle and source of both corruption and generation. For this reason it must be regarded as a divine principle, the Absolute itself. Indeed, Bruno's concept of *mater-materia* as the inexhaustible source of all forms is strongly reminiscent of Anaximander's *apeiron*.

However, it was Anaxagoras who provided the crucial element of Bruno's monistic ontology, for he asserted that everything can come out of everything, and he concluded that, if there was an initial separation of something out of some other thing, there must have been a principle for this separation as well. Anaxagoras called this principle of separation *nous*, generally translated as mind, although this concept does not exactly correspond to our modern concept of mind as intelligence; it was originally merely a principle of separation, the origin of the 'other'.

It did not take Bruno too long to discover that Anaximander's fecund *apeiron* was intimately related to Anaxagoras' *nous*. His synthesis of the *apeiron* with *nous* paved the way for the fusion of boundless *mater-materia* with the cosmic mind and, consequently, also to a markedly monistic ontology.

There was yet another insight Bruno needed to gain in order to arrive at his definitive and most elaborate concept of mind-in-matter. It concerned the internal dynamism of the cosmic mind. Bruno got this insight from Heracleitus' notion of incessant universal and eternal becoming – *panta rei* (everything is flowing) – but he applied it not only to the phenomena of visible reality, but also to the cosmic mind itself. In conformity with this view, Bruno understood Heracleitus' other famous dictum, 'war [is] the father of everything' as the incessant clash and struggle between dialectical opposites within the cosmic mind, and hence as the source and motor of all the transformations that matter goes through.

Thus the 'new philosophy of the Nolan' reveals itself first and foremost as a vigorous revival of the *antica filosofia* (ancient philosophy) of the Pre-Socratics.

However, Bruno's ideas about matter and the cosmic mind were influenced, not only by the Pre-Socratic philosophers, but to a large extent by the Stoics as well. In fact, it is possible to detect an impressive number of Stoic ideas underlying Bruno's thought. With regard to matter, although Bruno sided with Epicurus' and Lucretius' atomism (rather than with Zeno's belief in a continuum devoid of atoms and the void), he agreed with Stoic vitalism in the view that matter, far from being inert and passive, was very much alive, indeed, that every single body and atom was animated by the 'soul of the universe'.[1] This was perhaps the most important Stoic contribution to Bruno's ontology.

Stoic influence, however, goes beyond this crucial insight. The Stoics understood Nature as an organism, that is, as a whole whose parts are in harmony with each other and which collaborate towards the achievement of a common goal. Bruno, too, conceived nature and the universe as a living, growing organism. Furthermore, Bruno's idea of multiple worlds is likewise of Stoic origin. The boundless creative power of the cosmic mind manifests itself by bringing numerous worlds into existence.[2]

Before clarifying further Bruno's thoughts about the cosmic mind, it may be enlightening to notice how congruous such interrelated Brunian concepts as matter, mind, and becoming are with our contemporary theories of the origin of the universe. All subparticles and the four elementary cosmic forces of contemporary cosmology are obviously the result of becoming and differentiation, since they emerged from a continuous, amorphous, and undifferentiated primordial quantum of energy which instantly began to break up and give rise to specific and well-defined permanent forms in a process of successive transformations. In Aristotle's stunningly insightful words, 'There must have been a time when all things were indistinguishably one, and a time when the stirring of segregative movement began.'[3] Thus, the Big Bang theoreticians, despite their distaste for metaphysics, could hardly avoid such concepts as becoming and differentiation in their explanations of the origin of cosmic multiplicity and diversity. Although, as we have shown, Anaximander, Anaxagoras, Heracleitus, and the Stoics originally provided the first basic philosophical (non-theological) insights and a rudimentary conceptual apparatus to explain the order and origin of the cosmos, it was Bruno who came up with the most compelling post-medieval synthesis of Pre-Socratic and Stoic thinking on these subjects. He insisted that there must be a principle of all separation, becoming, and differentiation, and hence for all the multiplicity, diversity, and order observable in the universe. This principle, Bruno pointed out, is precisely what Anaxagoras called 'mind' and the Stoics 'the soul of the universe'.

Bruno contended that the source of cosmic order is not an external cause, but one single internal principle; that this principle pervades the entire universe and does not exist in and by itself either spatially 'outside' or temporally 'before' the universe, but rather that it is immanent in the universe, as the soul is immanent in the body, and form in matter. As in the Aristotelian conception of the unity of matter and form and of body and soul, so, too, according to Bruno, neither the matter nor the immanent form of the universe, its soul, can exist independently of each other. Thus the universal principle of organized complexity, the soul of the universe, is immanent in it. Moreover, it needs the universe and cannot exist without it. Consequently, the universe must be coeternal with its immanent universal intelligent principle, the cosmic mind, which, in turn, can only exist in indissoluble union with matter.

The soul of the universe was conceived by Bruno, not only as the dynamic principle of universal motion, but also as the organizational principle of the structure of all heavenly bodies, that is, of the linkage, association, and harmonious assemblage of their parts, and also as the steering principle that directs all cosmic bodies in their multiple self-preserving operations and functions. This particular immanent principle of movement, organization, and self-preserving activity is not material (as was the fire of Heracleitus and the Stoics, and the mind/spirit of Lucretius), but an 'ideal' form which, despite its mental nature, is intrinsic and essential to matter, and, like matter, incapable of existing in and by itself. Precisely this conception is at the root of the crucial Brunian insight that all matter is intelligent and all intelligence is material, the cornerstone of Brunian monism.

Hence, the 'souls' with which Bruno allegedly equipped the cosmic bodies are not separate entities embodied in each individual;

in fact, they are not individual souls at all, but rather the vital energy universally imparted to all bodies by one single cosmic principle of motion and complex organization – ubiquitous, imperishable, and immutable. Hence, there is not an infinite number of individual souls, but one single cosmic soul, undivided and indivisible[4], present and immanent in every body as well as in every single atom of matter. This clarification should suffice to absolve Bruno from the charges of crass animism and panpsychism.

If the universal soul is immanent in everything that exists, then, of course, everything is, to a certain extent, 'alive', but the presence of soul in every existing individual being by no means implies the fragmentation of the universal soul into myriads of individual souls. As the soul or principle of life of a tree is present, all of it, in every part of the tree, from the roots to the fruit and the seeds, so is the universal soul present in everything that exists. Thus, everything has, in itself, its own immanent principle of life and movement, which it shares with everything else in the universe. Such is the import of the so-called Brunian panpsychism and panzooism, every bit of matter is alive and informed by the cosmic soul.

Thus, the cosmic soul, according to Bruno, is not a transcendent cause, but a metaphysical principle immanent in the totality of physical reality. This intrinsic principle is the necessary and sufficient reason for the movement and the order, as well as for the variety and complexity, of all patterns and structures in the physical universe. In order to explain this order, a principle is required for organizing the discrete constituent elements into integrated wholes, an ubiquitous principle with the ability to subject, harness and direct these elements towards the actualization of the specific blueprint of the organized whole. This principle is the universal intellect.

What is the exact relationship between the world-soul and the universal intellect? According to Bruno, the universal intellect is an inherent power (*potenza*) of the universal soul; it is both the efficient physical cause and intrinsic principle of everything that exists in the universe, and it operates from the inside as an internal artificer (*artefice interno*) which 'from inside the trunk drives out the branches, from inside the branches the formed twigs, from inside these unfolds the buds; from the inside it forms, shapes, weaves, like nerves, the foliage, the flowers, the fruits . . .'[5] This union and unity of the universal soul with the universal intellect may be appropriately referred to as the 'cosmic mind'.

'Explication' or unfolding thus becomes the true principle of individuation of the cosmic mind.[6] Accordingly, the ability to manifest itself as extension, plurality, variety, individuality, negation, limits must be seen as essential to the cosmic mind. The universe is, therefore, the actualization and individuation of all these virtual potentialities of the universal intelligence which become real only through its unfolding. The cosmic mind itself is not extended, but it manifests itself through the extension and discreteness that its unfolding grants it.[7]

Since it is essentially linked to physical reality and cannot exist 'outside' or independently thereof, it would also be mistaken to consider Bruno's cosmic mind as existing before and outside of spacetime, in a sort of Platonic extracosmic metaphysical *topos*. The cosmic soul and intellect, in Bruno's view, are consequently in some sense themselves spatio-temporal, albeit, as all metaphysical principles, totally inaccessible to empirical knowledge. They are postulated only by reason, specifically, by the principle of sufficient reason.

It must be noted that the 'knowledge' attributed by Bruno to such an immanent principle of organized complexity does not necessarily imply self-awareness, or even any awareness, for that matter, which would render it capable of representing to itself, as a knowing subject, all the individual particular entities that issue from it, or of becoming gradually aware of itself in and through the process of their production and representation, as Hegel would later maintain. Nor is it necessary to attribute to this mind a will, a definite purpose, or a specific intentional cosmic design. It would suffice that the 'knowledge' of the cosmic mind be identical with what, in contemporary terminology, is commonly referred to as the entire algorithmic systemic network inherent and operative in the universe. Bruno's cosmic mind is, therefore, not to be confused with the traditional personal theistic or deistic designer, the great 'architect' or 'watchmaker' of the universe. It could just as well be a sort of 'blind watchmaker', as the metaphor coined by Richard Dawkins vividly suggests[8], or even not a 'maker' at all, if this notion necessarily implies a subject different and separate from the product it brings forth.

A pertinent and illustrative analogy may be established

between this essential and necessary union between the Brunian cosmic mind and the physical world, and the necessary linkage – also transempirical and metaphysical – established by Einstein's general theory of relativity between mass/energy and spacetime. Indeed, contemporary cosmology generally holds that the cosmos is the totality of mass/energy in all of spacetime. These four abstract concepts (or intuitions) of the mind: mass, energy, space, and time, constitute a sort of ideal interrelated and unified 'quaternity', a metaphysical construct rationally postulated as the indispensable matrix of all physical phenomena. Their interrelatedness is so essential that none of the four elements of the quaternity may be conceived as capable of existing independently of the other three. Thus, after Einstein's formulation of the special theory of relativity, it is no longer possible to think of time independently of space, nor is it possible to think of mass independently of energy. Moreover, it is equally impossible to think of the two bonded pairs, namely spacetime and mass/energy, independently of each other, so that every unit (or quantum) of mass/energy carries along with it its own spacetime, and every section of spacetime necessarily holds within itself some quantum of mass/energy.

In addition to these four concepts, there are two others particularly highlighted by contemporary cosmology, namely those of force and field. They, too, remarkably branch out into a fourfold conceptual construct, namely the four forces (and fields) known as electromagnetic, gravitational, nuclear weak, and nuclear strong. Indeed, it does not seem possible any more to theorize about the totality of physical reality without recourse to these categories. Consequently, they build the necessary conceptual matrix within which the emergence and permanence of order in the cosmos must be explained.

Thus, Bruno's cosmic mind could be understood, in terms more familiar to us today, as the underlying principle of the unified four or fundamental quaternity, and the ultimate source of their specificity, difference, integration, and harmony. Only a cosmic mind would seem to satisfy the demand that the principle of sufficient reason imposes on the otherwise utterly incomprehensible facticity of the fundamental quaternity of Einstein's comprehensible universe. Indeed, by postulating an intelligent immanent principle that would account for the order of the universe – and hence for the interconnectedness, harmony, and boundless fecundity of the quaternity matrix – Bruno actually provides a plausible metaphysical solution to Einstein's paradoxical conundrum of the incomprehensible comprehensibility of the universe. The crucial difference between Einstein's rational cosmological postulates and Bruno's untestable metaphysical assumptions is, of course, that Einstein's have been borne out by extensive experimentation and dramatic scientific accomplishments, whereas Bruno's haven't, and obviously never will. But Einstein's own metaphysical speculations were obviously not too distant from Bruno's, since he kept insisting, until the end of his life, and in spite of quantum mechanics' strong disagreement, that 'God does not play dice with the universe'.

The cosmic mind needs infinite space, time, and matter to produce successively infinite (in quantity and quality) forms and concrete entities; but the unfolding of the cosmic mind does not entail their eternal immutable permanence, but rather the constant flux of their becoming. Thus Bruno's metaphysics reveals itself as the synthesis of Heraclitus' *panta rei* (everything is flowing) and Parmenides' *hen kai pan* (One and All).

We understand now how foreign this Brunian concept of the cosmic soul is to Descartes' 'thinking substance', or 'the ghost in the machine' as Gilbert Ryle pointedly calls it. The Cartesian dualistic metaphysical construct is independent of, and extrinsic to, the physical bodies it happens to inhabit or inform, while Bruno's universal soul is immanent in, and inseparable from, physical reality.

The baffling paradox of Bruno's cosmic mind is that, although essentially one and immutable, it cannot be without constant change and individuation, thus it is, in a sense, always the same and always different. It is invisible and yet needs to become visible. It is omnipotent because it has the power to actualize constantly and eternally its infinite potentialities, and perfect as well, because it lacks nothing, for nothing exists besides or outside the cosmic mind that can effect or measure any deficiency in it. Yet, at the same time, it appears as unfulfilled and vain,[9] for it needs to display its omnipotence and intelligence constantly and forever. Indeed the cosmic mind is the perfect example of Cusanus' coincidence of opposites.

Bruno's infinite universe was neither static nor stable, but eminently dynamic. He envisaged an eternally evolving universe with new forms incessantly emerging from the impetuous and relentless drive of the cosmic mind. If we take into consideration the dialectical bent of Bruno's mind as well as Heracleitus' influence on his thought, it is not surprising that Bruno conceived an eternally evolving universe engaged in a relentless and inexhaustible display of new forms. However, this in no way implies that the cosmic evolution Bruno had in mind was progressive towards a certain pre-established goal. As there is no center, there is also no goal or *telos* in Bruno's universe. It is acentric and aimless as well. What Nietzsche asserted about man – 'Since Copernicus man is rolling out of the center unto X' – applies just as well to the entire universe: Since Bruno, the universe is rolling out of its center unto X.[10]

The main metaphysical importance of Bruno resides in the fact that he, before Schelling and Hegel, conceived the Absolute, that is the totality of reality, not as two substances – one material and the other spiritual – as Descartes had done, nor even as two attributes of one and the same substance, as the pantheist Spinoza maintained, but as mind manifesting itself in and through matter. Such conception implies that mind is one with nature, indeed that it constitutes its very essence.[11]

According to Hegel, the Absolute Spirit is self-moving, for it contains in itself its own principle of movement, which is dialectical negation, and, driven by negation, it is constantly changing and progressing towards its *telos*, which is perfect self-awareness. This is where Bruno would have disagreed with Hegel's extreme idealism. Bruno's cosmic mind is also self-moving, but it has no aim or goal. Thus, also according to Bruno, the cosmic mind needs to unfold and actualize itself in nature and human history, although not necessarily 'in order to' become aware of itself in the process. Its necessity to evolve is therefore non-teleological and non-progressive, for it does not drive nature and humankind towards increasing perfection. Bruno conceives the cosmic mind rather as driven by the irrepressible need of an eternal playful display of true omnipotence.

Among all the innumerable forms produced in the universe by the cosmic mind since the Big Bang, the one that displays the most complex organization and is capable of successfully performing the most complicated calculations is unquestionably the human mind. Particularly, human self-awareness and memory demand a satisfactory and plausible explanation within the conceptual frame of the totality of physical reality. Anthropology, neurophysiology, as well as molecular biology, all conspire to suggest strongly that human self-awareness and memory presuppose huge concentrations of order and organization in the human brain. Now what determines the orderly disposition of the myriads of quanta of mass/energy in the supremely complicated circuitry of the human brain and in the astonishingly clever system of nerve-signal transmission along the axons of the one hundred billion neurons in it is nothing but huge collections of those mysterious mathematical entities called 'algorithms'. They are mysterious, among other things, because it is difficult, perhaps impossible, to establish exactly where they are located. As a computational formula establishing and determining the arrangement and operations of quanta of mass/energy, an algorithm seems, on the one hand, to exhibit purely mental characteristics and hence to suggest that its existence is merely subjective. On the other hand, it is operative in and upon the objective physical reality that science is presently constrained to conceive through the categories of the quaternity. This would suggest that algorithms are themselves also in spacetime and therefore share the objectivity proper to the four elements of the quaternity. However, the algorithmic universe seems to occupy an intermediary position such that it cannot be said to be located either in spacetime or in an entirely extraterrestrial, indeed extracosmic, Platonic realm of pure ideas, forms and archetypes.

The comprehension of the relationship between the physical universe of the quaternity and the algorithmic universe responsible for the order that the former exhibits encounters almost insurmountable barriers as long as we persist in understanding this relationship in dualistic terms, that is, in considering the algorithms essentially different from, and independent of, the physical reality they help to structure and organize.

In fact, the algorithmic nature of the universe seems to coincide with what Gregory Bateson calls the 'larger mind'.[12] This larger mind, according to him, is immanent in the universe, that is, it cannot be considered the 'cause' of the universe, as both theists and deists conceive it, nor can it be conceived as existing 'outside' or 'prior' to the universe, nor as independent and essentially different from it. The larger mind is in the universe; indeed it can even be properly said to be the universe, however not in the fashion that a crude panentheism would imagine it to be, that is, as the soul of the cosmic body. A much more appropriate metaphor would be 'the software of the cosmic hardware'.

The rigorous monism that Bateson propounds rejects even the moderate dualism that continues to underlie the panentheistic conception of the universe as the body of God. On the other hand, it unambiguously endorses Bruno's and Schelling's monism.[13]

We have now completed our exposition of the basic features of Bruno's ontology. Together with his cosmology they constitute what Bruno called 'the philosophy of the Nolan', a most coherent and original synthesis and revival of the ancient philosophy of the Pre-Socratics and the Stoics. To conclude this exposition and discussion of Bruno's cosmology and ontology, let us now summarily recapitulate the main cosmological and ontological insights of Bruno's philosophy:

I The infinite universe:

1 The universe is infinite.[14]
2 It is infinite because it has no borders or limits, neither does it have a surface, and hence neither circumference nor figure.[15]
3 The universe has no center.[16]
4 Space is an homogeneous and infinite continuum.[17]
5 The ether is identical with the void or absolute space.[18] Thus, so understood, the void is not impossible.[19] There is interplanetary and interstellar space (or void).[20] The universe is not solid. The heavenly bodies are not in a vacuum, but in this medium called ether; this is their only and universal 'place'. There are no absolute voids or perfect vacuums in the universe, nor outside of it.[21]
6 The universe is one single whole.[22]
7 The infinite universe does not need an external motor to move it. In itself it is immovable, since there is nothing else it can move towards or away from; however, everything in it is in constant motion.[23]
8 From the infinite universe new abundance of matter is always born.[24]

9 The universe is homogeneous and isotropic; there is no hierarchy in cosmic matter resulting from its relative distance from the human observer on Earth; the universe looks the same from wherever in the universe an observer may look at it.[25] All heavenly bodies are made of the same elements and have similar composition, consistency, and structure. Neither the Sun nor the Earth have any cosmological privileges over other heavenly bodies in the infinite universe. There is no essential difference between the sublunar and the supralunar world.[26]

10 Motion is universal. All heavenly bodies are endowed with several kinds of movement, and none of them is perfectly regular.[27]

11 The universe had no beginning in time; it will have no end either; it is eternal.[28]

12 There is no absolute time. In the universe, the number of times correspond to the number of celestial bodies.[29]

13 The material universe consists of space, ether, atoms, and light.[30]

14 Light is not made up of atoms.[31]

II The innumerable worlds:

15 There are innumerable, indeed infinite, suns and planets in the universe.[32]

16 These innumerable suns and planets are in themselves finite.[33]

17 Heavenly bodies move freely in space. The celestial vault or firmament – the ultimate sphere of fixed stars equidistant from the Earth – is an illusion.[34] All heavenly bodies have in themselves their own immanent principle of movement (soul); they are automotive and animated; they do not need to be pushed or pulled by other bodies; their source of movement is internal vigor, not external impulse (mechanical push or pull).[35]

18 The Sun is a star and the stars are suns. They are not made up exclusively of fire, but of the same elements that make up the Earth as well as all other celestial bodies.[36]

19 The Sun, like all heavenly bodies, moves; it revolves around its center.[37]

20 Besides the visible planets, there may be other invisible ones

rotating around the Sun which we cannot see because of their distance or size.[38]

21 There are probably other planetary orbits around other suns besides our own solar ones.[39]

22 The farther the planets are from the Sun, the longer are their orbits, and the longer their orbits, the slower they move around the Sun.[40]

23 The Earth is a planet not unlike many others in the universe. It moves freely in space,[41] and is not a perfect sphere.[42]

24 There are probably living beings in other worlds.[43]

III The soul of the universe:

25 The universe is one because it has one single immanent principle that holds all its parts together, just as the human soul is the one single principle that holds together and interrelates all the parts of the body. It is the soul of the universe (*l'anima de l'universo*).[44]

26 The soul of the universe must be conceived as the principle and substance of the universe, although its true nature is extremely difficult to grasp.[45]

27 The universal soul is found in everything, and there is no corpuscle, however tiny, that is not animated by it.[46]

28 The universal soul is able to produce all from all.[47]

IV The universal intellect:

29 There is order in the universe; this order is not the result of chance, as the atomists would have it, but rather the effect of an efficient cause, the universal intellect. The universal intellect is the only single immanent principle of organized complexity in the universe: Mind, God, Being, the One, Truth, Fate, Reason, Order.[48]

30 The agent that governs, orders, and directs everything in the universe is the intellect of the soul of the universe; the intellect is not only formal cause and principle of the universe, but its efficient cause as well.[49]

31 The efficient cause of the universe, the universal intellect, must also be conceived as the final cause of the universe, for it may

be conceived as having an immanent (not transcendentally pre-established) purpose, namely that all possible forms of matter it contains be actualized, for it must become everything that it can possibly become. It so strives to achieve perfection through a full 'explication' (in Nicholas of Cusa's sense) or unfolding.[50]

32 The universe is not complete and perfect; the infinite universe is open and can therefore never reach perfect completion.[51]

V Matter and form (Bruno's hylemorphism):

33 Matter and form, the passive and the active metaphysical principles of all physical reality, are inseparable, infinite, eternal, and indestructible.[52]

34 Matter is divine and animated from within by the equally divine formal principle.[53]

35 All the individual forms existing in the universe are not received by matter from outside, but all proceed from the infinitely fecund bosom of matter animated by one single form, which is the soul of the universe.[54]

36 The One (universal intellect or cosmic mind) effects an infinity of forms out of uncreated matter throughout eternity. There was never a single initial act of creation that produced, out of nothing, a complete and perfect universe of immutable forms.[55]

37 All the infinite different forms in the universe are subject to constant transformations.[56] All forms on Earth are incessantly changing into other forms, and all bodies in the universe are equally transmutable and susceptible to incessant changes.[57]

38 In the universe, only space and ether are continua; the rest are either discrete, perfectly solid, indivisible atoms, or the bodies composed of such atoms. The atoms are the most elementary particles of matter.[58]

39 Matter comprehends a lot more than atoms; it includes ether and light as well.[59]

40 Atoms are automotive and animated, that is, they have in themselves the principle of movement (they have 'souls'). Their movements produce infinite combinations which settle down to innumerable forms.[60]

CHAPTER ELEVEN

Bruno's God

During the eight long years of Bruno's imprisonment and trial by the Venetian and Roman Inquisitions not once was mention made of Bruno's book *The Expulsion of the Triumphant Beast*, despite the fact that the Inquisitors instructed the Jesuit, Robert Bellarmine, to submit to a most severe scrutiny all the works that had become available to them. This Italian ethical dialogue, written and published in London, contained by far the most scathing indictment of the Church that Bruno ever made. Nor did Bruno himself, in the many interrogations he endured, or in any of the numerous spontaneous declarations he made in his own defense, ever mention this dialogue. One must, therefore, conclude that he carefully avoided any reference to it out of fear of fatally incriminating himself. This supposition becomes almost a certainty when we learn that the only book that was mentioned in his death sentence was precisely *Lo Spaccio della bestia trionfante* (The Expulsion of the Triumphant Beast). The Inquisitors, only weeks before his execution, had finally laid their hands on a copy of the book. After reading it, they unanimously arrived at the conclusion that Bruno was an atheist.[1]

From then on it was no longer possible for Bruno to proclaim his innocence with regard to his Catholic orthodoxy, nor to hide his true feelings about the Church and the Papacy. His credibility collapsed, his simulation became apparent to all, and the first one to realize the hopelessness of his cause once *Lo Spaccio* had fallen into the hands of his judges was Bruno himself. He knew now, for sure, that even if he managed to escape death by confessing his errors and humbly asking for forgiveness, he would still have to spend the rest of his days in the dungeons of the Inquisition, for a man who harbored such contempt for the Church and its ministers could never be allowed to become a free man again. The danger, indeed, was too great that one day he would manage to escape from Italy and conduct, from abroad, the impious rebellion, against the Church (Roman Catholic) and the entire Christian religion, which he was secretly planning. For his greatest crime, the Inquisitors agreed, was that he was not only a heretic himself, but a leader of heretics, a heresiarch, committed to the definitive expulsion of what they thought he was symbolizing by 'the triumphant beast'. The Pope was understandably outraged, and the Cardinals were furious, as the following accusation evidences:

> After having consigned other writings to the acts of the Holy Office, addressed to the Holiness of Our Lord [the Pope] and to us [Cardinals Inquisitors], from which it appears manifestly that you remained pertinaciously in the above mentioned errors; and also having received notice that in the Holy Office of Vercelli you have been charged with being an atheist while you were in England and of having composed a book of the *Triumphant Beast*, on the tenth of the month of September of 1599 it was imposed on you a term of 40 days to repent. . .[2]

Thus, the Cardinals' examination of *The Expulsion of the Triumphant Beast* – the book that contains the grand manifesto of the Brunian ethical and political revolution – extinguished in Bruno the last hope of ever initiating and carrying out personally that revolution, and of becoming the 'Mercury' sent by the gods whom the Hermetic prophetic Lament[3] announced, to bring light and new life to a rapidly decaying civilization. Once all hope of freedom had vanished, Bruno dropped the mask; he had worn it for ten years, only to save himself for the great task he had envisioned. He therefore openly declared, thus signing his own death sentence, that he had nothing to recant, for he knew of nothing that needed to be recanted. If his revolution was ever to take place, only his courage and his writings would remain to inspire it.

Was Bruno really an atheist? Was he a pantheist? What was Bruno's real concept of God? In order to answer these questions we have to look more closely into his views on the relationship between the cosmic mind and the universe.

We saw in Chapter Nine that the eternal *mater-materia* was characterized by Bruno as 'the inexhaustible bosom of worlds, of forms, of individual beings, of images, the substance always remaining the same; for it is but one – one divine, immortal Being'.

Bruno thus clearly regarded matter, and hence the entire universe, as divine. Furthermore, Bruno wrote in *De la causa*, that the universal intellect, 'from the interior of seminal matter welds the bones, extends the cartilages, hollows out the arteries, inhales the pores, weaves the fibers, branches out the nerves, and with such admirable mastery arranges the universe'.[4] Thus, Bruno's universe is divine and the universal intellect is immanent in it. However, although these views unquestionably bring Bruno very close to theological pantheism, their ambiguity does not yet allow us to conclude that he was a true pantheist.

Bruno often insisted on the fact that the human mind is capable of conceiving utterly regular geometrical forms which are never found in nature in absolute perfection. This power of the human mind renders it remarkably similar to the divine mind, which traditionally was thought to conceive all possible forms in their ideal perfection. Furthermore, such power was, in principle, common to all human minds and identical in all of them. This could arguably be attributed to the fact that the cosmic mind is immanent and operative in all human minds. Bruno supported this view by pointing out that the universal intelligence is present and operative in (he often uses the words 'pervades') everything that exists, from those huge 'animals', the heavenly bodies, to the most minute atoms, the minima, of matter.

Do these views imply a total identification of God with the universe? Not necessarily, because precisely Bruno's conviction that geometrical figures and mathematical equations never achieve in physical reality the perfection which they have as human mental phenomena is an indication that Bruno did not propound a total identification of God with the universe. The cosmic mind is, according to Bruno, most certainly present in nature, indeed immanent in it, since it thoroughly pervades it; but if nature never reaches the perfection of the divine mind, and hence is never an exact reproduction thereof, then it cannot be totally identified with it. Although the imperfection of the universe is not an argument against its divinity, it does forbid, in Bruno's mind, an outright identification of the universe with a transcendent God.

Despite the ability of the human mind to reproduce the perfect forms of the cosmic mind, Bruno repeatedly asserted that God was not accessible to conceptual human knowledge. God cannot properly be said to be either physical or mental, either material or spiritual. In fact, God does not have essential properties or attributes (as Spinoza's God); only His existence is postulated by reason, and assigned the negative title of 'ineffable'. In this point, he totally agreed with Nicholas of Cusa's assertion that the divine unity precedes all plurality and hence all diversity, difference, opposition, inequality, division and anything that accompanies plurality, and hence that it belongs to no kind, has no name, and no shape, even though it is all within all. Thus it is clear that, far from being radical rationalists and pantheists like Hegel and Spinoza, both Bruno and Cusanus subscribed to the *via negativa*[5] as the only possible non-mystical cognitive approach to God.

Bruno shared with Cusanus a decidedly Neoplatonic approach to the question of God. Following Plotinus they agreed that God was totally beyond every concept and knowledge; in fact, as Plotinus asserted, God was even beyond 'being', understood in the sense of 'being something specific and determinable'. It was therefore unthinkable that this utterly transcendent God could be immanent to the universe. On the other hand, Bruno was totally convinced of the immanent presence of the divine in the universe. Thus, due to Bruno's undeniably Neoplatonic theology – despite his rabid anti-Neoplatonic cosmology – he had no choice but to resort to Plotinus' 'hypostases' or emanations from the 'One' – the *nous* (intellect) and the *psyche* (soul) – if he was to provide a rational explanation for the immanence of the divine in the universe. Bruno's cosmic mind is, in fact, remarkably similar to, if not identical with, Plotinus' *nous*, the divine principle generated by the One, which contemplates in the One and derives from it all the forms, archetypes, and numbers actualized in the cosmos. Bruno's *anima mundi* (the soul of the world, which, as in Plotinus, cannot be conceived as existing separately from the cosmic intellect or mind) is in turn analogous, if not identical with, Plotinus' *psyche* – the divine principle of movement and hence the agent of all changes and transformations in the universe.

However, Bruno's refusal even to attempt any conceptualization of the utterly inaccessible divinity cannot be interpreted as a surrender of rational thinking in favor of mystical experience for the attainment of some knowledge, however imperfect, of God. Unlike Plotinus and Nicholas of Cusa, Bruno was not a mystic. As a philosopher and metaphysician, however, he did postulate a divine principle of complex organization and movement immanent in the universe. This metaphysical principle accessible only to reason attested merely the immanence of the cosmic mind in the universe. It was postulated merely to provide a sufficient reason for cosmic order. Thus, Bruno explains the immanence of the divine in the universe in a way that is not detrimental to the transcendence of God; for this reason he must be absolved from the charges of crude atheism and pantheism.

Neither did Bruno conceive the universe as the body of God, as a crude panentheism would maintain, but rather as the necessary manifestation of the immutable, infinite, unknowable One, which, precisely because of its omnipotence, had no choice but to unfold itself without detriment to its immutability, infinitude, and perfection; only its cosmic manifestations are finite, since they are multiple, bounded, and discrete in space and time.

The proposition that would unequivocally make Bruno a pantheist would be one that totally identified the universe with God, and, if not a full-fledged pantheist, he certainly would have to be considered a panentheist[6] should he have described the universe as the body of God. Neither of these two propositions are found anywhere in Bruno's writings. What we do frequently find there is the assertion of the inextricable union of the infinite cosmic mind with the infinite universe – a union so intimate and indissoluble that neither one can exist without the other.

Although it is true that Bruno never endorsed distinctly pantheistic or panentheistic views, he certainly was a monist and for this reason an adversary of Christian dogma and all other dualistic (both theistic and deistic) doctrines concerning the origin and nature of the universe.

However, in the Frankfurt didactical poems (in which Bruno's cosmology and ontology reached full maturity) he sometimes expressed his thoughts in terms which strongly suggest pantheism. 'God is infinite in the infinite, everywhere and in all things,' he wrote, 'not above them, nor outside of them, but absolutely intimate to all of them.'[7] This definition – or rather description – emphasizes God's absolute immanence in the universe. This is precisely what the insistence on the double negation preceding the prepositions 'above' and 'outside' intends. In any case, Bruno's radical monism clearly contradicts the theistic as well as the deistic concepts of God, for it challenges the central Judeo-Christian belief in a God who freely created the universe out of nothing in the beginning of time. The idea of a God who is in the universe 'not above . . . nor outside' all things, who therefore cannot exist separately and independently of an eternal and infinite universe, is utterly incongruous with the theistic Judeo-Christian tradition, and even with a deistic concept of an utterly free Creator-God.

However, if clearly not the universe itself, is Bruno's God perhaps the soul of the universe? Although a number of Brunian texts point in this direction, Bruno explicitly avoided this identi-fication as well.[8] God, he wrote, is not the soul, but the 'soul of the soul' of the universe. Although Bruno regarded the cosmic mind as the ultimate source of movement and order in the universe, he shied away from making it the Absolute; no less than the universe, the cosmic mind, too, must have a cause or a principle, and that could only be God. A refusal to acknowledge some kind of sub-ordination of the cosmic mind to God would inevitably have been interpreted as an outright denial of the fundamental orthodox Christian dogma of creation, something that Bruno was not prepared to do. However, if not necessarily the origin, certainly the order of the universe could, in principle, be attributed directly to the cosmic mind. Moreover, the universe was not regarded by Bruno as having its origin in time. Consequently, the cosmic mind does not seem necessarily to require an additional transcendent principle to justify the existence of the universe. Inextricably and eternally united with the cosmos they would have, exclusively and entirely in themselves, the reason for their absolutely neces-sary existence; the union and unity of cosmic mind and cosmos would constitute the Absolute.

Had Bruno totally excluded God from his cosmological reason-ing he would have made himself even more vulnerable to the charge of pantheism. However, we must point out that making God the transcendent principle of the cosmic mind and hence of the cosmos, is not postulated by the principles of natural philoso-phy which alone Bruno professed to follow, but rather by theolog-ical considerations which clearly lie beyond the parameters he himself established for his philosophical inquiry. We therefore cannot but conclude that Bruno's decision not to leave the tran-scendent God completely out of his cosmological and ontological speculations was not due to philosophical reasons, but rather to the justifiable fear of putting his entire philosophy in jeopardy by challenging the fundamental Christian dogma of creation. We will never know for certain whether Bruno was, from the bottom of his heart, a convinced pantheist or panentheist, for prudent dissimulation was considered a necessary, indeed even a laudable virtue in those dangerous times.

Thus, Bruno conceived God, although utterly inaccessible to human comprehension, as intimately united with the universe through the agency and mediation of the soul of the world and the universal intellect. This is the essential trait and most specific characteristic of the Brunian God. If in his earlier writings Bruno carefully distinguished God from the visible universe and even from the cosmic mind in order to avoid the accusation of impious atheism, this distinction cannot be understood as an endorsement of the traditional view that the transcendent God exists separately and independently from the universe He created. When we look at the visible universe, Bruno would point out, it is not God we are directly looking at, but rather only at His unfolding and manifestation.

At first sight, it would seem that there is little, if any, disagreement between Bruno and Thomas Aquinas in the view that God is everywhere present in the universe. But there is, in fact, a radical difference between their understanding of this presence. The key to understanding their disagreement is provided by Bruno's concept of the cosmic mind. According to Bruno, the divine mind is essentially 'cosmic' because it is intimately and indissolubly linked to matter and therefore constitutes the very essence of physical reality. This is precisely what is meant by the term immanent, as opposed to transcendent. According to Aquinas, however, the divine mind itself never becomes the substance of physical reality: in its total aloofness it merely creates, conserves, and governs the universe. Aquinas' utterly transcendent God keeps the universe 'at a distance'; there is an insurmountable gap between them. Although both Bruno and Aquinas coincide in affirming the epistemological transcendence of God – God, according to both, is incomprehensible and ineffable – Bruno unambiguously maintained the ontological immanence of the divine mind in the universe, whereas Aquinas resolutely rejected this notion as too redolent of pantheism. Already Nicholas of Cusa had been suspected of heresy because of his explanation of God's creation as an 'unfolding'; it sounded too much like a Neoplatonic emanation. But, as we have extensively documented, Bruno asserted, in terms far more explicit than those ever used by Cusanus, the ontological immanence of the cosmic mind.

Bruno's God is, therefore, neither the universe nor the soul of the universe. He is conceived rather as 'the soul of the soul', that is, as the ultimate metaphysical principle of the cosmic mind which, in turn, irresistibly drives the universe to its unfolding. God, cosmic mind, and universe are thus intimately united. Moreover, the intimate union of the cosmic mind and the universe must be understood as a unity, not unlike the unity that Aristotle conceived as resulting from the union in the human being of those two inseparable ontological principles constitutive of all physical reality, matter and form (body as matter and soul as the form of the body).

However, even in Bruno's later more elaborate cosmological and ontological poems, the immanence of God in the universe, realized through the intermediary of the cosmic mind, remains shrouded in deep mystery because of its utter inaccessibility to human conceptualization. Thus, it is not clear whether Bruno conceived Cusanus' unfolding as a Neoplatonic emanation, a view which Christian orthodoxy unambiguously condemned. In any case, Bruno's concept of God is decidedly anti-Platonic and unorthodox, for it is based on a monistic ontology that vigorously rejects the radical separation and absolute autonomy of mind and matter, and consequently also of the divine mind and the universe.

Can this more sharply delineated Brunian concept of God still in some way be considered pantheistic? We would have to answer affirmatively, should we understand pantheism merely as a general proclamation of the divinity of the All, for Bruno did indeed regard the universe as divine – *mater-materia* is divine, and its form, the cosmic mind, is likewise divine. However, we must answer this question negatively if pantheism is taken to mean that this visible universe is the only existing material God, uncreated and eternal, existing with absolute necessity and being its own cause.

In the following text, Bruno comes even more dangerously close to outright pantheism, as he clearly identifies God with nature:

> You see then that there is one simple Divinity found in all things, one fecund Nature, preserving mother of the universe insofar as

she diversely communicates herself, casts her light into diverse subjects, and assumes various names.

Texts such as these in *Lo Spaccio* prompted the Cardinal-Inquisitors to accuse Bruno of 'atheism', which was the word used then to refer to pantheism. Most objectionable was Bruno's contention that the universe is necessary, for God could not but create, although, as Bruno cautiously pointed out, this necessity does not contradict God's freedom. In God, he argued – using the principle of the coincidence of opposites – freedom and necessity are one. This conviction Bruno shared with Cusanus, who we know exerted a very powerful influence on his thinking.[9] According to Cusanus, God, as *possest*, is the actual realization of all of God's potentialities. If God has the power to create an infinite world without center and circumference, then He cannot but create it; for why would an omnipotent God choose to restrain his power and impose limits on what he can do? An omnipotent God needs to create an infinite universe. He simply cannot exist without it. The irony of the omnipotent is that He is needy . . . of infinitude.

The paradox of Bruno's concept of God – considered impious and atheistic by the Cardinal-Inquisitors – is that it is actually profoundly orthodox-Christian and anti-gnostic, since he took the *unio hypostatica* (the union of one divine hypostasis – the second person of the Christian Trinity – with the human nature of Jesus Christ) so seriously that he literally raised it to the cosmic level. The essence of gnosticism is to hold matter in contempt and to believe in the essential immateriality of reality. In opposition to gnostic beliefs, Orthodox Christology, definitively victorious in the Council of Chalcedon (451 A.D.), solemnly pronounced the humanity of Christ to be totally real. How could the Word really have become flesh, the orthodox bishops argued, if matter is either an illusion or evil, and therefore utterly contemptible? Thus, by proclaiming the immanence of God in the universe, Bruno was taking the orthodox dogma of the Incarnation to its ultimate consequences.

Blumenberg is keenly aware of this and explicitly contends that Bruno was neither a pantheist nor a polytheist because Bruno's immanentism implied that the universe occupied the place that the Incarnate Son of God had traditionally occupied in Christian dogma.[10] Blumenberg, however, does not draw the unavoidable conclusion from his own argument, namely that if the universe was indeed the incarnation of the divinity, it could hardly avoid being considered the body of God, which is a downright panentheistic conception totally foreign to Bruno. Although the universe for Bruno was neither God nor the body of God, it certainly was the unfolding of the divinity and hence ultimately itself divine. However, to conceive the end-result of this unfolding as the material body of a purely spiritual God would introduce into Bruno's thinking an ontological dualism he vehemently opposed.

Bruno is a true precursor of 'process thought' or 'process theology', which holds that the universe is not teleological, that is, is not willfully directed by a mind (immanent or transcendent) towards the production of certain highly intelligent beings as the ultimate goal which would give meaning to the entire process of cosmic evolution. According to Bruno – a firm believer in the Heracleitan primacy of becoming over being – new forms, structures, and systems of the greatest variety and complexity are continuously and eternally emerging, because fecund *mater-materia*, driven by the cosmic mind that immanently informs it, is endowed with a playful freedom to incessantly explore, test, and bring the viable ones to fruition. This principle of complex organization thereby manifests true omnipotence and, at the same time, absolute freedom since it has not set for itself, once and for all, a fixed goal it must attain. Thus, compounding the cosmic mind's rationality with contingency, mutability, and freedom, Bruno anticipates the 'dipolar God', rational as well as contingent, of process theology.[11] For indeed the cosmic mind (which furnishes the higher organizing principles – irreducible to laws of physics – that monitor and control the behavior of complex systems) is both contingent and rational, mutable and algorithmic, both affecting and affected by the matter it informs, and its activity resembles more the work of a creative artist inventing and experimenting with new forms than that of an architect or watchmaker holding a definite blueprint he must perforce implement.

The ethical and religious consequences of Bruno's concept of God and the universe are noteworthy. First of all, not only does it allow for human freedom, it also provides the perfect leeway for it. On the other hand, its similarity with the Brahman of Hindu philosophy is very striking. In the earlier Upanishads the absolute un-manifest Brahman was considered the supreme reality sustaining the universe, whereas the manifest, qualities-bearing Brahman contained the universe. Bruno's God – who, as he repeatedly stated, lies beyond any possible conceptualization – is therefore comparable to the absolute un-manifest Brahman, whereas the manifest Brahman may be assimilated to Bruno's cosmic mind, which is immanent in the universe. Thus Bruno's God and Brahman have in common that they are both at the same time inclusive and exclusive of the universe, immutable as well as the ultimate principle of all change.

However, Bruno does not side with a particular Vedantist (and also Western idealistic) understanding of the relationship between Brahman and the universe, a sort of 'acosmic pantheism' which views the universe as a mere illusion or deceitful dream. The universe is supremely real for Bruno, and the rational knowledge thereof that we can obtain is basically trustworthy, provided that we detect and correct the illusions caused by our sensorial misperceptions. Our cognitive limitations refer only to God, not to the universe. On the other hand, Bruno equally rejects the panentheistic conception – espoused by some Vedantists (among whom Ramanujan is perhaps the most prominent) – of the universe as the body of God.

We may now summarize Bruno's views on the relationship between God and the universe as follows: The universe is an eternally ongoing process. The agents that initiate and regulate this process, the world-soul and the universal intelligence, are immanent in the process; they are not parts of the divinity, since the divinity has no parts, but they do partake of it since they unfold from God (perhaps as Neoplatonic hypostases of the One). The universe is neither God nor God's body. Neither does the universe emanate from God or the cosmic mind. The divinity is in the universe as the soul is in the human body, although inseparable from it and forming a unity with it. God, cosmic mind, and universe are infinite and eternal. The universe is necessary. An utterly solipsistic divinity, capable of existing in and by itself without the universe, is absurd.

Bruno's supreme achievement in the philosophy of religion was to bring God back from the remoteness of his extracosmic domain into the universe. The Brunian God is a truly cosmic God.

Nowhere does this become more manifest than in Bruno's argument with Palingenius.[12] This Italian poet-cosmologist, contradicting Aristotle, had come close to asserting the infinitude of the universe. However, he identified the last sphere of the Aristotelian-Ptolemaic universe, the firmament, with an infinite realm of divine light, the dwelling of God and assigned three separate regions for three different kinds of light: the light of our world, the light of the heavenly bodies, and the divine light of the Empyrean, which he paradoxically considered a part of the universe. Thus Palingenius' God was cosmic and extracosmic at the same time, for he divided the cosmos into three separate regions, one of which was the exclusive dwelling of God.

Bruno emphatically rejected this view. Light, he argued, is one and the same throughout the entire universe. God does not dwell in a secluded realm of divine light; He is everywhere in the universe. In fact, not only is He everywhere, but He is everything in the universe, as the following passage explicitly states:

> Before anything else the One [*l'unità*] must exist eternally; from His power derives everything that always is or will ever be. He is the Eternal and embraces all times. He knows profoundly all events and He himself is everything. He creates everything beyond any beginning of time and beyond any limit of place and space. He is not subject to any numerical law, or to any law of measure or order. He himself is law, number, measure, limit without limit, end without end, act without form.[13]

Palingenius was wrong in assuming the existence of a special cosmic divine light, different from the light of the heavenly bodies and of this world. Based on his fundamental cosmological principle of homogeneity Bruno argued that there is only one kind of light in the entire universe. Whatever light may be, and Bruno never claimed to know what it was, one thing was certain for him, namely that light does not exist in and by itself, independently of a corporeal substratum. Light and body, light and matter are indissolubly bound together.

Bruno's concept of God is indeed that of a truly cosmic God. As such, it represents the most radical rejection not only of the God of Plato and Aristotle, but also, and above all, of both the gnostic and the Manichean God. Paradoxically, this Brunian concept of

God signals the complete and final victory of the orthodox Christian dogma of the Incarnation – driven by Bruno to its ultimate consequences – over both Manicheism and gnosticism.[14] This is also the conclusion of Paul Henri Michel, who, referring to Palingenius, writes:

> . . . does not the imprudent poet-cosmologist concur in the errors of the Manichees in assigning two realms impenetrable each by the other to Good and Evil?
>
> If the universe is indeed divided and if a zone of pure light becomes the dwelling place of God, then the worst has happened for our world: evil alone reigns there; it is wicked and therefore sprung from an evil principle: *Si hic mundus esset malus, a malo esset principio.* On the final pages of *De immenso* the Monist affirmation is forcefully repeated: God is everywhere and in everything, not above, not below, but in the heart of everything.[15]

Bruno actually says in the final pages of *De immenso* even more: God, he writes, is everything. (Only the inverted proposition, 'everything is God' would be outright pantheistic.) In any case, what this poem unambiguously proclaims is the total immanence of God in the universe, mediated by the cosmic mind and soul, and hence the existence of a truly cosmic God – 'not above, not below, but in the heart of everything'. This is the essence of Bruno's 'monist affirmation'.

What kind of religion could conceivably result from this Brunian concept of God? Bruno surely did not ignore that absolute certitude in metaphysics is impossible, but he firmly believed that a compelling ontology could be built on the basis of a sound cosmology, and further, that a plausible ontology could provide a legitimate and commendable foundation for a universal religion. Indeed, there seems to be no other alternative for achieving universal consensus about such basic concerns, common to all religions, about the origin and fate of the universe, the cause or principle of the stunning order we observe in it, and the meaning of human existence.

There was certainly no longer room for prayer, as it was traditionally understood, in Bruno's new religion. God's necessary cosmic unfolding can perhaps be somewhat influenced by human activity, but ultimately the minimal change that human minds can bring about in the universe depends largely on their ability to decipher the code of the cosmic mind and bring this knowledge to bear upon the transformation of the physical world. In Bruno's new religion, humanity's prayer, rather than a request for God's special intervention and favors in human affairs, becomes a dialogue – a dialogue between the human and the cosmic mind; this prayer would lead further to action that would render possible the attainment of even greater knowledge of the cosmic mind. This, in turn, would contribute significantly to the realization of the Brunian Utopia by urging reason – rather than greed and ambition – to bear on world politics and economics, in such a way that more and more human beings would be able to enjoy those elementary living conditions which alone make possible the development and education of their minds.

Since the main theist argument for the existence of God, the cosmological argument, no longer seems to be compelling, the fact that it nevertheless does appeal to reason, rather than to faith, for supporting its validity only encourages reason to seek to establish sound ontological and cosmological foundations for a rational, universally acceptable religion. Indeed, the monumental theological works of Thomas Aquinas and Francisco Suárez, as well as of many other great Scholastic theologians, had only one purpose, namely to show the rationality of the Christian dogma, which is precisely the reason why Thomas Aquinas used the philosophy of Aristotle to explain and defend Christian doctrine.

Should the opinion prevail that religion does not need such philosophical underpinnings and that faith in the revealed word of God is sufficient, the road would be blocked to a universal religion, for this is precisely what every religion based on particular revelations and special sacred books tries to become, as their active proselytism clearly demonstrates.

As long as there are human beings who wonder about the origin of the universe, about the marvelous order that is perceptible everywhere in nature, and as long as they feel a desire to understand this universe and whatever may be its cause or principle, human beings will continue to ask who or what this cause or principle of the universe may be, and whether they have any obligations or duties towards this principle or cause, and what exactly these duties are. In other words, the need for religion will probably continue to be very strong in the future, and will grow even stronger, in the measure that our amazement at the stunning wonders of both macrocosm and microcosm increases.

It is obvious that a religion which appeals to reason has a better chance of being accepted by the peoples of all nations than a religion which either sidesteps or spurns reason. Such was the religion that Bruno wished to propose to a humanity torn by religious wars – wars among peoples and nations that had embraced religions based on the authority of the revealed word of God as recorded in allegedly divinely inspired sacred books. Bruno felt strongly (and in this point he agreed with the Florentine Humanists) that mankind was finally ready for such a religion, now that the old world view, and the entire cosmology and ontology with which it was interlocked, had collapsed.

The cosmic age, inaugurated by Bruno and now coming of age, has developed very sensitive and eager ears for a new cosmic religion that no longer demands blind faith in obscure propositions, miracles and myths (which was unquestionably the major stumbling block in the way of universal acceptance of all historical religions), but rather appeals only to human reason, common sense, and that special intense love of life, the planet, and the universe that an increasing number of human beings all over the world are now experiencing. For, indeed, a religion that views nature as divine and professes reverence for all forms of life is capable of instilling and promoting in all human beings love and respect for the environment as well as for others. And, a religion that understands human existence as a participation in the divine process of constant creation, and as an extension and continuation thereof, sets clearly for humanity a lofty goal in the kind of self-fulfillment that generally results from art production, scientific research, and the technological improvement of living conditions on the planet and in the universe. Although it is true that this religion does not promise individual immortality and eternal bliss any more – rewards that are unquestionably the most ambitious human beings have ever dreamt of, a bit too ambitious perhaps – it might very well contribute to the survival of the human race by helping to build a world in which peace, harmony, and beauty finally begin to prevail.

CHAPTER TWELVE

The New Road to Knowledge

A well-known astronomer of NASA's Goddard Space Flight Center recently made the following statement: 'The greatest astronomical discoveries have always been made by better technology, rather than by the brightest minds.' This statement seems to underestimate the crucial role that mental images and a vivid imagination play in scientific speculation and discovery. The fact is that there have been numerous instances of bright minds anticipating the greatest astronomical discoveries long before the technology that later confirmed them was invented and applied.

Giordano Bruno did not live long enough to know that the Milky Way was made up of stars. This was discovered by Galileo only seven years after Bruno was burnt at the stake. Yet Bruno achieved in less than ten years of intense speculation a considerably more accurate picture of the universe than the one Galileo reached after several decades of incessant calculations and experimentation. Indeed, almost sixty years after Bruno had grasped that the universe was infinite, open, and acentric, Galileo, on his death-bed, was still clinging to the Copernican view that the Sun was the center of the universe, and that the outermost stellar sphere, the firmament, was immobile, despite the considerable technological advantage he had gained over Bruno with his telescope, and despite his routine use of mathematics and experimentation in the modern science of physics he had founded. Thus, although Galileo actually beheld the immensity of the universe when he pointed his instrument for the first time to a sky that suddenly became populated with millions of stars never seen before by the naked eye, he never dared to admit that the universe is infinite.[1] It was Bruno who, despite his serious technological and methodological handicaps, proclaimed the infinity and acentricity of the universe loudly and clearly wherever he went.

This undeniable historical fact prompts us to ask questions concerning the ability of the mind to arrive at certain truths about the universe long before technology and experimentation confirm them. These questions are intimately related to the larger problem Einstein referred to as 'the most incomprehensible thing about the universe: its comprehensibility'. Einstein's mind was unquestionably one of those brightest ones that repeatedly succeeded in beating technology in the race towards the goal of unraveling the secrets of the universe.

Bruno realized that the new cosmology, inaugurated by Copernicus, could not develop fully and eventually debunk the established one unless it broke loose from the fetters that held it in bondage, namely the philosophical systems of Plato, Plotinus, and Aristotle, as well as the Church's contention that the authority of the Bible extended also to strictly cosmological matters. To accomplish this difficult and hazardous, but long overdue emancipation of cosmology from those philosophical and theological shackles, Bruno relied on the attentive observation of astronomical phenomena, a sharp speculative reason, a most vivid imagination, a profound knowledge of the Pre-Socratic philosophical tradition, and a novel epistemological theory. Equipped with these tools, he set out to construct his cosmological model.

Bruno obviously had no idea of such basic concepts of classical physics as gravitational force, fields, waves, magnetism, and electricity, not to mention the forces and sub-particles of quantum mechanics. And yet, despite the extremely rudimentary state of physical and astronomical science in Bruno's time, his cosmological model is strikingly congruous with some of the most compelling contemporary ones. The question then arises, by what means did Bruno arrive at such astonishing anticipatory insights?

Most contemporary cosmological models are, like Bruno's, to a large extent, speculative, for it is mostly imaginative assumptions and inferential extrapolations that ultimately generate these models. In this respect, there is not much difference between Bruno's cosmological model and those of contemporary cosmology. Nor is there much difference between them in their determination to firmly ground their theoretical speculations on empirical data, since in both cases it was uncompromising. Bruno, in fact, was never willing to sacrifice observational data in favor of preconceived metaphysical assumptions. His cosmological speculations were prompted and supported by attentive observation of natural phenomena and all the empirical knowledge he could muster. In this respect, he was much more of a modern thinker than some of his critics are willing to admit.

The crucial difference between Bruno's cosmological model and contemporary ones lies in their authors' discrepant assessment of the role and cognitive power of mathematics in cosmology. Bruno challenged the claim of certain mathematicians of his time to possess the only adequate and reliable means to grasp the essence of physical reality. In this he proved to be in opposition not only to Pythagoras and Plato, but also to some of his most influential intellectual contemporaries, the Italian Renaissance Platonists. Bruno's main objection, against the mathematicians, was based on the fact that Ptolemy's exceptional mathematical skills – ingeniously applied by him in support of his compelling and highly successful model – had not been able to prevent humankind from being in gross error for more than thirteen hundred years about such fundamental facts as the movement of the Earth and the other planets around the Sun, as well as the size and shape of the universe. Even Copernicus, who in Bruno's estimation was a mathematician rather than a *fisico*, that is, a philosopher of nature, had been unable to draw the most pertinent and crucial conclusions from his cosmological breakthrough because of his predominantly mathematical approach. Bruno rated the heuristic power of philosophy of nature higher than that of mathematical computations of astronomical phenomena, and considered the latter utterly inadequate, indeed misleading, if divorced from rational thinking based on observation.

The main reason for Bruno's objections to the superior heuristic power of mathematics when applied to physical reality was his correct understanding of the basic homogeneity of all matter in the universe. He had no trouble in siding with both Plato and Aristotle in their view that imperfection was inherent to all sublunar bodies. The reason why they believed that mathematics and geometry could be legitimately applied to describe the structure and movements of the heavenly bodies with absolute mathematical precision was that none of the four terrestrial elements was found in them. But once Bruno realized that the stuff of the heavenly bodies in no way differs from the elements that make up the Earth, he concluded that imperfection was not limited to the sublunar world, but that it was the essential common characteristic of everything that exists anywhere in the universe and, consequently, that mathematics and geometry have the same restricted heuristic and cognitive value, regardless of the cosmic topography in which they are applied. It made no difference whether it was the sublunar or the supralunar world.

Bruno's reservations regarding a purely mathematical understanding of the universe, far from betraying an unscientific mind, make him a forerunner of most contemporary scientists who consider all physical laws statistical, and hence merely approximate. Indeed, most of them would agree that perfect regularity and exactness, a distinctive feature of geometrical figures and mathematical equations, exist only in our minds. Bruno's firm conviction that natural phenomena resist adequate and exhaustive elucidation of their nature by mathematical equations and geometrical figures clearly reveals the strong anti-Platonic and anti-Pythagorean drift of his thinking. Bruno even attributes acceleration to heavenly bodies, something totally inconceivable for Aristotle, who considered uniform circular motion the only possible motion for them.

Bruno, however, did not absolutely deny the existence of regularity in the universe. He explicitly admitted degrees in regularity and regarded mathematics as indispensable for measuring them, as his sporadic recourse to mathematics in his own cosmological speculations clearly demonstrates.

In contrast to these strongly anti-Platonic views of Bruno's, it is interesting to note that all of Kepler's laws of planetary motion were based strictly on Pythagorean and Platonic assumptions. Kepler shared the traditional belief that perfection and geometrical exactness existed in the heavens. He was so convinced of this that he initiated his inquiry into the planetary movements by postulating, *'more pythagoreico et platonico'* (in the manner of Pythagoras and Plato) that the orbits of the only five planets that were thought to exist corresponded exactly to the perfect spheres that inscribed or were inscribed in the only five regular solids that Euclid proved were possible. Kepler was, of course, wrong, but his next attempt, by far more successful than the former (in fact the one that really made him famous), was hardly less Platonic than the previous one. For although Kepler replaced the circular orbits by less perfect elliptical ones in order to explain planetary

motion, mathematics raised its triumphal crown even higher
when he produced the equations which accurately accounted for
those elliptical gyrations. Kepler had thereby succeeded in fulfill-
ing Pythagoras' and Plato's goal of grounding astronomy entirely
on geometry and mathematics. Subsequently, it was Galileo who
introduced mathematics into physics as well. Finally, Newton
accomplished the total mathematization of science by expanding
the scope of Galileo's terrestrial physics to encompass the entire
universe.

Newton, however, relying on Galileo's discovery of inertia and
Gilbert's discovery of magnetism, actually undermined the
Platonic presuppositions of Kepler's laws, for he put the finishing
touch, with his law of universal gravitation, to what Bruno had
initiated a century earlier, namely the introduction of sublunar
physics into the realm of the supralunar. Newton thereby definitively debunked the millenary dogma of the essential inequality
of celestial and terrestrial phenomena, and consequently also that
of the irreducibility of celestial to terrestrial physics. He also
delivered the final blow to the Aristotelian notions of firmament
and transporting spheres (which Bruno had already undermined),
since universal gravitation rendered those mental constructions
utterly superfluous and obsolete. Newton was further compelled
to introduce absolute infinite space as the necessary receptacle of
all those celestial bodies moving about and attracting each other,
as well as ether as the indispensable medium for the transmission
of the force of gravitation. In effect, he introduced the idea of
infinite space (an insight which again Bruno had reached a hundred years earlier) in order to avoid the otherwise inevitable
conclusion of a universe eventually collapsing unto itself as a
result of universal mutual attraction.

Newton, however, never succeeded in explaining the nature of
the gravitational force he postulated. He did give us the equation
that measures it, but he never told us what it is, and truly, the
notion that two bodies mutually attract as a result of just being
present to each other is very odd indeed, and it eventually turned
out that this hypothesis was not only odd, but also incorrect.
Contemporary cosmology informs us that Newton's metaphysical assumption that there is a universal force of gravitation transmitted through the ether is no longer tenable; bodies don't attract
other bodies by virtue of a universal gravitational force. Einstein

has shown that heavenly bodies move along the geodesics formed in spacetime by the warping of its fabric by the massive bodies embedded in it; they simply roll down the 'rails' without a 'locomotive' to provide the pull. Thus, the most profound and revolutionary cosmological insight of this century may be compressed into the following stunningly succint proposition: gravity is ultimately nothing but geometry! Although it obviously confirms the primacy of mathematics in physics, Einstein paradoxically arrived at it in virtue, not of mathematics, but rather of a stunning image of his powerful imagination.

The general underestimation of Bruno's cosmological accomplishments by contemporary scientists is based mainly on his alleged neglect of experimentation and mathematics. Indeed, in comparison with Galileo and Newton, who heavily relied on them to arrive at their scientific conclusions and to corroborate them, it is understandable that Bruno generally does not appear to modern scientists as anything but a 'mystic', a 'magus', and a Neoplatonic dreamer. The remarkable thing about this 'dreamer', however, is not only that his model of the universe is actually much more in conformity with contemporary cosmological models than those of his most famous contemporaries, and even of the leading scientists who lived in the century following his death, but also that he established, for the first time, some of the basic principles of modern cosmology, which in turn have never been either proved or disproved by mathematics or experimentation.

The charges leveled against Bruno that he was insensitive, if not hostile, to the genuinely scientific approach inaugurated by Galileo and Newton because of his disdain for mathematics and neglect of experimentation, and particularly because of his excessive reliance on allegedly unfounded metaphysical speculations, arise in part from overlooking that cosmology was not an experimental science even for Galileo and Newton, or for anybody else who pursued it until the advent of astrophysics, which in turn was made possible by the relatively recent discoveries of spectroscopy, electromagnetism, and nuclear physics. With regard to cosmology, Newton was not even a nose ahead of Bruno in the race to understand the cosmos with the help of experimentation. The truth is that Newton's extrapolation of terrestrial into cosmic physics – the necessary presupposition for his insight into universal gravitation – was not the result of any particular experiment,

but rather a bold assumption made possible by Bruno's preliminary insight into the isotropy and homogeneity of the cosmos. It
is true, Newton's equations did indeed confirm the validity, and
account for the stunning accuracy, of Kepler's laws of planetary
motion. But this was achieved mainly by Newton's keen intuition,
bold mental images, and highly sophisticated theoretical speculation, with little if any help from experimentation.

Far from holding mathematics in contempt, Bruno considered
it useful for corroborating the intuitions about the universe that
he believed only philosophy could provide; he was also the first
modern thinker to become keenly aware of the opposition
between the two principal symbolic languages at our disposal in
our efforts to comprehend physical reality. The former consists of
concepts rooted in mental images, the latter of numbers. Contemporary physics uses both. Thus, when it speaks of waves, particles,
fields, strings, inflation, and black holes, it resorts to purely
qualitative-conceptual, and therefore inevitably, also to metaphorical language. On the other hand, when it brings forth an
equation such as $e=mc^2$, in which energy, mass, and speed of light
are concepts, it still operates with numbers, for these concepts are
converted into numbers in the equation. Thus, although this equation establishes a mathematical equivalence between mass and
energy, it still leaves us totally in the dark as to what mass and
energy really are. In order to clarify these concepts, physics is
compelled to resort again to other conceptual images. The circular
impasse is unavoidable, since mental images are simply not
reducible to numbers.

Positivist astrophysicists and cosmologists do not tire of insisting that truth is not in the picture, but in the algorithm. If you want
to understand, they warn us, disregard the images and trust the
numbers. The irony of the matter, however, is that the most
spectacular recent breakthroughs in relativistic and quantum
theories about the origin of the universe, such as the inflationary
and the string theories, have been achieved thanks mainly to the
epistemic and heuristic power of bold mental images. Although
the validity of these theories does indeed ultimately depend on
the stringency of the mathematical apparatus developed to
support and corroborate them, it is very unlikely that they would
have ever been conceived in the first place had those images not
inspired them. Science simply cannot do without mental images,

metaphors, and qualitative concepts. They make up the ideal 'biosphere' in which genuinely creative scientific minds thrive and become most prolific.

Although it is true that quantum mechanics has given up all efforts to visualize subparticles, it still cannot avoid images and concepts to describe their odd behavior. If reality can be represented at all by mental processes, it is not possible to dispense altogether with conceptual language. In Heinz R. Pagels' words, 'They [language and mathematics] are both symbolic means of representing the world; language is richer, while mathematics is more precise.'[2] This superior richness of language and the relative poverty of mathematics obviously refers to their respective power of representation. Notwithstanding, some quantum physicists (like Dirac and Heisenberg) were convinced 'that a consistent mathematical description of nature was the road to truth in physics'.[3] Because the laws of physics and chemistry can be formulated appropriately only by means of algorithms and mathematical equations, it is obvious that these sciences cannot dispense with mathematics. It does not follow, however, that physical reality can be fully understood by mathematics. This is not possible if indeed conceptual language is 'richer', that is, has greater representative power than mathematics.

For Bruno, to know was not just to measure. Only the quantitative properties of matter are accessible to mathematics; the qualitative ones lie beyond its reach. The alternative for those who believe that knowing and understanding physical phenomena is equivalent to accurately measuring them is either to deny the existence in nature of qualitative properties irreducible to quantitative ones or, if the former are acknowledged, to give up all hope of ever achieving true knowledge of them.

This was the point Bruno was trying to make in his polemic against those mathematicians of his time who claimed to have the only truly reliable key to the comprehension of physical reality. Bruno was critical of mathematics not because it could be dispensed with in astronomical and physical speculations, but because of its inherent weakness to penetrate, explore, and discover the essence and true nature of these phenomena. In sum, mathematical language was, for Bruno, utterly inadequate to represent, describe, explain, and therefore ultimately to comprehend the phenomena of physical reality.

The contention that Bruno was hostile to a genuinely scientific approach in astronomy and cosmology can easily be dismissed if we listen to Bruno's laudatory references to the remarkable astronomical achievements of Tycho Brahe. Moreover, in the construction of his own cosmological model, Bruno shared with the famous Danish astronomer the same basic methodological and heuristic principles, namely most careful observation of phenomena, total confidence in the ability of the observer's own thinking processes to interpret those observations, and the readiness to give up hypotheses not warranted by empirical evidence. Whatever failed to satisfy the standards set by these rigorous heuristic and epistemological requirements was seldom accepted and incorporated into his model, including some of the most compelling views of his much admired Pre-Socratics and Hermes Trismegistos. In fact, it was precisely Aristotle's occasional disregard for these essential prerequisites of scientific research that made his speculations so vulnerable in Bruno's eyes.

One of the traits of Bruno's mind which most clearly manifests its critical – and hence truly scientific – frame, is his keen awareness of the principal source of error to which his adversaries frequently succumbed, namely their tendency to give undue credence to visual appearances and their failure to realize the inherent fallacy of the senses. The theological prejudice underlying this generalized view was that God could not possibly have endowed human beings with senses so feeble and imperfect that they could lead them to such grave errors in their understanding of the universe. Bruno flatly rejected this unwarranted assumption and unambiguously denounced the deceitfulness of the senses.

Bruno's main handicap in the construction of a scientific cosmology was that a new physics had not yet been worked out after the bankruptcy of the Aristotelian, which he so strenuously labored to bring about. Consequently, Bruno had to develop his own novel cosmology in an almost complete scientific vacuum. With regard to physical theory, almost all of Bruno's energies were spent in refuting and undermining the firmly established Aristotelian physics. As a result, his undertaking, although successful, was mainly destructive. However, since he was neither a physicist nor an astronomer, but a cosmologist, it would not be fair to brand him as unscientific merely for not having anticipated and practiced the rigorous scientific method Galileo was about to inaugurate.

Bruno's initial strongly Neoplatonic epistemology had undergone a profound crisis as a result of his study and intense intellectual exchange with Copernicus' cosmology. It signaled a gradual but steady retreat from the positions he had held until then in the Neoplatonic field of Plotinus, Pico della Mirandola and Marsilio Ficino[4] towards the Pre-Socratic, Epicurean and Stoic camp, which he usually referred to as *'antica vera filosofia'*. It was in this ancient true philosophy that Bruno sought and found the ontological and epistemological foundations most congruous with his new cosmology.

We have the first signs of this evolution in Bruno's epistemological work *De sigillis sigillorum*, which marks a significant progress with regard to the earlier treatise he had written in Paris, *De umbris idearum*. However, it is not until the publication of the three Italian dialogues in the following two years that a radical ontological, cosmological, and epistemological transformation becomes clearly manifest.[5] From then on, Bruno no longer lodged in the Neoplatonic camp. He had definitively moved his intellectual home back to the territory of the Pre-Socratics.

Bruno's merger of metaphysical opposites such as principle and cause, matter and form, act and potency, and so on, laid the groundwork for an entirely new epistemology. Bruno's thinking had gradually become dialectical. The rigid, separate, and immutable forms of Platonism, as well as the fixed categories of Aristotelianism lost their rigidity, became fluid, and could turn into their opposites. This transformation had taken place mainly as a result of Bruno's reflections on the philosophy of Nicholas of Cusa, and makes Bruno one of the most significant precursors of Hegelian dialectics. Indeed, Bruno not only matched his dialectical epistemology with the Heraclitean ontology of universal becoming, but grounded it on the dialectical principle established by Cusanus of the coincidence of opposites. Never before in the history of Western thought had mental categories been endowed with such powerful internal dynamism. Thus, Bruno's vigorous vitalism penetrates even his epistemology; it pervades his entire philosophical system.

Besides his dialectical thinking, there were some crucial principles which led Bruno to the discovery of cosmological truths that so many astronomers and astrophysicists after him failed to envision. The basic premises of Bruno's epistemology were clearly established at the beginning of the dialogue, *De infinito, universo e mondi* (On the Infinite, the Universe, and Worlds). Here he distinguishes between sensorial knowledge, the knowledge that our reason gives us, the knowledge that we can acquire through the intellect, and finally the knowledge that is attainable only by the mind, which is the highest form of knowledge. Reason, explains Bruno, merely argues and discusses, the intellect leads us to origins, principles, and conclusions, but it is only the mind that in the end vitally perceives the truth.[6]

Bruno's conviction that the human mind was 'the eye of divine intelligence' may have prompted him to 'tune in' with the cosmic mind. Man had first to set his mind free from all the prejudices that held it imprisoned in the dark dungeon of ignorance so as to render it capable of establishing contact with the cosmic mind. He simply had to let the 'larger mind' take over.

This conviction of Bruno's was ultimately rooted in a bold, but compelling, metaphysical assumption. Since the universe was comprehensible, it was not possible for the human mind to discover and comprehend the basic features of the universe unless it was in some way finely tuned with the cosmic, 'larger' mind that informs the universe and consequently all human minds as well. The naïve-realistic doctrine that an omnipotent transcendent mind created out of nothing microminds capable of accurately mirroring the universe is gnoseologically implausible and has long been discredited. Likewise, Leibniz's doctrine of 'pre-established harmony', designed to explain how it was possible for the purely spiritual – the human mind – to accurately reflect the material universe, considering that any interaction between these utterly heterogeneous substances was totally inconceivable, is even less convincing. The most sensible explanation for the fine tuning between the human mind and the 'larger' mind that renders it capable of comprehending the universe was given by Bruno himself, undoubtedly inspired by Stoic philosophy: The cosmic mind is immanent in the human mind; this is the reason for the remarkable harmony that exists between them (as we know, the concept of 'harmony' was central to Stoicism). Bruno illustrated this harmony by means of the analogy of the human 'soul', which, without diminution or fragmentation, is totally in every part of the human body, and also by the analogy of the human voice, which is present in many listeners without ceasing to be one.

To illustrate this crucial Brunian doctrine concerning the metaphysical foundations of his epistemology – the union of the human with the cosmic mind – Bruno even resorts to graphic, openly sexual imagery. This is what he wrote in *De umbris idearum*:

> Hence in order for you to acquire a consummate and absolute art, it behooves you to copulate with the soul of the world, and once you have copulated with it, to act, for it is teeming with rational forms, and it generates a world full of similar rational forms. And these forms (Plotinus would agree) shape and form in seed everything that exists, like tiny worlds. Hence since the soul is everywhere present, all of it in the whole and in every part of it as well, you may be able to behold, as the condition of matter will allow, in every thing, no matter how small and cut off, the world, not to speak of the semblance of the world, so that we may without fear say with Anaxagoras that everything is in everything.

From a contemporary perspective, it is possible to interpret Bruno's view in the following manner: if the cosmic mind is immanent in the human mind, it is not unreasonable to conjecture that the same algorithms operative in the universe were also impressed on the human mind, and that consequently the same cosmic codes and programs were copied there as well.

Thus, the epistemological argument with Neoplatonism which Bruno initiated in Paris with his book, *De umbris idearum*, reached its culmination in London after Bruno completed there his other major epistemological work, *De sigillis sigillorum*. By then he had drawn a clear line between Neoplatonism and his own new philosophy. Two major gnoseological insights signal Bruno's definitive break with that philosophy: first, the ultimate principle of reality, the One, was transposed from the *mundus ideatus* – the intelligible world of Platonism – to the level of physical reality, that is to the physical universe; and secondly the *triplex mundus* of Platonism, the physical, the metaphysical, and the logical were seen as homologous. Thus, the subject as well as the object of knowledge participated in the same basic structure, whereby the universe became comprehensible, however not by virtue of a subjective mirroring of objective reality, but through a basic synchronicity of the three levels of reality which were ultimately the expression and unfolding of the same One.

In this crucial overturn of Platonism, Bruno retains one of its basic insights (which it nonetheless shares with Parmenides), namely that true knowledge is only of the One, and consists in grasping the unity in multiplicity, and the identity in variety. By transposing the One from the realm of ideas to the physical world, true knowledge can henceforth be achieved only by mind in a 'vital' intuition that grasps the knot that binds the three worlds. So physics was inextricably linked to metaphysics, and both to Bruno's dialectical epistemology.

Thus, Bruno's cosmovision may hold key elements for a possible solution of Einstein's conundrum. The universe is indeed comprehensible, because *mater-materia* brought forth the human brain and impressed therein the figures and patterns of mind's logico-dialectical processes by copying them from the information codes proper to the universal intelligence immanent in matter. Thus human knowledge of reality would find its ultimate explanation not in the mirroring theory of naïve realism, nor in the pre-established harmony of Leibniz's deism, but in the 'copulation' of the human with the cosmic mind, and ultimately in the fundamental oneness and identity of mind and matter as two interdependent, complementary, and dialectical aspects or moments of reality, rather than in the total absorption of one by the other, or in the sheer reduction of one to the other (as in pure idealism or crude materialism).

It is amazing how many rivers of thought converge in this fundamental Brunian insight. First of all there are Schelling and Hegel, who clearly made nature and the universe an essential and necessary moment of the Absolute. There is also Plotinus, who asserted that the human mind is an emanation of the divine One. Above all, there is the basic insight of the philosophies of Hinduism and Buddhism, that the mind and the All are one. The language and metaphors may change, but the fundamental insight is shared by some of the greatest philosophical minds the world has ever known.

However, Bruno's epistemology was not based exclusively, in fact, not even primarily, on metaphysical assumptions.[7] We will understand this better if we follow closely the successive steps his thinking took in the process of overcoming the Copernican cosmological model.

It appears that the factor that most decisively contributed to Bruno's deconstruction of the Copernican model was not a set of metaphysical axioms, but rather his uncanny ability (in conjunction with his prodigious memory) to form visual and mental images of the physical universe that seemed to incorporate and integrate in a simpler, more economical, and aesthetically more satisfying manner the data provided by astronomical observation. Thus, it would be most illuminating to detect in his confrontation with the Copernican model the precise elements of that model that struck him as being most crucial and at the same time most vulnerable.

In his intellectual journey towards a cosmological model capable of supplanting the traditional Aristotelian-Ptolemaic one, Bruno initially received with enthusiasm, and started to build upon, the Copernican model, until he detected in it a serious flaw. An unwarranted metaphysical assumption interfered with and blocked the way to the formation of a Gestalt fully congruous with the astronomical data Copernicus had assembled and based his model on. Bruno had no difficulty in agreeing with Copernicus on the fundamental insights of the Earth's movement and the central position of the Sun in the solar system, but he found neither empirical nor theoretical justification sufficient for making the Sun the center of the entire universe; a heliocentric universe would still require the whole apparatus of transporting spheres and consequently also an edge and a shape for the same finite and closed universe, in addition to the highly implausible vertiginous rotational velocity of the remotest sphere of fixed stars around the Earth. Now Aristotle's strongest argument in favor of placing the Earth at the center of the universe was his concept of weight, defined as the tendency of bodies to move towards their natural place. Since of all the four elements earth was the heaviest, it tended to occupy a place beneath the places occupied by the other three lighter elements. The result was that the extraterrestrial material constituted by those other elements had to be stacked around the Earth. Since the element earth was not to be found in Copernicus' Sun, Aristotle's main argument pleading for a cosmic center could no longer be applied to the Sun. If Copernicus, in spite of the necessary forfeiture of the only physical justification for a cosmic center ever suggested and widely accepted, still insisted on making the Sun the center of the universe, he had to do so on the basis of purely metaphysical (not excluding theological) considerations.

Once the flaw was discovered, the way was open to an entirely new image of the universe, for no longer was there any physical reason why the Sun should be the center of the universe. Suddenly a new mental image of the universe emerged in Bruno's mind: an infinite, acentric universe filled with innumerable worlds probably inhabited by other extraterrestrial intelligent beings; all heavenly bodies set free and made of the same stuff, the same elements and the same atoms; infinite space filled with ether; an infinite, acentric universe in constant change and transformation that had no beginning and will have no end.

As a result, cosmological dualism – the partition of the universe into two separate, heterogeneous regions, the sublunar and the supralunar – as well as the idea of a closed and finite universe were rejected. A new cosmovision was born, the result of eliminating all unwarranted metaphysical assumptions from the other models and vividly imagining what the universe would look like then. The final test would be the capacity of the new model to incorporate and integrate coherently and consistently the data provided by the most reliable astronomical observation. However, what most commended the new cosmovision was its simplicity, its elegance, and above all, its capacity to render the available ensemble of astronomical data more comprehensible to the human mind.

Thus, Bruno's main tools in the elaboration of his new cosmological model were his reliance on the ability of the human mind to form adequate pictures of physical reality, a most vivid imagination, and a sharp philosophical acumen to detect the unwarranted metaphysical and physical assumptions underlying the predominant models.

One of the most important, if not the most important, guiding principle of Bruno's epistemology is total intellectual independence and honesty. He firmly believed in the power of his own intellect, and of reason in general, to discover truth. This, of course, in turn presupposes a conviction that the universe is rational and comprehensible. Thus, Bruno anticipated, indeed made possible, the rationalist philosophical approaches of Descartes, Spinoza, and Leibniz. Actually, with this insight, Bruno set up the continental divide that separates the Middle Ages and the Renaissance from the Modern World, for the basic prerequisite for the advancement of astronomy and cosmology, indeed for the general progress of all sciences in Europe, was the emancipation and encouragement of free and independent minds to doubt, question, and challenge all accepted and widely held views about the universe, particularly those that had been firmly established by the most authoritative philosophers and astronomer-mathematicians of the past and most zealously defended by the theologians and philosophers of his time. It is precisely this belief in rationality that compelled Bruno to prefer the Copernican over the traditional Ptolemaic theory. It is, again, precisely this belief, compounded with his intellectual independence, that led Bruno to disagree with Copernicus with regard to cosmic acentricity and the existence in the universe of infinite worlds similar to our own planetary system. For Bruno, authority was never an argument in favor of a view. Rationality always had the last word, even if it contradicted the most venerable authorities.

More than anything else, particularly more than any specific controversial proposition about nature and the universe, what would upset the Cardinal-theologians of the Inquisition most was Bruno's revolutionary epistemology. They were keenly aware of the fact that Bruno was actually vindicating the rights of the human sensorial apparatus and reason to find out the truth about nature without the aid of revelation or ecclesiastical doctrinal authority. This amounted to upholding the autonomy and independence of reason from religious supervision, control, and censure in scientific matters. This was the decisive reason for Bruno's condemnation and execution, since his position posed the most dangerous threat to the power of the ecclesiastical authorities should they ever lose their tight grip on scientific inquiry. The eventual triumph of Bruno's epistemological stance in northern Europe, particularly in Protestant countries, resulted in the foundation of increasingly autonomous academies of science which contributed decisively to the rapid development of science and technology in those countries, and consequently also to their greater economic and political power.

The key to understanding the crucial difference between contemporary scientific epistemology and Bruno's in the common business of discovering cosmological facts and laws is not the exclusion of mathematics and experimentation, on the one hand, and the reliance on intuition and the vivid imagination, on the other, but rather in the total refusal of contemporary science to accept anything as true that is not falsifiable by experimentation

and corroborated by exact mathematical computations and measurements. Thus, whereas mathematics is not a prerequisite for
scientific discovery in the initial phase, it certainly is essential for
the validation of theories in the final stage. Bruno was, therefore,
not overly reprehensible for his low esteem of mathematics as a
powerful heuristic tool, but he certainly was unmodern in his
willingness to accept unfalsifiable non-empirical entities as
adequate explanations for physical phenomena.

In spite of this, it is undeniable that in the end Bruno proved to
be astonishingly successful, by virtue of his reliance mainly on
intuition and a vivid imagination, in anticipating a remarkable
number of truths about the universe whose validity it took centuries for the scientific community to accept. It seems that, in this
respect, both Bruno and Einstein shared the same 'hot line with
the Old One'. Of course, Einstein's overwhelming advantage over
Bruno lay in his firm grasp and mastery over the means to prove
that the messages heard were correct. However, in spite of the
obvious considerable differences in their theory and practice of
scientific epistemology, we find Heinz Pagels' remark equally
applicable to both of them:

> Extraordinary geniuses are quite different [from ordinary ones]. It
> is not at all clear how they think. They seem to work by an ordinary
> set of rules of their own invention and yet arrive at remarkable
> insights. They cannot tell you how they got there: their reasoning
> seems devious. The ordinary genius may have many students. But
> the devious genius rarely has any, since he cannot communicate
> his methods of solution.[8]

CHAPTER THIRTEEN

Was Bruno a Magus?

Some further considerations are still necessary to clarify Bruno's interest in magic. After all, the assertion that Bruno was 'nothing but a Renaissance magus' is the central thesis of Frances Yates' highly influential book, *Giordano Bruno and the Hermetic Tradition*. There is probably nothing wrong about being a Renaissance magus, particularly if we understand magic the way Bruno did. What is certainly very wrong is Frances Yates' contention that he was 'nothing but' that.

There is no question about the fact that Bruno was profoundly interested in magic. This interest grew even more intense towards the end of his life, after his ontology and cosmology had been fully developed. Thus, in the summer of 1589, after his departure from Wittenberg and during his sojourn in Helmstedt, he composed at least five *opere magiche* (magic works) which he never had the opportunity to publish: *De magia* (On Magic), *Theses de magia* (Theses on Magic), *De magia mathematica* (On Mathematical Magic), *De rerum principiis et elementis et causis* (On the Principles of Things and Elements and Causes), and *Medicina lulliana* (Lullian Medicine).

Bruno's unquestionable interest in magic, however, does by no means justify Frances Yates' characterization of him as 'nothing but a Renaissance magus', for this view fails to acknowledge his powerful insights and remarkable anticipations in the fields of cosmology and ontology, which we have tried to clarify and appraise in the preceding chapters of this book. Frances Yates was interested mainly in tracing Bruno's thought back to Hermetic sources. To this effect, she focused primarily on Bruno's earlier works, in which the Neoplatonic influence was strongest, and on those later ones dealing specifically with magic, whereas Bruno's Frankfurt writings, which contain the bulk of his mature

cosmology and ontology, do not receive in Yates' book the attention they deserve. Nor does the distinguished Renaissance scholar
trouble to explore the motives that Bruno may have had for his
interest in magic, or to take notice of the crucial role Bruno
assigned to magic in his plans for a radical ethical and socio-
political revolution in Europe. This biased approach prevented
Yates from acknowledging the acumen, originality, and depth of
Bruno's ontological and cosmological discourse.

Bruno's interest in magic must first of all be reassessed in the
context of his criticism of popular Roman Catholic apologetics.
Bruno was undoubtedly aware of the enormous importance of
miracles – not only of Jesus's miracles, but also of those attributed
to his disciples, to the Virgin Mary, and to countless other Catholic
saints and relics – as conclusive evidence of the truth of the
Catholic faith. He realized that, if he failed to provide a rational
explanation for those miracles, his new religion had no chance of
being accepted by the educated public as an acceptable substitute
for the popular Catholic 'superstition'. Magic offered him the most
probable and compelling rational explanation. Thus, to attribute
miracles to magic was, for Bruno, unquestionably of the highest
strategic importance, indeed a necessity, if he had any hopes of
success for the sweeping religious, ethical, social, and political
revolution he was planning to launch.

However, Bruno's interest in magic had deeper roots; they
reach all the way down to his ontology and 'Pan-theology'. It is
only at this deeper level that Bruno's interest in magic can be fully
understood. Magic was, for Bruno, ultimately nothing but the
mental activity most effective for gaining access to the forces of
nature ensconced in the cosmic mind. Traditional prayer was
considered by him incapable of establishing this contact. Only the
inquisitive human mind had the possibility of establishing communication with the cosmic mind and of gaining access to the
forces of nature hidden in it, provided it availed itself of the
language and tools that magic provided. Thus, magic made possible that particular 'copulation' of the human with the cosmic
mind which alone rendered it capable of acquiring knowledge of
the hidden forces of nature and of the means to exploit them.

Bruno distinguished between nine meanings of the word
magic, and nine different types of magic.[1] Only one of these
meanings refers to the much maligned black magic or necromancy

which Bruno, too, held in contempt. The kind of magic that interested him most was the so-called theurgic magic, because of the unique heuristic and gnoseological potential he attributed to its esoteric language. This language, he thought, had once been mastered and spoken by the ancient Egyptian sages and theurgic magicians, who had allegedly succeeded in performing with it all sorts of prodigious feats in nature. However, its power did not depend on incantations or invocations of supernatural beings, but rather on the fact that it was the language of nature itself – the language of the soul or intellect of the universe.

Bruno was convinced that nature's code was not made up either of numbers or of abstract concepts. Instead, it was a highly complex system consisting of interrelated signs, symbols, and images. Vestiges of these signs and images could still be found in dreams and in the symbols and figures of the Cabala, of alchemy, astrology, Greek mythology, and the Lullian art of memory.[2] The only language that had ever had access to that secret code, the language once spoken by the ancient Egyptian sages and theurgic magicians, was now dead; it had been long forgotten after having been displaced in the course of history by other languages with considerably less cognitive and heuristic power. In light of this, Bruno's argument with the Aristotelians, the Neoplatonists, the Pythagoreans, the Renaissance Humanists, and the mathematicians must be understood mainly as a critique of the languages they relied on to understand nature and the universe and to unravel their secrets.

Thus, rather than being unscientific, Bruno's interest in magic was prompted by an intense desire to discover the most appropriate scientific language, the one which allowed access to the hidden code of nature, for, indeed, Bruno understood science as an intercourse of the human mind with the mind of the universe, and since the cosmic mind had its own language, and that language had a code, in order to communicate with the cosmic mind the human mind had to discover that code and learn that language.

Thus, the main reason for Bruno's life-long interest in magic is that he anticipated and shared modern science's conviction that the universe is comprehensible, that beneath the astonishing complexity of cosmic phenomenality lies a hidden underlying order, accessible to the human intellect. All the efforts of Bruno's predecessors to understand the universe mathematically had been unsuccessful. The metaphysical assumption underlying all those efforts was the old Pythagorean-Platonic belief that the essence of supralunar reality was mathematical. It enabled the Aristotelian-Ptolemaic world-view to hold its ground and mislead humanity for more than thirteen hundred years. In view of this dismal failure, if the universe is at all comprehensible, Bruno argued, it must be comprehensible unmathematically. Now, the only epistemological categories available to Bruno, besides the mathematical ones, were abstract concepts, and images and signs. However, all the abstract categories developed by post-Socratic philosophies had been as useless as the mathematical ones to help us understand the universe. Bruno, consequently, set out to discover a set of categories capable of cracking the hidden code of the universe. Because this code is hidden, he searched for it in the occult. He, therefore, engaged in a life-long study of occult systems, among which the Lullian, the Cabalistic, and the Hermetic were the most elaborate, complicated, and rich in imagery, and for this reason they became the preferred objects of his research.

This is, indeed, the most plausible explanation for Bruno's interest in magic. Bruno, consequently, was undeniably un-modern by rejecting mathematics as the most adequate and reliable means to crack the cosmic code, but he was genuinely modern in searching indefatigably for the most appropriate language that would access the hidden underlying patterns of phenomenal complexity and thus provide a clue for solving the paradox of the incomprehensible comprehensibility of the universe.

Bruno's religiosity also provides an additional perspective from which we can better understand his interest in magic. For indeed, despite his total lack of interest in the official Scholastic theology, Bruno was a profoundly religious man. He anticipated and shared Galileo's belief that God reveals himself to humankind primarily in the 'book of nature', but, unlike Galileo, Bruno was convinced that the only way to communicate with God was through nature, for God does not 'talk to' human beings in their everyday human language. However, natural magic was the only means available to humans for communicating with the cosmic mind. The magus was therefore the only possible 'priest' of the new Brunian religion. Indeed, Bruno's conversion from theism to ontological monism implied the transformation of the Catholic priest (which Bruno actually was) into the hermetic magus. If mankind was interested in receiving favors from the only accessible divinity, the cosmic mind in nature, conventional prayer was of no avail. Communication with this divinity could be established only by the magical discourse and praxis, for the only language the cosmic mind 'spoke' was not made up of ordinary human words, but rather of the signs and figures it had impressed in nature. Thus, the principal business of the magician, the priest and worshiper of nature, was to discover, decode, and interpret these signs and figures – 'the utterances of natural effects' – with the aid of his magical ceremonies, as Bruno lets the goddess Isis explain:

> Those worshipers, then, in order to procure certain benefits and gifts from the gods through the knowledge of profound magic, entered into the midst of certain natural things in which, in such manner, Divinity was latent, and through which she was able to, and wanted to impart herself to such effects. Therefore, those ceremonies were not vain fantasies, but live words which touched the very ears of us gods. Just as we want to be understood by these worshipers, not through utterances of language, which they may be able to contrive, but through utterances of natural effects, they wished to strive to be understood by us through these utterances, as well as through acts of ceremonies. Otherwise we should have been deaf to their prayers, just as a Tartar would be toward the Greek tongue, which he had never heard.[3]

Since there is no God outside of, or separate from, the universe, the only communication possible with the divinity is through 'reading its mind' manifested in and through the signs and figures – 'the species that are in the bosom of Nature'. Thus Bruno's magus may be seen as the precursor of the modern cosmologist, who, as Carl Sagan pointedly observes in his Prologue to Stephen Hawking's *A Brief History of Time*, is doing nothing but trying to read God's mind from its manifestation in the universe. This is why the concept of prayer as 'petition' and request of favors was clearly rejected by Bruno in *Lo Spaccio*. Prayer is only possible in theism since it presupposes a personal, provident, and caring God, but Bruno had definitively abandoned the camp of dualistic theism and established himself firmly on the grounds of monism . . . and sometimes even very close to downright pantheism, as the following text shows:

God, as absolute, has nothing to do with us except insofar as he communicates with the effects of Nature and is more intimate with them than Nature herself. Therefore, if he is not Nature herself, he is certainly the nature of Nature, and is the soul of the Soul of the world, if he is not the soul herself . . .

Divinity reveals herself in all things . . . , she is found and is seen in things said to be most abject, although everything, from what is said, has Divinity latent within itself. For she unfolds and imparts herself even unto the smallest beings, and from the smallest beings, according to their capacity. Without her presence nothing would have being, because she is the essence of the existence of the first unto the last being.[4]

Consequently, man's most important religious duty is not to give an utterly transcendent God honor and glory (as the Calvinists proclaimed), since God has no need of human praise, but to explore the occult forces of nature and to try to harness them to the benefit of mankind. Through the knowledge of those forces, human beings would effectively increase their knowledge of God; and through mastering and using these forces, they would become more similar to God by imitating the constant creative activity of the cosmic mind. Magic, thus, became for Bruno the indispensable and central ceremony of a totally new religion for a reformed humanity. It consisted in the study and mastery of the occult forces of nature as the most adequate means to establish that intimate relationship with the divinity that true religion and mysticism seek.

Bruno's ontology of universal becoming played a crucial role in shaping this Brunian 'Pan-theology', for the cosmic mind is eminently Proteic, and consequently magic must be a spirited human activity in tune with this dynamic and constantly changing divinity. Magic certainly has no place within the frame of an ontology of rigid and immutable essences. Thus, to communicate with the Divinity implies not only to understand the language it speaks through nature, but also to follow the infinite unfolding of its relentless transformations. Thus, watching the waves roll on a sandy beach and deliver their inexhaustible bounty of exquisitely patterned shells – all of them showing the unmistakable imprint of the cosmic mind – can become a profoundly religious experience, reminiscent of the moment when the mythological hunter Actaeon surprised the naked Amphitrite wearing only her shell necklaces, playing and displaying herself in the sparkling waters. It is not surprising that Bruno saw himself as another Actaeon, for he, too, was in constant frenzied pursuit of the goddess of nature. When Actaeon finally found the goddess and watched her bathing naked, in punishment for his sacrilege he was metamorphosed into a deer only to be torn to pieces on the spot and devoured by his own hunting dogs. Indeed, this is a stunning prophetic allegory of Bruno's own life in constant pursuit of the elusive goddess of nature, and of his tragic death as punishment for having discovered and revealed her best-kept and inviolable secret! In light of this, it is understandable that even the wild polytheism of the Egyptians, not in spite of but precisely because of its innumerable animal gods, was seen by Bruno as the prototype of a unique form of profound religiosity. 'In all things and in all effects,' writes Bruno in *Lo Spaccio*, 'they [the Egyptians] contemplated the divinity.'[5] 'Magic,' writes Bruno, again in *Lo Spaccio*, 'inasmuch as she turns toward the contemplation of Nature and to the scrutiny of her secrets, is natural.'[6] Thus, Bruno's monism, naturalism, and profound religiosity were the basis of his high esteem of natural magic.

Bruno was not blind to the fact that fecund *mater-materia* often impresses its forms on things through number and geometrical configurations. However, he also knew that, if number and figure are indeed at the very root of every physical being, no perfect figure is found in nature – no perfect circle, square, triangle, or solid – for everything is in constant flow. For there to be perfect figures in nature, identity would have to be possible, the identity of a body with itself and with other bodies as well. However, nothing is identical either with itself, in successive instants, since reality is in constant flux, nor with anything else, simultaneously. Hence, no perfect figure can be found in nature. Yet, what is truly amazing is that nature, in its relentless creativity, seems to be unable to operate without the assistance of geometry and mathematics. Precisely in this, consists nature's rationality, or at least this is how we discover it, and yet Bruno disagrees with those who claim to understand fully reality by means of mathematical symbols and relations. Although nature's *modus operandi* is indeed to a large extent quantitative, its essence is elusive, certainly not merely quantitative. The *élan*, the *Drang* or thrust of life is manifestly not blind; it is supremely intelligent, and its intelligence

reveals itself through innumerable patterns of complex organization, frequently either geometrical or algorithmic. Consequently,
the only way to acquire power over nature and to collaborate with
it in its ongoing creative process is to discover the patterns through
which it operates. In this point, positivistic science is absolutely
right: metaphysics has nothing to contribute to scientific methodology. But this may well be due to the fact that science has become
our own contemporary version of magic. After all, we are still
trying to read God's mind!

As we can easily see, Bruno's insight into the nature of nature
is profoundly modern. Only the way proposed and used by Bruno
to acquire this knowledge is unscientific in the modern sense,
because it is not based on the direct observation of the structures
themselves as they are found in nature and on their analysis with
the powerful aid of highly sophisticated technology and experimentation, but rather on associations of figures and symbols
found in the rich storehouses of the occult sciences of his time. This
is where Bruno really falls behind true modernity, not in his
ignorance or denial of the geometrical patterns underlying reality
– in this he was basically in agreement with modern science – but
in his methodology of gaining access to the figures that lurk at the
bottom of physical reality. Bruno was convinced that those figures
become reality in the nerves and fibers of all organisms as well as
in the patterned structures of inorganic matter. Unfortunately he
did not have at his disposal a microscope to detect them, so he
resorted to the only means available to him, at that time, to
penetrate into the hidden figures which he believed pervaded and
sustained all structures in nature. It was almost like a Jungian
search for archetypes in nature, and Bruno sought these archetypes in the symbols of mythology and the Hermetic writings, in
the numerology of the Cabala, and in the Lullian art of memory.

There is yet another important question we must ask regarding
Bruno's true identity and his relation to magic: Was Bruno a
gnostic? There are, indeed, at first sight some gnostic traits in
Bruno's ontology, although few if any in his cosmology. We must
therefore take a closer look into Bruno's ontology in order to detect
possible gnostic ingredients in it.

As opposed to both Judaic theological, and Platonic ontological, transcendentalism which interpose an unsurmountable
chasm between God and man, the gnosis abolishes the gap and

proclaims the identity of God and man. Paradoxically, this is not the result of overcoming transcendentalist dualism, but of driving it to its ultimate consequences. For transcendentalist dualism had merely separated, albeit drastically, the spiritual from the material, whereas the gnosis utterly devalued and often even rejected and denied corporeal reality. Hence, it refused to attribute any power, or even real existence, to matter. This explains the tendency of Christian gnosis to docetism, which refused to accept the physical reality of Jesus' body, and hence also of his suffering, death, and resurrection, and particularly the power of Jesus' blood to wipe away the sins of humankind, and the redeeming value of sacrifice in general. In this respect, Bruno is definitely not a gnostic, for he unambiguously proclaimed the dignity, power, and fecundity of matter.

However, some gnostic resonances are still detectable in Bruno's identification of the human with the cosmic mind and in his opposition to both Platonic and Judaic transcendentalism. Also, his rebellious rejection of authority, his staunch individualism, and his belief in the power of the human mind to reach out and tune in with the cosmic mind have a familiar gnostic ring. There are also, undeniably, some affinities with the gnosis in his devotion to magic as a privileged channel for establishing communion with the cosmic mind.

However, unlike in the majority of historical gnostic sects, the source of Bruno's 'gnosis' was neither a secret book of revelation nor a private illumination, but, as we have repeatedly stated, reason, observation, and a vivid imagination. Above all, his doctrine was definitely not esoteric; instead, it was intended to be shared by all human beings who were willing to think by themselves about God and the universe.

Frances Yates could not but sharply disagree with this view. Bruno was not only a Renaissance magus, but a full-fledged gnostic as well, for magic and gnosis, she contended, always go hand in hand. But how did Yates handle the undeniable fact of Bruno's divinization of matter? Based on Festugière's alleged distinction between an optimistic and a pessimistic gnosis, she hastened to label Bruno as an optimistic gnostic, for unlike pessimistic gnostics he didn't demonize matter. However, was there ever truly such a gnosis, or was the 'optimistic gnosis' just an oxymoron fabricated by Yates and falsely attributed to Festugière?

Plotinus, who wrote against the gnostics and even had some gnostic friends, surely must have been quite familiar with their doctrines. The founder of Neoplatonism, however, profoundly disliked the gnostics, wrote treatises against them, and fought them mercilessly mainly because 'they despise and hate the material universe and deny its goodness and the goodness of its maker'.[7] Had there been an optimistic gnosis, surely Plotinus would have known about it. It is therefore quite probable that the 'optimistic gnosis' that Yates discovers in some Hermetic writings is nothing but Plotinian Neoplatonism, for Plotinus, like Bruno, thought highly of matter. This seems, indeed, to be the case, for she claims to have found the distinction between optimistic and pessimistic gnosis in a footnote of Festugière's book *La révélation d'Hermès Trismégiste*.[8] Actually in that footnote Festugière does not speak about pessimistic and optimistic gnosis, but about optimistic and pessimistic Hermetic writings, which is an entirely different matter. The *Corpus Hermeticum* was mainly of Neoplatonist, not of gnostic origin. At least this is what Casaubon (the man whom Yates proclaims as the true watershed between Renaissance and Modern world!)[9] tells us about these writings after discovering that they were not attributable to a contemporary of Moses. Casaubon, Yates reports, discovered that the works falsely attributed to Hermes 'do not contain the doctrines of an ancient Egyptian but are made up partly from the writings of Plato and the Platonists and partly from Christian sacred books'.[10] There is no reference at all to the gnosis in Casaubon, according to Yates herself! Only those Hermetic writings that held matter in contempt may perhaps have been exposed to some Christian-gnostic contamination; the rest were simply Neoplatonic. Thus, it is totally unwarranted to deduce from Festugière's footnote the existence of an 'optimistic' gnosis, and even more so to consider Bruno a gnostic, notwithstanding his optimism. It seems that Yates, in her eagerness to make Bruno appear as a gnostic – since she believes that 'gnosticism and magic go together' – touched Festugière's footnote with her own magic wand.

In conclusion, it is possible to acknowledge that Bruno was a magus, provided we understand this word in the sense that Bruno himself understood it. However, Bruno was much more than 'just' a Renaissance magus. This is precisely what Frances Yates never could or would understand.

PART FOUR

Bruno's Anticipation of Contemporary Cosmology

CHAPTER FOURTEEN

The Vanishing Centers

Bruno's cosmological model, among all the models of the universe proposed before the relativity and quantum revolutions, is unquestionably the most congruous with contemporary views of the cosmos. However, few Brunian insights, of the many which inspired his model, are more impressive than his insight into the acentricity of the universe. Bruno arrived at this in the least propitious historical moment. The Earth had just been dethroned from her privileged position at the center of the universe by Copernicus, who, however, had felt compelled to put the Sun in her place. A dramatic cosmological upheaval had taken place, certainly long due, but welcome at first only by a handful of scientists and philosophers both in Anglican England and in Protestant Central Europe, who slowly became persuaded by Copernicus' arguments. For this tiny group, and Bruno belonged to it, the authority of the great Polish astronomer had become decisive. At the other end of the spectrum, the Italian Renaissance Humanists had prepared the ground for the triumph of the Sun over the Earth by their enthusiastic reception of the Hermetic writings, which they believed contained the revelations of Hermes Trismegistos, the legendary Egyptian sage thought to be contemporary of Moses. In these writings, the Egyptian Sun-God had undergone a radical conceptual transformation that made him almost undistinguishable from Plato's Supreme Being. However, although Bruno shared the erroneous belief of the Italian Humanists with regard to the authenticity and authority of the Hermetic writings, he did not allow himself to be dazzled by Copernicus' authority nor to be mesmerized by the Italian Humanists' rapturous celebrations of the Sun. He thereby proved to be a true republican – cosmologically speaking – by refusing to participate in the coronation ceremony which Copernicus and the humanists had staged for the new King of the Universe.

The stubbornness with which mankind clings to centers was demonstrated by the fact that it still took more than two hundred years for it to be persuaded that the Sun was not the center of the universe, as Bruno had predicted. For it was not until 1780 that Herschel discovered that the Sun was a part of the Milky Way galaxy, along with millions of other stars like it. However, even Herschel clung to the idea that the Sun was the center, not of the universe, for sure, but of the galaxy in which it was located.

It was not until 1917 that the American astronomer Harlow Shapley discovered that the Sun was not located in the center of the Milky Way either, but rather in one of the outermost arms of that spiral galaxy, tens of thousands of light years away from the center. Thus, Bruno's bold imagination and remarkable lucidity anticipated by more than three hundred years the conclusion that experimental astronomy finally arrived at in the second decade of this century.[1]

However, Shapley's conclusive observations still did not succeed in curing us of our obsessive addiction to centers.[2] Shapley hypothesized that certain stars forming globular clusters form a fairly symmetrical swarm about the center of the Milky Way. So, even though he had driven the Sun out of the center of the Milky Way, he still felt compelled to consider the Milky Way as the center of the globular clusters of stars whirling around it.

This new center, however, like all its predecessors, was also doomed to vanish, and, indeed, very soon did. Only six years later, Edwin Hubble, another great American astronomer, discovered that the Andromeda nebula, until then believed to be a part of the only galaxy we knew of, our own Milky Way, was in fact another galaxy situated far beyond the boundaries of the Milky Way; furthermore, he predicted, and very soon discovered, that there were, in the universe, besides our own, countless other galaxies like the newly discovered Andromeda galaxy. Hence, if the Milky Way was only one among many galaxies, the Milky Way could not possibly be the center of the universe either. Again, another center had vanished.

Would we try again? We had now realized that our galaxy, along with other nearby galaxies, formed clusters of galaxies. Could at least our cluster of galaxies be the center of the universe?

The final disappointment came when it was discovered that, besides the local group of galaxies that form our cluster, there are countless other clusters of galaxies, all of them receding from each other at fantastic speeds approximating the speed of light.

If we had been definitively disappointed in our quest for centers in space, there was still a recourse we had never tried before – to postulate a center in time. This new center was, of course, the singularity of the Big Bang, that theoretical entity which Hubble himself had been so instrumental in introducing, as the most plausible explanation for the beginning of the universe, after discovering and convincingly proving that the clusters of distant galaxies are all moving away from us, and consequently that the universe is expanding. And, if it is indeed expanding, cosmologists would soon conclude, it must once have been compressed into a point of infinite density, temperature, and curvature of spacetime – the primordial singularity – out of which everything that exists burst out and has been expanding ever since.

Although indeed not in the center of absolute time – before the Big Bang there was no time! – the singularity does function as a center of sorts, since its explosion created spacetime, and the early universe dispersed in all directions just as spacetime was being created.

A spectacular astronomical discovery finally seemed to signal the end of the endless center-fugue and to give us back our feeling of security. The Big Bang hypothesis has been spectacularly confirmed (at least in its modified inflationary version) by the irregularities discovered by the COBE satellite in the cosmic background radiation. It now seemed incontrovertible that our universe, after all, does have a center, not a center in space, but certainly a center in time.

However, our sigh of relief was short-lived. Once more, humankind's craving for centers was profoundly disappointed, for we are now warned against the complacency that is liable to arise from the almost unassailable certitude of a beginning in time of this, our universe, by a most unsettling consideration. The Big Bang singularity may well have been the temporal center of this universe, but we are not sure that this, our universe, is the only one that exists! Instead of one single Big Bang, there may have been countless other Big Bangs. Consequently, there may be millions of other universes that we know nothing about and with which we cannot communicate now and may even never be able to communicate with at all. As a matter of fact, there are several cosmologists today, perhaps the most famous are the Russian Andrei Linde and Harvard's Sidney Coleman, who believe this to be actually the case. But even here, in this most recent theoretical many-universes scenario, our inveterate center-obsession makes its last stand. The ensemble of universes, some defenders of this theory suggest, was spawned from the froth of our early universe as autonomous bubbles to which our universe remains linked by infinitesimal channels dubbed wormholes by Coleman. In this hypothesis, our universe, as the single matrix of the multiple universes, would still have some claim to be considered the center of the multiple universes.

However, the final blow to our center-mania was delivered by Andrei Linde himself when he came up with the ultimate acentric many-universes model.[1] Our universe, he contends, is probably not the primordial egg from which the other universes were hatched; our universe is, in fact, only one of the many bubbles which were released from the froth of another universe, which in turn was spawned from another, and this from yet another, *ad infinitum*.

Here, at long last, the long voyage towards total acentricity, initiated by Bruno, has come to an end. Bruno's discovery of the infinitude, isotropy, and homogeneity of the universe has thus been carried by Linde to its ultimate consequences. The All is no longer necessarily a sea of billions of galaxies and clusters of galaxies; the All may be an infinite ocean of infinite universes! In this ocean, our insignificant tiny universe is only an island in the infinite archipelago of universes. Humanity has thereby been stripped for good of all its cherished centers. Riding on its speck of dust, humankind drifts aimlessly along the endless pathways of the labyrinth of universes – a labyrinth with no center and no edges, no beginning in time, and no end. Thus, Linde finally arrived at the very notion that Bruno, the prophet of acentricity, had formulated four hundred years earlier: the notion of an eternally self-reproducing universe, of universes breeding offshoot universes without end. 'The evolution of the universe as a whole has no end,' Linde says, 'and it may have had no beginning.' Furthermore, he agrees with Bruno on that other point, a consequence of the former: 'The fact that somewhere else there is life like ours is to me almost certain.'

Looking back at the history of the centers of the universe, it appears as a long succession of receding and vanishing centers, a stubborn dynasty of pretenders to a throne that does not exist anywhere, neither in space nor in time. This obsessive center-mania does reveal a lot about ourselves, for it strongly suggests the presence, in all of us, of a desperate need for security, and of a resolute refusal to accept the now undeniable fact of our utter cosmic insignificance. However, there is really no need for despair: by discovering our appalling spatio-temporal insignificance, we have come to realize the only title to greatness we still possess, and which has become, precisely in the process of this millenary quest for centers, all the more manifest and inspiring: the boundlessness and almost unlimited power of the human mind. Alas, is the mind the real center we have been looking for so relentlessly?

To persuade us that the mind indeed constitutes a center, there is, of course, the awareness of our ability to recall things from the boundless storage room of memory with a simple command, and the ability to make projects with the help of the recollections we conjure to consciousness out of the unconscious. How, then, can we avoid the conviction that there must be an invisible central control in our mind where the commands originate and from where they are transmitted?

Computer technology, however, is contributing a lot to undermine this conviction. Bulk is no longer necessary for the most sophisticated programming, and software doesn't have or need a topographical center.

Ironically, now that we have been forever banished from the illusory center of the universe and driven to the fringes of utter insignificance by the latest astronomical and cybernetic discoveries, the realization that the human mind is in tune with a 'larger' cosmic mind, and perhaps even identical with it, unexpectedly brings us back to the center. This time, however, humans are not believed to dwell at or near a topographic center. Instead, the human mind manifests itself as the information center of the universe. The topographic center has become a cybernetic center. We are, indeed, no longer the center of the cosmic hardware, but we may well be the loose and ubiquitous center of the cosmic software.

Why does mankind need centers so badly in the first place? The psychological reasons for man's need for centers are not difficult to understand. This need arises from the fear and anxiety over man's fundamental insecurity. Thrust into the quicksand of existence, man needs something to grab and hang on to in order to survive. His most reliable life-belt is the center, any center. In fact, the principal business of civilization has been to create centers, and its ultimate goal to spin a gigantic network of centers on this planet and beyond.

Not only does our desperate craving for centers, but also our addiction to dichotomy result from the unconscious awareness of our own fundamental acentricity. How could we have a center if our essence is temporality? Center-seeking inevitably leads to dialectics, for to our mind's voracity for centers, reality always responds with a refusal to provide it with the coveted prey. The best it can offer it is a pair of inseparable, mutually attracting as well as repelling poles. Still the mind refuses to surrender and give up its obstinate quest for centers; so it now looks for the center of the poles! But a center of poles can never be found; every fancied new center inevitably begets yet another pole, and so the center hunt goes on indefinitely; it is called dialectics. Paradoxically, the truth about dialectics is that it is an acentric center-seeking thinking process.[2]

There is also a more profound reason for this need for centers. This reason we must seek on the ontological rather than on the psychological level; as Heidegger pointed out, the ontological dimension, characteristic and specific of man, is existential. Existence, Heidegger contends, is temporality. But the two dimensions of time, the future and the past, are always sighted from the fleeting center of the present; it separates, like a continental divide, the two great watersheds of the past and the future dimensions of temporality. But the utterly volatile present is perhaps the most illusory center of all.

Man emerges from the subhuman condition the moment the center of temporality is formed, for only then does he really begin to exist. Existence is being-there, and being-there is being-in-time. Animals, like humans, have memory; consequently they too have a past. They also have projects, which they carry out most efficiently; hence they also have a future. But they seem to lack the fleeting and illusive center from which the two great temporal watersheds are simultaneously beheld. Thus, man's specific temporality results from a center-illusion, and man's existence is therefore inextricably bound with centricity.

Because human existence is temporality, and because temporality needs and presupposes an illusory center, humankind constantly projects centers into everything it tries to understand. Indeed, understanding tends to, and culminates in, forming illusory centers and projecting them into things. Thus, Kant's three ideas of pure reason – God, ego (soul), and the cosmos – are mankind's much-needed centers of understanding. Deprived of them, reality becomes incomprehensible. Not only are these 'ideas of pure reason' taxonomically useful umbrella-concepts intended to cover entire phenomenal realms of reality; above all, they are the indispensable centers from which all phenomena are comprehended. These three centers of understanding, like the original center of human temporality, are mental fabrications, which, although necessary, are utterly illusory.

There is also a metaphysical explanation for our need for centers, at least from the perspective of Nietzschean philosophy. arguably, nature's will-to-power is ultimately nothing but will-to-center, for order requires centers; hence power, too, needs centers, for it results from order. Consequently the all-pervading vital impulse of nature, will-to-power, irresistibly leads to centers. The most compelling proof of this is the fact that in biological evolution, cells become capable of reproduction, thereby achieving unlimited power and a sort of immortality, the moment the nucleus is formed. Clearly, the highest known instance of order in the universe, the center of the nervous system, the human brain, results from nature's relentless drive to produce centers.

Man has learnt from nature the basic strategy of power: if he wants power, he must create order; and if he wants order, he must first create centers. Thus, man's relentless center-production is nothing but mimesis of nature. It is therefore not surprising that every culture has a mandala and every empire a throne.

One is, therefore, compelled to conclude that living without centers is impossible, and that all efforts to eliminate all centers would be as suicidal as casting away one's life-belt if one has been shipwrecked and is drifting in the middle of high seas. Thus, total acentricity reveals itself as being not only psychologically disruptive, but existentially impossible as well.

Bruno was not a center-destroyer out of sheer rebelliousness.

He did not arrive at the insight into the total acentricity of the universe out of his intense hatred of Aristotle, the pedantic Aristotelians, or the Church theologians. Copernicus did, indeed, remove the bandage from his eyes and did shake him out of the dogmatic slumber, but that was only the initial push in the right direction. Once he became convinced of the truth about the Earth's movement around the Sun, Bruno advanced further and transcended Copernicanism all the way to the final insight into universal acentricity, driven by his own reasoning, logic and common sense, and, of course, also by his courage, for only Bruno's fearlessness prompted him to allow logic and common sense to dominate his thinking. He already had lost much respect for authority in his early youth when he was a novice in the Dominican monastery at Naples, but after he read Copernicus, the little respect for authority he had left vanished completely. For how could he respect authority any longer if it had maintained humanity in ignorance for two millennia about the basic facts about the universe and our position in it? And if the 'pedants' (as he used to call them), out of respect for authority, refused to acknowledge what had become obvious to him, thereby prolonging humanity's deceit indefinitely, his intellectual honesty left him no choice but to attack them mercilessly.

It is not difficult to understand that the surest and easiest way to turn a social group into an enraged mob, and to get lynched by it, would be to seriously threaten it with the destruction of its most sacred centers. It is therefore quite understandable that Giordano Bruno, the apostle of universal acentricity, had to be burnt at the stake. Only the fact that Bruno was convinced he was right – and eventually also proved right – and the admirable moral integrity evidenced by his courage to speak out, invalidate the otherwise almost unavoidable conclusion that he was either a madman or a fool.

CHAPTER FIFTEEN

The Cosmic Blueprint

The universe appears to have been designed by a great
mathematician . . . [it] begins to look more like a great thought
than like a great machine.
SIR JAMES JEANS

Contemporary cosmologists are interested, almost exclusively, in
discovering and explaining the primordial state as well as the
forces, particles, constants, laws, and parameters of the early
universe which determined the elements, structure, internal
dynamism, and size of the present observable cosmos. However,
whatever mechanisms were involved in the production of the
universe, the most remarkable thing about them is precisely that
they were actually the case, in other words, the utter facticity of
the laws and parameters (the fundamental constants) of the early
universe. 'The point at issue,' writes Paul Davies, 'is not the way
in which the very special form came about, but that the world is
so structured that it has come about.'[1]

Facticity, however, is inaccessible to physical explanations; it is
a metaphysical problem. The question why this and only this
mechanism obtained, why these and only these natural laws and
parameters were actually the case, can never be satisfactorily
settled by any scientific explanation. Particularly the fact that
precisely these mechanisms, laws, and parameters, in virtue of
their stunningly fine tuning and coordination, would have
originally coalesced in such a way as to allow, after billions of
years, the emergence of intelligent observers in the universe, is
essentially impervious to scientific explanation.

All the particles, forces, laws, and parameters of the early as
well as of the present universe constitute, in their entirety and
complex interrelationships, one single cosmic system encompassing

a huge network of algorithms. Such a system presupposes a blueprint.[2] This is obviously a purely metaphysical assumption, because there is no way of proving scientifically that such a blueprint exists; it is postulated exclusively by the principle of sufficient reason. However, its rejection would be equivalent to attributing cosmic order to pure randomness, which in turn is another metaphysical principle, only this one, besides having the same inconvenience of being just as unfalsifiable and consequently as unscientific as the previous one, has the additional disadvantage of being downright absurd, for there was obviously not enough time – in the four-and-a-half billion years that have elapsed since the formation of a life-supporting Earth – for the billions of different species of highly complex living organisms, with their stunningly clever biological systems and functions, to have originated as a result of random collisions of trillions of trillions of subparticles. We are therefore rationally compelled to assume the existence of a cosmic blueprint.

Why and how did this cosmic blueprint originate? There seems to be no way of circumventing the problem of the physically unexplainable facticity of the cosmic blueprint. The necessary and sufficient reason for its existence is once again metaphysical: the universe must have had in itself, from the very beginning, a principle of complex organization. Such a principle had originally been called *psyche* (soul) by Plato and Aristotle, and the Stoics applied it later on to the cosmos.[3] Bruno referred to it as the soul of the world and the universal intellect, thereby associating 'soul' with Anaxagoras' *nous* (mind). If we are willing to admit that such a cosmic mind is the most plausible rational explanation for the order of the universe, the problem remains whether this 'larger'[4] mind is immanent or transcendent to the universe.

Contemporary cosmology conceives the primordial fireball as a plasma-continuum of pure energy where discrete particles had not yet arisen. Consequently, the very first elementary particles that emerged in that energy-plasma were extremely simple and had no internal structure, but they were numerous and identical to each other. This was the origin of ontologial categories such as multiplicity, number, quantity, distinction, and identity. Nuclear physics informs us further that eventually scores of different types of elementary particles and subparticles appeared, and that each type included innumerable identical entities. But this implies that,

in addition to those other ontological categories, otherness, difference, quality, limitation, and becoming – in sum, the basic array
of Hegel's logico-ontological categories – were already present in
the very early universe, or at least, in our conception of it. Indeed,
it is impossible for the human mind to conceive the emergence of
the early universe from the initial singularity without resorting to
these categories.

Despite the lack of internal structure, the very first elementary
particles that emerged within the original energy-plasma (in the
first infinitesimally small spacetime bubble that the Big Bang
singularity produced) already represent a progressive transition
from chaos to order, since immediately they would either
become or give rise to slightly more complex and internally
structured particles. In light of this, we can hardly avoid the
conclusion that order emerges out of chaos, a proposition very
hard indeed for the logical mind to comprehend and accept,
unless the algorithms determining the nature and structure of
those particles were already virtually contained in the primordial energy-plasma as a set of initial conditions. In this case, the
primordial plasma cannot be viewed as sheer chaos, but rather
as a hotbed of order, no matter how undifferentiated that initial
plasma-continuum of energy may have been. We are thus faced
with a stunning paradox: the seeds of order are already
embedded in the dark womb of chaos![5]

There is yet another highly paradoxical cosmological fact
which, until now, has not received a satisfactory scientific explanation. It is the apparent contradiction between the second law of
thermodynamics and the continuous emergence in the universe
of countless systems of the highest complexity and order. There
are, in fact, two opposing arrows of time in the evolution of the
universe: the arrow of growing entropy and the arrow of ever
increasing complex organization. Science has provided conclusive evidence to account for the first arrow, but it has hitherto
utterly failed to present a satisfactory explanation for the second.
This paradox is compounded by that other equally perplexing
one: the primordial energy-plasma must be conceived as having,
on the one hand, maximal 'negentropy' (negative entropy) and,
on the other, maximal symmetry and total lack of structural
complexity. Thus, it does not seem possible to simply identify
entropy with disorder and negentropy with complex order. The

ordering algorithms that were immediately to become operative in the undifferentiated and highly symmetric 'cosmic broth' of the early universe must already have been virtually present in the Big Bang singularity itself, for only to them are we compelled to attribute the power of effectively initiating the evolutionary process which eventually resulted in the stunning complexity of a universe which at the same time is relentlessly (and perhaps also irreversibly) tending towards the 'heat death'.

Science, until quite recently, has not been interested in, or capable of, providing an explanation for this paradox. It did not hesitate to discard as 'metaphysical', and hence totally unscientific, the few timid attempts undertaken in this direction. In this, science was only being consistent, since it had long been accustomed to provide, for natural phenomena, strictly reductionist 'Lagrangian' explanations, consisting exclusively of mathematical equations and algorithms; however, since any solution to the double-arrow paradox must be non-algorithmic, non-mathematical, and hence unscientific, positivistic science has simply ignored it. However, the burning question still remains, a challenge only for metaphysics; it has accepted it and come forth, more defiantly than ever before, with more pressing and embarrassing questions for positivistic science.

Thus, in the light of contemporary cosmology, Leibniz's crucial metaphysical question – the one he thought was capable of delivering the most powerful shock and shudder to thinking individuals – namely, 'Why is there something at all rather than nothing?' must be reworded thus: 'Why is the universe the way it is, indeed why is it so cleverly ordered and organized, rather than not at all?'

We mentioned above that the categories of the mind developed by Hegel in his *Logic* must be perceived by dialectical thought as immanently present in the Big Bang singularity. The emergence of plurality, difference, and identity; of replication, interconnectedness, pattern, symmetry, and above all – upon the appearance of the first living organisms – of synergy and *telos* (finality, particularly conspicuous in the regenerative processes, the immune system, and all the self-regulating, homeostatic processes of these organisms) presents an insolvable riddle for scientific explanations. Only a dialectical ontology can provide, at most, highly plausible, although never absolutely certain, explanations, since they are, and will always remain, untestable and unfalsifiable.

Science informs us that we are all made up of the same identical elementary particles and subparticles, in fact, that the entire universe is formed of these particles. The 'metaphysical' consequence of this fact is that we humans are all interconnected, and intimately related, not only to each other, but also to the entire cosmos, which thereby becomes a single holistic system.

In the measure that we discover more and more complex order in the universe and become increasingly convinced of the intimate interconnectedness and harmony of everything, it becomes more and more difficult to accept the view that this stunning order and fine tuning is merely the result of blind chance and mind-boggling luck. Above all, baffled by the synergy we have detected in our planet Earth, in our solar system, in our galaxy, and in our original supernova, we find it extremely difficult to accept randomness as the correct explanation thereof, even if we take the weak anthropic principle into account.[6] For in the relatively short time that has elapsed since the formation of the solar system and the birth of planet Earth, or even since the Big Bang, it appears incomprehensible, indeed unacceptable, to the mind, that so much concerted synergy displayed in the myriads of different forms of life on Earth could have emerged without a principle responsible for bringing about such high levels of teleonomic organization. There was simply not enough time for sheer luck to achieve that result. If we call this principle of organization and order 'mind', how unreasonable is it to conclude that there must be a cosmic mind at work in the universe? For the inescapable dilemma is none other than this: either inconceivable luck or the cosmic mind; *non datur tertium* (there is simply no third solution). We may still quarrel about whether this principle of organized complexity is transcendent or immanent in the universe, but agree we must on the existence of a cosmic mind, unless, of course, we don't mind indulging in metaphysical absurdity.

The search for answers to questions such as these is metaphysical by nature. The principle of complex organization is, by definition, transempirical; it is not accessible to scientific inquiry. Although numerous recent scientific discoveries have strengthened our conviction that there must be such a principle, science by itself cannot discover it, for science is essentially empirical, but how reliable are our metaphysical speculations about the universe?

The answer of most pre-Kantian philosophers to this question was encouraging. Yes, they insisted, reason compels us to assume a principle or cause of cosmic order, indeed, it can even clearly prove its existence. Kant, however, strongly disagreed. Pure reason, he argued, can neither prove nor disprove the infinitude or the eternity of the universe. In the light of this, he would have equally denied the possibility of proving or disproving the existence of a cosmic principle of complex organization; the most reason could do is to show the antinomies, the inconsistencies and contradictions of the conflicting hypotheses about such a principle. Does Kant's conclusion further imply that there is no other way left for us to get to the truth about the origin and structure of the universe? Perhaps, but he may have been wrong about this.

There seems to remain only the mystical solution, the Oriental experience of pure Self and the universal commonality of pure Self. However, Einstein was neither a mystic nor an agnostic. According to his own testimony, what helped him most, in discovering special and general relativity, was intuition and an unshakeable conviction that God doesn't play dice with the universe; in other words, the metaphysical assumption that the universe is rational and comprehensible. Einstein was convinced that God's mind contains supremely simple and beautiful algorithms, and that this infinite simplicity and beauty are at the very heart of nature, indeed are the very essence of nature.

What Gregory Bateson says about Samuel Butler with regard to evolution applies just as well to Bruno with regard to the cosmic mind: 'I don't think Butler ever looked at anything except his own cat, but he still knew more about evolution than some of the more conventional thinkers.' This remark indicates that Bateson had succeeded in ridding himself of his former positivistic anti-metaphysical prejudices. In fact, he arrives at the following conclusion, which he presents as a new approach to cybernetic epistemology:

> The individual mind is immanent but not only in the body. It is immanent also in pathways and messages outside the body; and there is a larger Mind of which the individual mind is only a subsystem. This larger Mind is comparable to God and is perhaps

what some people mean by 'God', but it is still immanent in the total interconnected social system and planetary ecology.[7]

This, in essence, is the conclusion Bruno arrived at three hundred and fifty years before Bateson.

What makes Bateson's thought about the 'larger mind' so similar to Bruno's? What basic common insight links these two thinkers over a span of more than three centuries? As we have shown, it is the insight that mind is immanent in the universe, rather than transcendent, as the traditional theistic and deistic doctrines of creation postulate.

What is then, according to Bateson, this immanent 'larger mind'? The expression 'larger mind' is used by Bateson in *Steps to an Ecology of the Mind* to denote the presence of structures, functions, and operations analogous to those of the human mind in the all-encompassing context of total cosmic reality. This universe is, for Bateson, an immense closed circuit where information is transmitted, stored, and otherwise processed in a way similar to the way information is transmitted, stored, and processed in the human mind, and where interactions among the elements of the system are regulated by the information-exchange process obtaining between them.

Thus, for Bateson the 'larger mind' is not an independent and privileged center of information, utterly different and separate from the universe, which it nonetheless unilaterally controls and regulates from a safe distance, but rather an all-encompassing cybernetic system, consisting of innumerable subsystems of circuits and pathways through which 'negative entropy', that is information, or 'the difference that makes a difference', travels, is stored, and otherwise processed for further feedback. Thus, the boundaries of the system would be ill-conceived as epidermic, as the tight skin of a tuber holding in and back its compact mass, for they are constantly expanding in the measure that the unrelenting process of positive feedback unfolds the intricate network of the gigantic rhizome.

Thus, information theory is seriously undermining the basic tenets of popular epistemology and, we may add, of popular theology as well. The 'larger mind', traditionally conceived as the transcendent center and cause of the universe or, in Bateson's words, as a 'chunk cut off and visualized as against the surrounding matrix',[8] is slowly giving way to the concept of an immanent cosmic mind, that is, a 'relevant total information-processing, trial-and-error completing unit', the all-encompassing systemic information rhizome that links everything together, and along whose pathways 'transforms of difference are transmitted'.

This is obviously an extrapolation, an assumption which can neither be verified or falsified. However, there are strong indications that some of the cybernetic processes which take place in the human mind also obtain in vast segments of reality hitherto commonly considered to be utterly different from the human mind.

In order to identify those processes observable 'outside' of the human mind that Bateson was referring to, we have selected one particular segment of reality where transmission and processing of information plays a decisive role, namely the human immune system.

In the language that microbiology uses to characterize the functions and processes of the large variety of cells which make up the immune system, we recognize the very same cognitive and volitional terminology usually ascribed to mental phenomena, such as sensitivity to difference, registration of difference, discrimination, selection and choice, memory, purposiveness, intentionality, communication, and command.

The undeniable presence of such 'mental' operations in segments of biological reality considerably smaller than the human mind is what prompts Bateson to resort to a concept such as the 'larger mind' to account for them, for it seems that they have to be attributed to one single immanent entity as the necessary and sufficient reason for their presence throughout the universe. It appears that not only the structure and functions of each particular type of cell is determined and regulated by one specific algorithm, but also, considering the synergy and remarkable coordination of all the subsystems of the immune system, that this larger system, too, as a whole, is determined and regulated in turn by another superior algorithm, a sort of blueprint – or the 'idea' – of the immune system. So, for example, we know that DNA holds the exact blueprint of one particular organism; but doesn't the DNA itself – not a particular DNA but all DNAs – also presuppose a blueprint? For individual DNAs to exist, it seems that there had to be a DNA blueprint – the idea of the DNA. If this is so, how does the blueprint of the DNA, the meta-program of the program originate? Does the fact precede the concept or is it the other way around? If the idea precedes the fact and is instrumental in bringing it about, then there is indeed a blueprint for the fact, and it exists in a mind. This may sound terribly Platonic, but what is the alternative? Perhaps that the first successful DNA molecule resulted from natural selection? And that once it was formed it was concurrently blessed with the power of self-replication? The fact is that natural selection presupposes random mutations and a set of already relatively successful individuals competing with each other for survival. That such stunningly clever inventions of nature as the DNA- and RNA-self-replicating molecules and their concerted interactions resulted from lucky random individual mutations and from the successful competition of the ones favored by such mutations with their less lucky rivals in the power game seems, to say the least, highly improbable. The hypothesis of a higher principle of organization immanent in nature taxes our credibility considerably less. The main positivistic objection against this assumption is, of course, that such a principle is not empirical and verifiable. But how empirical is the 'luck principle'?

The astounding power and efficacy of the 'larger mind' is evidenced by its ability to harness and assemble trillions of quarks into structures of enormous complexity capable of performing amazingly efficient functions. What is even more mind-boggling is the fact that it operates within the coarsest blobs of matter in almost all of the life-sustaining and life-reproducing systems of organisms. There is hardly a more vivid and compelling image of absolute chaos than those gooey porridges of organic matter where the remarkably clever operations of the reproductive and digestive systems are constantly taking place. It looks as if the algorithms that underlie chaos depend on and thrive in these turbulent pockets of organic broth. Here again the dialectics of order/chaos is at play: order needs chaos in order to be, and chaos harbors order in its bosom.

Thus, it seems perfectly reasonable and justifiable to extrapolate the larger mind all the way back to the Big Bang singularity. This would not be much more arbitrary than attributing to it infinite density, temperature, and spacetime-curvature, but this is precisely what quantum theory is doing with regard to the Big Bang singularity. On the one hand, it admits that it can predict absolutely nothing about the inner structure of any singularity (both black-hole and Big Bang), and on the other, it holds that it was infinitely dense, hot, and absolutely curved in itself. The only reason for concluding this is that these, and only these, initial conditions could have made the universe at all possible as we know it now. Yet, it doesn't seem any less reasonable to conclude that the larger mind, as universal source and principle of organized complexity, is the most fundamental and necessary of all initial conditions, and if this is the case, then we must think of the larger mind as immanent in the singularity and in the universe that evolved from it as well. The fact that we are compelled by reason to conclude that, since bosons and fermions, and the four known elementary cosmic forces were to emerge within the expanding early cosmic universe immediately after the Big Bang, their algorithms had to be present, at least virtually, in the singularity, prompts us also to conclude that the source and principle of all forms of complex organization ever to materialize in the universe (the superalgorithm of all algorithms) also had to be present in the singularity.

The metaphysical nature of the quantum physicists' speculations about the Big Bang singularity appears very clearly when they resort to the term 'infinite' to describe its density, temperature, and spacetime curvature. Obviously, infinity cannot be perceived by the senses; it is utterly inaccessible to empirical knowledge and can only be inferred by reason. Quantum mechanics is therefore compelled to transcend the senses and resort to metaphysical speculations if it insists on making predictions concerning the Big Bang singularity. This is precisely the reason why philosophy was incorporated into contemporary astrophysics, as a result of which the strongly speculative science known as quantum cosmology was born.

Also the positivistic contention that classical physics had finally rid itself of all metaphysical underpinnings is naïve and false. Supporting the Cartesian, Newtonian, and Laplacian cosmological model there was a set of very specific, clearly metaphysical assumptions. Some of these assumptions were that the universe is one; that it is composed of elements placed in infinite and absolute space; that these elements are material and parts of a material whole; that matter is nothing but three-dimensional extension in space; that besides quantitative extension, matter has no other determinable qualities; that all the other perceptible qualities of the universe are the result of the impact of matter on animal sensorial apparatus, ultimately then of the impact of quantitative extension upon quantitative extension; that all material elements of the whole are quantitative and hence measurable; that these elements are intimately interrelated; that these relationships are stable, unalterable, universal, and necessary, and hence purely quantitative and measurable; that all changes that occur in the universe are necessarily determined by events in the universe prior to these changes and are intimately and necessarily connected with them; that the law of necessary and universal causality is the law binding all phenomena in the universe; that all phenomena are accurately predictable once the laws regulating phenomena are discovered; that these laws are knowable and can be adequately formulated mathematically; that there is a fixed and necessary order in the universe; that the universe functions with the regularity of clockwork, and finally, to cap it all, that the universe behaves like a perfect machine.

Not a single one of these propositions can be proved empirically; they are merely speculative assumptions made in order to construct a model that allows us to better understand and predict phenomena. Because most of the predictions were accurate, the model, and, along with it, the assumptions on which it rested, were considered until the twentieth century to be in total conformity with reality. Mathematics was to be regarded as the only reliable road to knowledge, and scientific knowledge as the only true knowledge. Metaphysical, and all other non-mathematical, transempirical assumptions were ruled out, at best, as untestable and unverifiable opinions, and at worst, as sheer mystical rubbish.

This is what has been called the classical mechanistic model, since it was based on the analogy of the machine. The father of mechanism was Descartes, the great mathematician who invented analytical geometry – the algebra of space, and hence the mathematics of three-dimensional bodies in space. According to Descartes all bodies are nothing but machines – even animals are machines – and since machines tend to function like perfect clockwork, he thought he finally had found the key to how nature works, the mathematics of his analytic geometry. Only motion escaped his measurements, but that problem was soon taken care of by Leibniz and Newton, who added force to the mechanics of purely quantitative matter as the cause of movement, and invented calculus to deal with the new dynamics. From then on, the mechanistic model was mathematically fully equipped to undertake its rational conquest of the universe, and for more than two centuries it was extremely successful... until Einstein, Planck, and Heisenberg proved it defective. The mechanistic model collapsed, and in its fall it took down along with it all its metaphysical underpinnings.

CHAPTER SIXTEEN

The Metaphysics of the Third Scientific Revolution

Philosophy is written in this grand book – I mean the universe.
GALILEO GALILEI

We are witnessing, in the last decades of the twentieth century, the total bankruptcy of the Cartesian-Newtonian mechanistic, deterministic, and reductionist paradigm as a suitable, let alone as the only possible and acceptable, explanation for the emergence in the universe of the highly complex organization required by biological and psychic processes. Following the two great scientific revolutions of modern times (the Newtonian and the Einstein-Planckian), a third revolution is now under way that may well radically change, by introducing entirely new paradigms and concepts, the way science looks not only at biological and psychic phenomena, but at all natural phenomena as well. Referring to this 'third revolution' Paul Davies writes:

> There is a widespread feeling among physicists that their subject is poised for a major revolution. As already remarked, true revolutions in science are not just rapid advances in technical details, but transformations of the concepts upon which science is based. In physics, revolutions of this magnitude have occurred twice before. The first was the systematic development of mechanics by Galileo and Newton. The second occurred with the theory of relativity and the quantum theory at the beginning of this century.[1]

This radical turnabout in the way scientists conceive and interpret natural phenomena is mainly the result of a new, more interdisciplinary approach, a change of focus from analysis to synthesis, and the introduction of entirely new concepts into scientific discourse. Paul Davies points out precisely where this profound change is taking place, namely

> . . . at the interface of physics and biology, where the goal is to understand not what things are made of but how they are put together and function as integrated wholes. Here, the key concepts are complexity rather than simplicity, and organization rather than hardware. What is sought is a general 'Theory of Organization'.

The fundamental insight behind this third scientific revolution is the view that the existence of states of higher organizational complexity cannot be fully explained merely by lower-level laws and system-components, in opposition to the reductionist view, 'founded on the outdated and now discredited concept of determinism . . . that all levels of complexity can in principle be explained by the underlying laws of mechanics that govern the behavior of the fundamental fields and particles of physics'.

The crucial issue here is then

> . . . whether the surprising – one might even say unreasonable – propensity for matter and energy to self-organize 'against the odds' can be explained using the known laws of physics, or rather whether completely new fundamental principles are required.

What are these new fundamental principles that now seem indispensable to explain 'the origin of life, the evolution of increasing biological complexity, and the development of the embryo from a single egg cell, all [of which] seem miraculous at first sight, and all remain largely unexplained'?[2] What is the source of nature's astounding organizing potency? Everything points to an immanent principle of complex order and organization, precisely what we have been referring to in this study as 'mind' and Bateson calls the 'larger mind'.

The growing dissatisfaction of scientists with the ability of mechanistic-reductionist paradigms to provide plausible explanations of biological and psychic phenomena is evidenced by the number of books penned by leading scientists, and published after the mid-seventies, that are highly critical of the traditional approach. Already the titles and subtitles of some of these publications betray the increasing malaise inside the scientific camp: *An*

Inventive Universe[3], *The Self-Organizing Universe*[4], *Wholeness and the Implicate Order*[5], *A New Science of Life*[6], *God and the New Physics*[7], *The Intelligent Universe*[8], *The Left Hand of Creation*[9], *Order Out of Chaos*[10], *The Unfinished Universe*[11], *The Cosmological Anthropic Principle*[12], *God and the New Biology*[13], *The Emperor's New Mind*[14,] *The Cosmic Blueprint. New Discoveries in Nature's Creative Ability to Order the Universe*[15], and *The Mind of God. Science and the Search for Ultimate Meaning.*[16] Since I have listed these books according to their date of publication, the most recent titles suggest that the idea of God seems to be coming on strong in the scientific community. Why is this happening?

Characteristic of these new approaches is that they are all trying to provide a rigorously rational and scientific explanation for the emergence of highly organized biological and psychic systems in the cosmos while at the same time carefully avoiding the pitfalls of the traditional theological (both theistic and deistic) and supernatural paradigms. They all seek to identify new transempirical, and hence metaphysical, principles of order and complex organization that do not abrogate, contradict, supplant, supersede, or even operate independently from the constants and laws of nature whose validity for lower levels of organization has been experimentally demonstrated and firmly established by modern physics. They tend to agree on the fact that different levels have their own specific organizing principles, and that the lower principles are subordinated to the higher ones, which in turn guide, encourage, or even 'harness' the lower ones.

Philosophically, the decisive insight underlying and inspiring this new scientific approach and contributing so effectively to breaking the dominance, until recently unchallenged, of the deterministic-mechanistic-reductionist paradigm is one which Hegel masterfully compressed into admirable concision and pregnancy: *das Wahre ist das Ganze* (the true is the whole). This principle, which is at the basis not only of Hegel's ontology but of dialectical materialism as well, re-emerges now as the theoretical cornerstone of holism and general systems theory. It states that in every organized system the behavior of the whole cannot be fully explained by the behavior of the elements constituting the system. The whole is not the sum of its parts, but something qualitatively, indeed essentially, different from its constituents. Thus, according to this view, an atom is totally different from a quark, a cell cannot be reduced to molecules, the brain cannot be adequately explained by the colony of neurons, a thought cannot be fully accounted for by particle physics, and the universal mathematical and logical systems shared by all humanity resist all efforts undertaken to reduce them to mere psychic phenomena. In all these levels of organization there are immanent organizing principles which are not present in the inferior levels despite the fact that all these levels remain intimately connected with each other. The organizing principles of one level reach out and extend their influence to the inferior levels, 'guiding', 'encouraging', 'harnessing' (tentative metaphors for an undeniable interconnectedness whose precise mechanism still remains shrouded in mystery) the principles and laws specific to those levels.

Thus, according to this basic holistic principle, a tree is not merely the sum of its constituent cells, molecules, atoms, and quarks, but something radically different from its constituent elements. What makes the difference is the specific organization of the aggregate, and what generates this organization is the information encoded in the DNA of the individual concrete tree. Now, this information is algorithmic, and constitutes the program or blueprint for development of amorphous matter towards a specific form. Because encoded information leads matter to form, form appears to be the *telos* or ultimate goal of the program,[17] and because the principle of organization underlying this process is algorithmic, hence logical and mental, it resists the assignation of a specific spatio-temporal localization. The system has no topographical center; it is diffuse and acentric.

This non-locality and acentricity of the principle of organized complexity was first assigned to a holistic system – the conceivably largest and most complex one, namely the entire universe – by Giordano Bruno. Indeed, if applied to the entire universe, general systems theory results in a totally Brunian cosmology: The universe is one, and it is a whole; it is a boundless system composed of infinite finite parts, all of them intimately and harmoniously interconnected, thereby making functional synergy possible. The universe is unfolding, growing in complexity, and constantly generating new forms. It therefore resembles a gigantic organism, for it has in itself its own immanent principle of complex organization which harnesses and subordinates all principles of order which regulate the processes taking place at all inferior levels and is therefore ultimately responsible for the self-organization of the whole. This supreme principle of complex organization is the cosmic mind, acentric, non-local, and ubiquitous in a way analogous to the way the soul traditionally was considered to be all at once and indivisibly in every part of the body.

If we apply this holistic paradigm to our universe as a whole and view it as a system constantly evolving and growing in complexity, we would be pressed to take the 'anthropic principle' seriously. A number of so-called 'constants of nature' are generally accepted by the entire scientific establishment as necessary parameters of the universe we inhabit. The initial conditions of the universe were so finely tuned and harmoniously coordinated with each other that the slightest tinkering with the values of any of these constants would have rendered the emergence of life and consciousness in our universe utterly impossible. Is it by pure chance that they were so harmoniously coordinated at the beginning? Or can this fine tuning receive a plausible rational explanation?

If there is one and only one universe, the one we actually inhabit, then the hypothesis of a totally random but supremely successful coordination of initial conditions is highly improbable, indeed almost impossible. Only in this scenario would the strong anthropic principle acquire a respectable degree of probability, for obviously the initial conditions of the universe had to be such that life and consciousness would eventually emerge. Even the further claim, so highly favored by creationists, that the initial conditions were so set as to produce life and consciousness – and consequently that there was an initial teleological cosmic blueprint – would gain some plausibility. However, in the hypothesis of multiple universes the anthropic principle becomes less convincing, and in the hypothesis of infinite or even innumerable universes the anthropic principle already loses most of its punch. In billions of universes with different initial conditions it is not surprising that one of them did have those required to produce life, and then, of course, that the eventually emerging computing minds would conclude that only under those precise initial conditions life and consciousness were at all possible. Since we have no evidence of other universes beyond the remotest possible cosmic horizon (and most probably will never have, since they all lie by definition beyond the range of accessibility fixed by slower than speed-of-light communications), the strong anthropic principle remains plausible for this universe. In any case, it remains theoretically unassailable, since the existence of infinite universes will always remain a conjecture. Paul Davies has incisively bared the weakness of the multiple-universes hypothesis to unsettle the anthropic principle:

> To postulate an infinity of unseen and unseeable universes just to explain the one we do see seems like a case of excess baggage carried to the extreme. It is simpler to postulate one unseen God. This is the conclusion also reached by Swinburne:
> The postulation of God is the postulation of one entity of a simple kind . . . The postulation of the actual existence of an infinite number of worlds, between them exhausting all the logical possibilities . . . is to postulate complexity and non-prearranged coincidence of infinite dimensions beyond rational belief . . .
> Scientifically the many-universes theory is unsatisfactory because it could never be falsified . . . Worse still, you can use many worlds to explain anything at all. Science becomes redundant . . . Furthermore, there is something philosophically unsatisfactory about all those universes that go unobserved. To paraphrase Penrose, what does it mean to say that something exists that can never in principle be observed?[18]

This, of course, is very bad news for all those who have hopes that creationism, and all the religions that seek refuge under it, will eventually die out. They will almost certainly be around for quite a long time still. However, the outlook for evolutionist pantheism and panentheism is particularly auspicious, for it remains arguable that the harmonious coordination of the constants and laws of nature that have made intelligent life possible in the universe is neither the effect of an omnipotent and provident Creator-God nor the result of pure randomness and incredible luck, but is determined by an immanent principle of complex organization that has effectively led the universe to become aware of itself. This principle is suitably referred to as the cosmic mind, for it is conceived as containing, or being, the metaprogram or cosmic blueprint holding all the information and algorithms that have effectively guided mass/energy in spacetime to the spectacular levels of complex organization that have made life and awareness possible.

It would be unduly anthropocentric (and anthropomorphic as well) to attribute to this cosmic mind a definite purpose in its cosmic evolution (as the theists and deists assign to their Creator-God), particularly if this purpose were the production of the human race (or any superior form of intelligent life towards which humans would still be evolving), because it does not seem absolutely necessary that any particular form of life should have already emerged or will eventually emerge, including our own, considering the furtuitous and most fortunate mutations that have taken place and the enormous instability of the environment; humans may be, for that matter, just as contingent as dinosaurs – the result of chancy mutations and casual felicitous interactions with a constantly changing and highly unstable environment. The cosmic mind does not need to have a purpose, a goal, or an 'omega point' towards which it is necessarily moving, as Teilhard de Chardin suggested. Paradoxically, as Henri Bergson most insightfully pointed out, 'finalism . . . is only inverted mechanism.'

However, the rejection of teleology and finalism, particularly anthropocentric finalism, does not necessarily imply the rejection of teleonomy in nature. Teleonomy differs from teleology in that it denotes a goal-directed activity operated by a program; teleology, on the other hand, means a goal-directed activity caused by the goal it aims at. Thus in teleology the future causally determines the past, whereas in teleonomy the future merely results from the past. Bergson arrived at the view – originally held by Nicholas of Cusa and further developed by Bruno – that the universe is continuously creative, that is, as Paul Davies accurately summarizes, a 'universe in which wholly new things come into existence in a way that is completely independent of what went before, and which is not constrained by a predetermined goal.'[19] However, the universe is not completely independent of what went before, if it is indeed teleonomic, for the future depends on the program and the program is also in the past.

Thus, the main insight of the third scientific revolution tends to agree with the Bergsonian view – which ultimately goes back to Bruno and Cusanus – that the cosmic mind (in Bergsonian terms, the *élan vital*) may be appropriately conceived as free, playful, resourceful, creative, artistic, and experimental – a sort of cosmos-immanent, impersonal divinity. From this perspective the divinity would be seen as lacking its traditional monarchic, patriarchal, and judicial roles and functions, as well as its more popular philanthropic attributes, and seen rather as a 'dipolar God', contingent because immanent, but necessary because it is the indispensable and sufficient reason for all cosmic systems and organized forms. Creation is no longer seen as a singular, once-and-for-all event at the beginning of time, but as an eternally ongoing process. The process is necessary, but the forms are contingent, and they are such because indeterminacy and stochasticity are fundamental features of the quantum world of mass/energy. God, after all, may indeed be playing dice with the universe, but he refused to load the dice, precisely because he seems to be enjoying the game!

Thus the cosmic mind displays some of the attributes Greek mythology was wont to anthropomorphize as Morpheus, Proteus, and Dionysus, as they eternally execute their indefatigable morphogenetic dance. Of course, contemporary science abhors such metaphorical language with stark mythical overtones and disapproves of any language that smacks of the supernatural or suggests any form of what is usually referred to as vitalism and panpsychism. However, it must be said of Bruno's vitalistic and animistic proclivities, that while upholding both Aristotelian teleology in nature and Cusanus' concept of an unfolding universe, he resolutely rejected every form of anthropocentric finalism, and proclaimed instead the plausible existence of infinite worlds inhabited by other intelligent creatures. He was, after all, the main adversary of 'theological astronomy', and his image of an acentric universe was based on the fundamental principles of modern cosmology, namely cosmic homogeneity and isotropy, which stand in radical opposition to every form of geocentrism and anthropocentrism. He thereby became the first modern adversary of 'theological astronomy'.

With regard to Bruno's much vilified vitalism and panpsychism, often derided by scientists as unscientific and mystical, it is interesting to listen to some hard-core physicists of the 'third revolution' whose views seem merely to echo Bruno's thoughts on this matter. So, for example, physicist Freeman Dyson writes:

I think our consciousness is not just a passive epiphenomenon carried along by the chemical events in our brains, but is an active agent forcing the molecular complexes to make choices between one quantum state and another. In other words, mind is already immanent in every electron . . .[20]

Another physicist of the 'third revolution', Paul Davies, writes the following lines strongly reminiscent of Bruno's metaphors of a universe unfolding like a tree from its seed, and like an organism with its own 'life history':

Creation is not instantaneous; it is an ongoing process. The universe has a life history. Instead of sliding into featurelessness, it rises out of featurelessness, growing rather than dying, developing new structures, processes and potentialities all the time, unfolding like a flower.[21]

Thus, almost four hundred years after Bruno's death, his almost-forgotten insight into the ultimate principles underlying physical reality has been unexpectedly revived by some of the most prominent physicists of the third scientific revolution in words astonishingly similar to Bruno's own 'vitalistic' and 'animistic' formulations.

It is hard to find an acknowledgment more explicit than the following text of how genuinely metaphysical contemporary science has been forced to become by recent dramatic discoveries made particularly in the fields of particle physics, microbiology, and astronomy:

There is a growing expectation among scientists that neither mind, nor life, need be limited to organic matter . . . Now consciousness and intelligence are software concepts: it is only the pattern – the organization – that counts, not the medium for its expression . . . it is possible to imagine a supermind existing since the creation, encompassing all the fundamental fields of nature, and taking upon itself the task of converting an incoherent big bang into the orderly and complex cosmos we now observe; all accomplished entirely within the framework of the laws of physics. This would not be a God who created everything by supernatural means, but a directing, controlling, universal mind pervading the cosmos and operating the laws of nature . . . Our own minds could then be viewed as localized 'islands' of consciousness in a sea of mind, an

idea that is reminiscent of the Oriental conception of mysticism . . .
a universal mind could, in principle, control everything that happens by directing the behavior of every electron, every proton,
every photon . . . Such a picture of God might well be enough to
satisfy most believers.[22]

Giordano Bruno was not a mystic. He incessantly searched for a
rational explanation of the universe. He did embrace, however,
what Rudy Rucker calls 'the central teaching of mysticism',
namely that reality is One.[23] The oneness that he aimed at and tried
to grasp is that of a coherent whole and the immanent principle
that unifies it, but this oneness of the universe is also the basic
metaphysical assumption of modern science. The same laws, constants, and parameters are assumed to be valid everywhere
throughout the entire universe, but this is not possible unless the
universe is conceived as constituting a holistic system.

We pointed out earlier that anthropic arguments and the
hypothesis of a universal mind and a cosmic blueprint would
lose much of their punch if a vast ensemble of random universes
were to coexist with our own. However, we must agree with
Paul Davies' argument that a many-universes theory – designed
to attribute to pure randomness the appearance of most felicitous initial conditions in the early universe that eventually led
to conscious life – 'flies in the face of Occam's razor, by
introducing vast (indeed infinite) complexity to explain the
regularities of just one universe'. Thus he concludes that
'Occam's razor compels me to put my money on design, but, as
always, in matters of metaphysics, the decision is largely a
matter of taste rather than scientific judgment'[24]. Unfortunately
good taste does not abound in our world. But there is some
hope for those cosmologists who, like Einstein, had a sense for
elegance and simplicity.

It is interesting to listen to Rucker's use of the labyrinth
metaphor to refer precisely to the mystic in search of a non-
rational understanding of the universe. The mystic must 'jump
out' of the labyrinth to acquire instantaneous, immediate
mystical knowledge:

The One has variously been called the Good, God, the Cosmos, the
Mind, the Void or (perhaps most neutrally) the Absolute. No door

in the labyrinthine castle of science opens directly onto the Absolute. But if one understands the maze well enough, it is possible to jump out of the system and experience the Absolute for oneself. . . .[25]

Bruno does indeed seem to have understood the maze pretty well, but, unlike the mystic, he did not jump out of it to experience the Absolute. He preferred instead to remain inside his acentric labyrinth to experience it. Perhaps he succeeded in the end, and that unique experience was the hidden source of his joyous determination to brave the flames.

PART FIVE

*The Spiral and the Ring: Bruno
Contra Nietzsche?*

CHAPTER SEVENTEEN

Bruno's Revaluation of All Values

Bruno's new philosophy does not reach its full form – its completion and culmination – with just knowledge, be it cosmological or
ontological. It was Bruno's firm conviction that a person's full
realization as a human being can only be attained through action.
It is, therefore, not surprising that Bruno's comprehensive philosophical system has a strong ethical component. However, is
Bruno's ethics a mere corollary of his cosmology and ontology, or
was it rather the main driving force that propelled, from the very
beginning, his entire philosophical discourse?

Bruno's ethical concerns were frequently associated with his
ontological and cosmological speculations. Thus, ethical
reflexions appear in the prologues to the three cosmological dialogues he wrote and published in London; and his three strictly
ethical dialogues, *Lo spaccio della bestia trionfante* (The Expulsion of
the Triumphant Beast), *Cabala del cavallo Pegaseo* (Cabala of the
Pegasian Horse), and *Eroici furori* (Heroic frenzies) were written
immediately after or, perhaps, even during the composition of the
cosmological ones.

The Brunian Revolution does not limit itself to a revolution in
knowledge, however radical; it encompasses the entire human
endeavor. It aimed at a complete overturn of traditional values
and therefore had not only ethical, but also significant religious,
social, and political implications.

An entirely new concept of man underlies Bruno's ethics.
Human beings share the stuff their bodies are made of with that
of all other beings in the universe and, not unlike them, their
bodies are undergoing incessant transformations. And, as far as
the soul is concerned, human beings share the same universal soul
with all other living organisms. Thus, Bruno's philosophical
anthropology was free from the old strongly anthropocentric

overtones. He clearly considered man an animal, and came very close to seeing him as an evolving animal as well.

But there was more. After losing his privileged position in the center of a finite universe, man lost, as well, not only the feeling of uniqueness that Judaism, Christianity, and Islam had nurtured in him, but also that special dignity whose discovery the Renaissance Humanists enthusiastically celebrated: freedom, a godlike intelligence, and the passion for truth and beauty, hailed by them as the goal, and hence also as the true meaning of God's creation.

At the beginning of Nietzsche's *Will to Power*, we read the following characterization of the consequences of Copernicus' ideas: 'Since Copernicus man is rolling from the center toward X.'[1] Nietzsche elaborates further this thought in his book, *On the Genealogy of Morals* (III, 25):

> Is precisely the self-disparagement of man, his will to self-disparagement since Copernicus, not relentlessly progressing? Alas, the faith in his dignity, uniqueness, and irreplaceability in the hierarchy of beings is gone – he has become an animal, an animal, literally, utterly, unconditionally, he, who in his previous faith was almost God (Son of God, Man-God). Since Copernicus man seems to be on an inclined plane – he is rolling faster and faster away from the center – whereto? into nothingness, into the 'piercing feeling of his nothingness'?

'Since Copernicus', writes Nietzsche, but forgets to mention the man whose ideas contributed most to this 'self-disparagement', loss of dignity, and 'piercing feeling of nothingness', which man began to experience after having been pushed definitively out of the cozy position he held in the center of a universe made expressly and exclusively for him.

Bruno himself may not have been as nihilistic as Nietzsche about mankind's new self-image in the acentric universe. In fact, it is likely that Bruno may have even thought he had finally discovered the true foundation of man's supreme dignity, for now that the great illusion had been definitively dispelled, man's most important task was to become aware of his true identity and to come to terms with it, for true dignity had to be based on truth. This he would certainly achieve by pondering the intimate relationship that existed between the human mind and the cosmic mind, for this would inevitably lead man to the discovery of a hitherto unsuspected closeness to the divinity. It would result from his introspective journey into the most recondite recesses of his mind, as well as from the attentive observation of, and meditation on, nature, for it is here that the presence and supreme power of the cosmic mind becomes manifest. Thus, mankind will retain its sense of dignity by discovering the power of mind to understand nature. Not unlike Hegel's Absolute Spirit, the human mind needs nature to become aware of its own greatness and dignity, that is, of its power to comprehend, imitate, master, and transform nature.

If, according to this interpretation of Bruno's thought, our destiny and the meaning of human existence consists in 'realizing' (in the double meaning of the word: becoming aware and implementing) the cosmic mind's power, then our first task must be to constantly strive for more and more knowledge of both our minds and the cosmic mind, and of the intimate relationship which exists between them; and the second task, equally important, must be to join forces with the cosmic mind in the never-ending process of creation and transformation of the world. Bruno's revolutionary philosophical anthropology would thus lay the foundations for a viable universal religion, since it would offer a spiritual bond that had some chance of success in bringing humanity together, in leading it to peace and solidarity, and above all, in securing its survival. This has, of late, become extremely urgent, for, alas, in spite of his regained divinity, this man-god can now easily commit suicide!

This is the spirit and import of the Brunian ethics and religion. The world that would result from their universal acceptance was Bruno's ultimate goal, an Utopia no doubt and an impossible dream, but it appears that the main driving force of the Brunian Revolution was this vision of a radical ethical and religious upheaval that would utterly subvert the dominant value system. Thus, Bruno anticipated Nietzsche by launching a movement towards a radical reversal and transmutation of traditional Western values – a 'transvaluation', as Nietzsche later was to characterize the final overturn of classical Platonism, as well as of its principal offspring, 'Platonism for the masses'[2].

It is important to understand, however, that it was only the final elaboration of the Brunian cosmology and ontology that inspired in Bruno the faith in the success of his program for a radical ethical revolution and gave him the courage to attempt its implementation, for he was convinced that only the wide acceptance of his new philosophy by the leading minds of Europe would eventually pave the way for the total overturn of the traditional values of Western civilization. For, indeed, the Brunian revaluation drew much of its power to subvert and supplant the prevailing ethical and religious order from the fact that they were rooted in a primitive and obsolete cosmology.

Bruno's harsh criticism of Christian ethical values coincides, to a great extent, with Nietzsche's. Bruno's argument with Roman Catholicism, in his ethical dialogues, frequently voices his conviction that its values, far too contemptuous of this world, undermined human dignity by refusing to recognize the intrinsic value of human works, efforts, and accomplishments. Consequently, he sharply criticized the Church for urging alms-giving to the mendicant orders and for encouraging the idleness of the monastic life dedicated mainly to contemplation and prayer. He also shared with Nietzsche the view that the Christian doctrine disparaged the human body and also failed to address legitimate and urgent worldly concerns. In sum, Bruno held the Catholic Church partly responsible for bringing about the decadence and decrepitude (*vecchiaia*) that was becoming increasingly apparent in the European societies of his time, especially the typically Pauline contempt for reason (the great whore, as Luther called it), and Paul's insistence on faith alone to attain salvation. Bruno suggested that this contributed considerably to the obstruction of the progress that could otherwise have been made in the sciences as well as in social and political institutions, and consequently also in securing peace, harmony, and collaboration between all nations; it may have been different had reason and free critical inquiry been allowed and encouraged to play a significant role in their development.

It is, therefore, legitimate to draw a parallel between Nietzsche and Bruno, for there are some striking similarities between them. They both planned a radical ethical revolution, had the same enemies, and shared the same project and mission – a revaluation of all traditional values. They both launched a campaign to achieve it, and they used the same weapons in their struggle, namely their writings. They both arrived at the conclusion that the universe is infinite, acentric, and eternal, and that the old biblical

Creator-God was dead. They were both inspired by the Pre-Socratics, particularly by Heracleitus, and they shared with him the view that everything is in eternal flux and undergoes constant and endless creation, destruction, and renovation. They were both incurable optimists, and they passionately affirmed life. Both were also at bottom metaphysicians, despite Nietzsche's frequent disclaimers, although their fundamental metaphysical principles were different. Whereas for Nietzsche the Absolute was will-to-power, for Bruno it was rather the irrepressible will-to-form of the cosmic mind. They even worshipped the same immanent God – Dionysian for Nietzsche, Proteic for Bruno – since they both rejected theism as well as deism in favor of a strongly monistic conception of reality. Both were grossly misunderstood by their contemporaries and by many of their modern interpreters as well. Even one particular trait of this misunderstanding was similar: their highly subversive thinking was attributed by some of their enemies to mental derangement, and in the end, they both failed, for their radical ethical revaluation and their total cultural revolution never took place. Moreover, centuries after their disappearance, the bulk of humanity continues to think and behave as if neither one of them had ever existed and had anything of real importance to tell us.

Ultimately, what brings Bruno so close to Nietzsche is that he was, like Nietzsche, what the latter called a 'labyrinthian man'. While Nietzsche was working on his *Zarathustra*, he wrote down some notes that were never incorporated into the text. Among this material the following enigmatic aphorism is found: 'A labyrinthian man never seeks the truth but always his Ariadne – whatever he may tell us.'

This aphorism is enigmatic because we know that Nietzsche was passionately engaged in the search for truth. Why, then, did he say that the labyrinthian man never seeks the truth? Was it perhaps that Nietzsche did not consider himself labyrinthian? But how could he know what a labyrinthian man really seeks if he himself was not one?

Like his distorted image of the labyrinthian man, Nietzsche, too, was obsessed with Ariadne, and, whom did he have in mind when he used the name of the classical labyrinthian woman in the note we are referring to as well as in several other places in his writings? Walter Kaufmann explains:

Cosima Wagner, illegitimate daughter of Franz Liszt, and the wife of Hans von Bülow[3] before she eloped with Wagner, was – so at least it appeared to Nietzsche – the first woman of stature with whom he came in close contact. The difference from the small-town women who had dominated his childhood[4] was indeed striking. Nietzsche never outgrew her fascination: in his late notes and poems she appears as Ariadne, while he increasingly identifies himself with Dionysus – and Wagner must occasionally fill the role of Theseus. It was not until the first days of his insanity, however, that he sent out several notes that reveal who Ariadne was. Cosima herself received a sheet of paper with the sole inscription: 'Ariadne, I love you. Dionysus.' And on March 27, 1889, in the asylum at Jena, Nietzsche said: 'My wife, Cosima Wagner, has brought me here.'[5]

Nietzsche's sister, of course, could not agree with Kaufmann's interpretation of Ariadne as Cosima Wagner. She fancied that her brother loved only her. Consequently, she assured us that her brother was only using Ariadne as a symbol of the human soul, and Nietzsche, she argues (and here Kaufmann reluctantly agrees with Nietzsche's sister), must have indeed been thinking of something other than the physical person of Cosima Wagner when he wrote that enigmatic aphorism. It was actually the human soul, Kaufmann explains, but 'in C. G. Jung's conception of *Anima*: originally dependent on a mother image, it grows into the ideal which a man pursues through his adult life'[6].

If Ariadne was indeed Cosima Wagner for Nietzsche – and the only reason I can think of for not taking his word for it was Nietzsche's advanced mental derangement when he wrote these notes – then he could not be identified with Theseus, the prototype of the labyrinthian man, simply because Theseus was definitely not looking for Ariadne. What he really was looking for was the Minotaur, for after he found and destroyed him, and Ariadne insisted on going back to Athens with the hero, he deserted her on the island of Naxos. It was Dionysus who later found, rescued, and, in the end, loved Ariadne, but Dionysus was anything but a labyrinthian man. True labyrinthian men do not look for Ariadne, they look for the Minotaur. They are heroes, not woman-lovers. Which of the two was Nietzsche, really?

Kaufmann says that Nietzsche 'increasingly identifies himself with Dionysus', and that, in his madness, he sent a note to his beloved Cosima, signing it with the name of Dionysus. Why then, if Dionysus is not the labyrinthian man, does Nietzsche identify himself with him? And why did he think of Wagner as Theseus, the true labyrinthian man? If the real labyrinthian man is not looking for Ariadne, but the Minotaur, then it was Nietzsche, not Wagner, the real labyrinthian man, because his real life-long fascination was not with Cosima, as was clearly the case with Wagner, but with the labyrinth and the Minotaur lodged in its center. For will-to-power and the Eternal Return had been the sole objects of his life-long passionate quest.

There is no question about the fact that Bruno, like Nietzsche, was a true labyrinthian man. Like Theseus, his quest was not for Ariadne, but for the Minotaur, and this quest was truly heroic. He searched for the Minotaur all his life with what he called *eroico furore*, an heroic frenzy. Like Theseus, the prototype of the true labyrinthian man, Bruno, too, entered his labyrinth in search of the Minotaur. Unlike Theseus, however, he could not find his prey, for his labyrinth had no center. Nor did he need Ariadne's thread to retrace his steps; once inside the labyrinth he stayed there, for despite the fact that he could not find the Minotaur anywhere, he made a discovery that put an end to his search for the monster. The Minotaur, he finally understood, was not in the center of the labyrinth, for the labyrinth had no center; he was everywhere. The labyrinth itself became his Minotaur, and since it was indestructible and eternal, it could not be killed. If Nietzsche could announce one day that God was dead, not so Bruno. His god, the Minotaur-labyrinth, was very much alive and could never be killed. Instead, Bruno himself was devoured by the Minotaur, but not destroyed, for it was in the belly of the monster where he received his final enlightenment.

It is from this perspective that we can understand that Nietzsche, too, was a true labyrinthian man, despite the fact that in his mad ravings he considered himself Dionysus and Cosima his Ariadne. The real object of Nietzsche's life-long quest was not Ariadne but the truth about God, man, and the universe. In this, the two labyrinthian men totally coincided. Nietzsche's Minotaur was the Christian God, and the truth he thought he had found about Him was that He is dead, whereas Bruno's Minotaur was the acentric labyrinth, and this one could not die.

There is, however, another fundamental difference between Bruno and Nietzsche with regard to their metaphysical understanding of the universe. Nietzsche conceived it as will-to-power generating an everlasting recurrence of the same. This was, conceivably, the most unconditional affirmation of life, expressing the utterly remorseless satisfaction with everything, that had once been achieved, to the point of wanting it to be forever returning. Bruno's concept of the universe was very different. It was not will-to-power that drove the universe, but rather will-to-form. True omnipotence was displayed by the cosmic mind engaged in an eternal, non-recurrent, non-repetitive creation of infinite forms.

Bruno's concept of the cosmic mind as will-to-form stands in sharp opposition to the Nietzschean doctrine of the Eternal Return if we interpret it as a cosmological or metaphysical hypothesis.[7] Bruno, in fact, in an almost uncanny anticipation of Nietzsche's ideas, dedicated two whole chapters of *De immenso* (On the Immense), the sixth and seventh of Book III, to refute the theory of cosmic cycles and eternal returns. In Bruno's view, nothing can return, for the simple reason that nothing is the same. For if there is no permanence and consistency in anything, how can anything return? In reality, Bruno's violent rejection of the ancient Greek doctrine of the Eternal Return is a necessary corollary of his cosmological and ontological premises. Plato's, Aristotle's, and Ptolemy's spheres eternally returned, whereas an infinite, centerless, eternally evolving universe can never return to a configuration identical to any other one previously attained. More profoundly, an eternal return is ontologically impossible, for there is no sameness or identity at all in physical reality; as Bruno expressly pointed out, nothing is identical to itself successively in time, nor to any other thing simultaneously in space:

> For us, as far as number is concerned, matter and substance are eternal, underlying an eternal movement and (with regard to the composite bodies it produces) an eternal vicissitude. The form of this same matter, with regard to number, never was nor ever will be the same, as it is not possible to affirm with any truth at all that it remains the same in two different moments . . . everything that changes is always different either from itself, in two successive moments, or from everything else, in every moment.[8]

It is obvious: if there is no sameness, there can be no return of the same. With this argument, Bruno refutes all those who want to save the constancy of the universe (*'salvare eterno la costanza dell' universo'*[9]). He further clarifies his thought thus: 'Since it is not possible for any composite body to have the same arrangement and the same aspect in two diverse instants, it is strange that they believe that this can happen in a universe of such variety, so that all effects should appear the very same with regard to number.' 'There is no proof,' insists Bruno in *De minimo*, 'that all heavenly bodies are disposed in such a way that they [must] return once and again, in exactly the same position with regard to the Earth.'[10]

This eternal 'vicissitude', this constant succession and transformation, coincides with the Heracleitan flux in which *omnia fiunt ex omnibus*[11] (everything is made out of everything), as a result of the endless association and disassociation of atoms. The fact that in nature neither a perfect circle nor sphere exists – except perhaps in the atoms themselves, supporters of change, but not themselves subject to it[12] – is the logical consequence of the essential instability and inconsistency of all bodies. Thus, Bruno anticipates and refutes Nietzsche's theory of the Eternal Return. For him, everything is irreversible and therefore unique. No particular form that ever existed will ever come back again, nor any event that ever happened will ever recur.

Thus, Bruno's conception of the ultimate metaphysical principle of absolute reality (mater-materia indissolubly linked with the cosmic mind) may be symbolized by the god Proteus, *'poichè desidera divenire ogni cosa, e in ragione delle proprie forze, essere simile a ogni ente'*[13] (since it desires to become everything, and in virtue of its own powers, to be similar to every thing). In contrast, the strong quantitative aspect in Nietzsche's concept of will, as incessantly wanting more and more power, is so predominant that it logically leads to the concept of will-to-power as circular, eternally returning upon itself. However, is not the will continually to change form, endlessly to metamorphose, an even more powerful will-to-power? If so, then Nietzsche's will-to-power should be conceived rather as will-to-form, will-to-metamorphose, and thus, in mythological symbolic language, as Proteus' will. For Proteus is the symbol of the divine power that delights in constantly adopting new forms. Indeed, Proteus is driven by an irrepressible urge to transcend and discard, in the ecstasies of his frenzied transfigurations, every form it accomplishes. Thus, Proteus resembles the Hindu god Shiva, the divine annihilator; he symbolizes constant self-transcendence, for he needs unceasingly to leave himself behind in order to become another. Precisely because Proteus' will-to-form is unconditional, it can never return to the same, for true omnipotence manifests itself supremely in never repeating itself. Thus the will-to-form seems to exclude, indeed, even to contradict, the Eternal Return of the Selfsame. From this perspective the ironic conclusion seems unavoidable: Nietzsche actually underestimated the power of will-to-power!

In what, then, did Bruno and Nietzsche disagree? In return versus no-return; in finitude versus true infinity; in limited power versus true omnipotence. Nietzsche would eventually prefer Eternal Return and perpetual circularity to Bruno's eternal transcendence of immanence.

Thus, for Nietzsche the key symbol of his metaphysics is the ring; whereas for Bruno it has to be the spiral[14], which is truly the most suitable symbolic representation of the infinite acentric labyrinth. Indeed, the open, infinite helix[15] stands in marked contrast to the closed finite ring of the cosmic serpent biting its tail, the symbol Nietzsche regarded as most appropriate for his idea of the Eternal Return.

In contrast, the image most congruous with the Brunian concept of the Absolute is that of a spiraling universe, rather than that of an oscillating one that would rock back and forth from same to same. And, even if after the present observable expansion the universe should come to a halt and start to contract, in Bruno's view its regression would be just one more turn of the spiral to initiate another coil. This eternally spiraling universe has, of course, no center: it is an acentric labyrinth.

EPILOGUE

The Acentric Labyrinth

GIORDANO BRUNO

De claro de cielo en claro,
hacia la puerta esquiva
del laberinto acéntrico,
siempre avanzando,
siempre girando,
nunca llegando,
en su cosmonave
instantánea,
solo.[1]

Daedalus, the master architect, received the commission from King Minos to build a suitable abode for the Minotaur, the creature the king's wife had borne after mating with Poseidon's magnificent bull. Although fully aware of his cannibalistic cravings, Minos spared the monster's life, for mysterious reasons, perhaps political, for he may have foreseen that the Minotaur would become a symbol, and hence a source of power. Eventually it did, for, before long, Athens had to demonstrate yearly its subservience to Cretan Knossos by sending the flower of its youth – fourteen adolescent virgins, seven of them boys – to satiate the monster's appetite. The dwelling place of the Minotaur consequently had to serve two very specific purposes. First, it had to function as the monster's prison-cage, foiling by its very structure every attempt of escape; second, its shape had to ensure regular and certain delivery of the proper food for the monster's voracious gullet. The successful fulfillment of these two basic requirements resulted in Daedalus' masterpiece – the labyrinth.[2]

Daedalus' labyrinth had a center, the secluded but accessible stable which was the monster's permanent domicile. Converging on this center were numerous corridors, the dreary pathways trodden by the young garlanded victims in their funeral march to the final horrible encounter.

Although not strictly circular, the labyrinth encouraged circularity – circularity in space and circularity in time. It was possible never to reach the center, and to be doomed to eternal meandering, and yet, the classical labyrinth's undeniable power to generate infinity countered its architect's principal intention. The labyrinth was supposed not only to hold in the dreadful creature but also to lead to it every other living thing that ventured inside; for, indeed, besides being a prison cell, the labyrinth was also a trap. It was the insidious net, the inextricable spider-web.

Despite its unquestionable horror, the classical labyrinth misses the ultimate awesomeness. It is flawed because it has a center; it is weak because it needs a Minotaur. In fact, after the Minotaur was slain and the center vacated, the prison vanished, and the trap lost its purpose.

It was Jorge Luis Borges, the great Argentinian fiction-writer, poet, and philosopher, who discovered the definitive horror of the labyrinth. Borges's cosmological labyrinth – the absurd Order – remarkably resembles Nietzsche's will-to-power, eternally revolving and returning. To be thrust into, and trapped in, this labyrinth is the common fate of all its wretched inhabitants; along its endless, tortuous pathways they drift, in hopeful search for the center, but, the ultimate horror of this labyrinth is that it has no center.

In his Preface to Borges' *Labyrinths*, André Maurois shows that Borges was well aware of Giordano Bruno when he wrote 'The Library of Babel'. It is precisely the theme of the 'center' that establishes the connection between the two thinkers. Borges remembers that Pascal had written: 'Nature is an infinite sphere whose center is everywhere, whose circumference is nowhere', and he sets out to hunt down this metaphor through the centuries. Finally he finds it in Bruno: 'We can assert with certainty that the universe is all center, or that the center of the universe is everywhere and the circumference nowhere.'[3]

Borges's labyrinth, of course, is a library, and the library is the universe. 'The universe (which others call the Library) is composed of an indefinite and perhaps infinite number of hexagonal galleries . . ."[4] It has no center. 'The Library is a sphere whose exact center is any one of its hexagons and whose circumference is inaccessible.'[5]

It is true, some of the inhabitants of the library-labyrinth believed in a center, supposedly a secret hexagon, the dwelling place of the 'Man of the Book'. He was given this title because he was transformed into a god after reading the Book which was, Borges points out, the 'cipher and perfect compendium of all the rest: some librarian has gone through it and he is analogous to a god.'[6] But this turned out to be a superstition: 'Many wandered in search of him. For a century they exhausted in vain the most varied areas.'[7] Indeed, the awesome truth about Borges' library-labyrinth and the universe it symbolizes is that it has no center, the supreme symbol of its utter absurdity.

The horror of the acentric labyrinth arises from the chilling insight into its total absurdity, signified by its circularity, emptiness, and eternity:

> Perhaps my old age and fearfulness deceive me, but I suspect that the human species – the unique species – is about to be extinguished, but the Library will endure: illuminated, solitary, infinite, perfectly motionless, equipped with precious volumes, useless, incorruptible, secret . . . I venture to suggest this solution to the ancient problem: The Library is unlimited and cyclical. If an eternal traveler were to cross it in any direction, after centuries he would see that the same volumes were repeated in the same disorder (which, thus repeated, would be an order: the Order).

The genius of Borges discovered the perfect symbol for the universe: the labyrinthian library. He himself explicitly acknowledged that it was Bruno who suggested this idea to him. Thus, although Bruno himself did not use the labyrinth as a symbol for his infinite, acentric universe, Borges, who did see the connection, provided the perfect symbol for it.

The similarities between Borges' labyrinthian library and Bruno's labyrinthian universe are indeed striking: both are infinite, acentric, cyclical, solitary, useless, incorruptible, eternal, and above all, 'secret'. Here Borges, once more, with stunning insight, hit upon the most mysterious and paradoxical feature of the library-universe: although 'equipped with precious volumes',

Borges observed, it was 'useless', although 'illuminated' it was 'solitary', and, although saturated with 'order', the order was 'absurd', for it resulted from repeated 'disorder'. Borges even symbolized the infinite intelligence and wisdom accumulated in the Library by its innumerable books. And the absurdity of this order, Borges believed (in this view following Nietzsche rather than Bruno), resulted from the recurrence and repetition of the same.

This was the riddle of the library-universe and its most mysterious 'secret', which Borges refers to as the 'ancient problem'. Borges' insight was indeed remarkable because it focused precisely on the feature of Bruno's acentric labyrinth that we identified as its greatest conundrum when we described, in detail, Bruno's cosmological model, namely its apparently inexplicable order.

Inexplicable indeed, and absurd, was this order, for Nietzsche as well as for Borges, but not so for Bruno. Probably neither Nietzsche nor Borges believed in a cosmic mind, whereas Bruno, confronted with the order that pervades the universe, refused to admit its absurdity – the utter absurdity of an order that results from pure chance and luck (Borges 'disorder') – and gave it the only rational explanation, a potent cosmic intellect in a fecund *mater-materia* that gives birth to that order through their eternal copulation. All the other features of Borges's universe Bruno ascribed to his universe . . . except this one. It sets up the wall that separates Bruno from Nietzsche as well as from Borges: eternal cyclical return versus eternally spiraling advance, absurdity versus comprehensibility, limited will-to-power versus truly omnipotent will-to-form, and a dead God versus a living cosmic mind.

Borges believed that the library-universe would outlive its inhabitants, for the library-universe was indestructible and would endure forever, whereas its inhabitants were about to be exterminated. We know that this is true: whether we self-destroy or are destroyed does not make a bit of difference. In the end 'the human species – the unique species' will inevitably disappear from the universe. Bruno, to be sure, did not share Borges' dismal pessimism, which the latter attributed to his old age and fearfulness. Perhaps the reason for this disagreement is that, according to Bruno, even if one day this unique species, the human species, disappears, the cosmic mind will not, nor will other no less unique species living somewhere in the immensity of his infinite universe, for the spiraling cosmic mind and *mater-materia*, in their indissoluble bond and everlasting copulation, have the power, and perhaps also the irrepressible urge, to eternally bring them forth.

In Umberto Eco's novel, *The Name of the Rose*,[8] which was obviously inspired by Borges's labyrinth-library, the library of the Benedictine abbey where the action takes place has the form and structure of a labyrinth.[9] Less cosmological than Borges, but certainly more faithful to the classical myth, Eco restores the center to the labyrinth. Like Minos, he too places his Minotaur in this center, only here the Minotaur has been metamorphosed into a book. Indeed, what other body could the Minotaur have assumed after his cage became a library? But the new body of the Minotaur is not any book: it is – Borges again inspires Eco – the Book. This Book too, like the one in the secret hexagon[10] of the Labyrinth-Library of Babel, is zealously guarded and protected by the Man of the Book, not because it, too, was 'the cipher and compendium of all the rest', but because it is thought by its guardian to have the power to open the eyes of all those who read it and, consequently, like Borges' Book, to make them like gods . . . and this, of course, had to be avoided at all costs, for only gods are supposed to have open eyes.

As a homage to that great builder of labyrinths, Jorge L. Borges, and also as an honest avowal of his own indebtedness, Eco chooses an unmistakable name of his Man of the Book: Jorge de Burgos. Both Jorges are blind, and they live in libraries, hemmed in by countless walls of books.[11] But here the analogy ends; what makes all the difference is precisely the Book. For the book that Jorge de Burgos is so zealously guarding is surely the most dangerous book, indeed, in his opinion, the greatest threat to humanity should it ever fall into its hands. Jorge's logic is unquestionably most stringent, for his unshakeable premise is that humanity can only be saved by believing the preposterous, but surely the single thing that would make such a belief most difficult, if not impossible, is humor.

This explains why the book that Jorge de Burgos felt he had to conceal in the octagonal center of the labyrinth-library of the Benedictine abbey, is none other than the justification of humor, indeed, the conceivably most compelling justification of humor in a Scholastic world: Aristotle's Second Book of Poetics, an extensive discussion of comedy, commonly believed then to have been lost forever.

This is, indeed, the Minotaur of the Benedictine labyrinth. It, too, had to be put away in its innermost and remotest center, to which nobody except the Librarian and his trusted assistants could have access. The blind Man of the Book was thereby making sure that the eyes of the world would remain closed. A remarkable replica of Dostoevsky's Grand Inquisitor, Jorge de Burgos is once again ready to eliminate as many human beings as necessary in order to prevent the definitive advent of the Kingdom of Freedom.

Jorge de Burgos is indeed the prototype of the rabid zealot, the fanatic par excellence. Once the secret pathway to the center of the labyrinth was discovered and the Minotaur lodged in it in imminent danger of being let loose upon the world, the librarian-inquisitor had no choice but to destroy it and reduce the library-labyrinth to ashes, and himself along with it if necessary, in order to save humanity from the most dreadful adversary of faith. Thus, Jorge de Burgos reveals himself ultimately not as the double, but rather as the utter perversion of Jorge Luis Borges, the agnostic blind seer with a sense of humor, who had read almost everything readable and who wished everybody would do the same.[12]

The cosmic labyrinth that both Borges and Eco masterfully allegorized as libraries in their fiction is none other than Bruno's non-hierarchical, acentric, and infinite universe, in which, however, a marvelous and mysterious order is to be found everywhere.

Although all earthly labyrinths are always finite – at least in one sense: they are enclosed within limits – the idea of infinity is inseparable from the labyrinth-symbol because of the always possible endless circulation.

Also, like all terrestrial labyrinths Eco's library-labyrinth could not help but have a center, this is why in the end it was destroyed.

It seems that all labyrinths with centers are vulnerable and ultimately doomed to destruction, or at least to deconstruction, since for all of them an Ariadne's thread invariably turns up.

The acentricity of the cosmic labyrinth is the necessary feature of a universe with rhizome structure, systemic circuitry, and ubiquitous mental characteristics. Nietzsche emphasized the closed circularity of the cosmic system, whereas Bruno was already aware of what we would designate today as its 'positive feedback'. It operates by trial and error and has an inexhaustible creative power. The acentric labyrinth is indeed a sort of runaway labyrinth.

It is obvious that the acentric labyrinth has a unique potential of becoming a highly distinctive symbol of our world. For our world is, above all, a cybernetic world, a vast and constantly expanding network of interconnected closed circuits, where an immanent center is nowhere to be found, let alone a transcendent one that would be its cause or purpose.

Indeed, as Nietzsche pointed out, the old traditional values that supported the whole structure of Western civilization by providing a rich matrix of meaning to all of our human endeavors and institutions have become more and more questionable, and hence less and less capable of accomplishing their task. But Nietzsche, the incurable optimist, also believed that all that was needed in order to rescue the decadent Western world from its baneful value-crisis was finally to get rid of the old values and to replace them with new ones that contradicted and subverted them. Equipped with this new set of values man would be ready for his transformation into a new human being: the Overman.

However, the Overman's new world would predictably seem to many just as meaningless as the old one it was expected to replace, and the new values that would give it meaning just as arbitrary as the traditional ones that Nietzsche blamed for the decadence of Western civilization – and perhaps eventually even more disastrous to the whole of human society.

There was a mirror in the center of Eco's[13] library-labyrinth; and there was also a mirror inside Borges' Library of Babel. As a matter of fact, Borges delights, as André Maurois observes, in the magical interplay of mirrors and mazes.[14] If the acentric labyrinth is Proteus, we shall let the god have his way once more and transform himself into a mirror. This, of course, would imply that all the walls of the labyrinth become mirrors, and then Man, the lonely wanderer along its endless pathways, would himself become a center. For now, inserted between the endless parallel mirrors, he is the center of the infinite series of doubles he projects on them, and hence the moving intersection of two infinite lines, the circular line of his path and the straight line of his reflections. Thus, the endless recurrence of time – eternity – meets, precisely in this mobile center, for the first time, and only here, the endless recurrence of space – infinity. The wanderer's lonesome meandering along the corridors of the acentric labyrinth has now become the eternal march with his infinite doubles, the infernal nightmare he can escape only by looking incessantly straight ahead, his eyes riveted to the future.

Giordano Bruno led the way. When he marched almost naked and with a gag in his mouth, in appalling loneliness, to the Campo di Fiori, he knew he was just another speck of dust drifting along the pathways of the infinite acentric labyrinth. And yet, always looking ahead and beyond the stake, he was overwhelmed with joy, the supreme joy of total awareness.

Neither Nietzsche nor anyone else after him seems to have found the way out of the labyrinth. Perhaps there is no way out of it after all. Perhaps all Ariadne's threads actually lead to yet another labyrinth. Maybe the universe is nothing more than an aggregate of labyrinths, indeed a labyrinth of labyrinths!

Is this not precisely what Camus was telling us in the final pages of his *Myth of Sisyphus*? That the only 'meaning' of human existence is the supreme privilege of a lucid awareness of living in an acentric labyrinth, and of knowing of humankind's fate to wander in it with no goal until its turn comes to vanish? And that Sisyphus's joy resulted from his belated discovery that nobody had sentenced him? Perhaps this is what Camus meant when he concluded: '*Il faut imaginer Sisyphe heureux*' ('One must imagine Sisyphus as happy').[15]

Since for Bruno the Overman is everyone who, driven by heroic frenzy, resolutely enters the acentric labyrinth, we can think of no better guide than Bruno to take the bold by the hand through the terrifying gate into his awesome labyrinth, the living rhizome with the endlessly proliferating pathways, along which humankind strides with its dreams, carrying the center, like joyful Sisyphus, on its shoulders.

Notes

Introduction

1 'Already, for the past 33 years, scientists have been seeking signs of
   intelligent life elsewhere in the universe. NASA's Search for Extraterrestrial Intelligence – SETI – was recently expanded under the new
   name High Resolution Microwave Survey (HRMS).' *National Geo-
   graphic*, vol. 185, no. 1, January 1994, p. 40.
2 Inspired by this concluding sentence of Stephen Hawking's *A Brief
   History of Time*, Paul Davies has titled his most recent book on
   cosmology *The Mind of God. Science and the Search for Ultimate Meaning*,
   London (Simon & Schuster) 1992.
3 Among the most insightful and thorough expositions, interpretations, discussions, and evaluations of Bruno's cosmology, we must
   mention the publications on this subject by Emile Namer, Luigi
   Cicuttini, Hélène Védrine, Paul Henri Michel, Ernst Bloch, Hans
   Blumenberg, Fred Stern, Giuseppe Saitta, and Alfonso Ingegno. Also
   the works of Antoinette Mann Paterson and Ksenija Atanasijevic are
   worth mentioning. See the Bibliography for precise details of their
   publications.
4 John Bossy, *Giordano Bruno and the Embassy Affair*, New Haven &
   London (Yale University Press) 1991. Bossy frankly discloses his
   sympathy for Holmes in his introductory quote to Part I. He also
   admits in his preface 'To the Reader' that his story is a detective story
   (p. 2), and yet Bossy vigorously protests, and wants his readers
   always to keep in mind, that he is 'a historian, not a writer of fiction'
   (p. 1).
5 *Op. cit.*, pp. 21, 129–30, 141.
6 *Op. cit.*, pp. 16, 20–21, 168.
7 See H. R. Trevor-Roper, 'Was Giordano Bruno a Mole? Giordano
   Bruno and the Embassy Affair, by John Bossy'. Yale University Press,
   in *The New York Review of Books*, December 19, 1991, pp. 3–8.
8 See Chapter 3.

9 Dorothea Waley Singer's excellent book on Bruno, *Giordano Bruno. His Life and Thought*, is now both out of date and out of print, and Antoinette Mann Paterson's much less fortunate work is hardly heeded by anybody any more.

10 Accessible also to English-speaking readers is R. E. W. Maddison's translation of Paul Henri Michel's excellent study *La cosmologie de Giordano Bruno*, published in Paris by Hermann in 1962. Although Frances Yates' book *Giordano Bruno and the Hermetic Tradition* was published two years later, the British scholar seems not to have taken notice of Michel's work, for there is absolutely no reference to this important French study of Bruno's cosmology in her book. Nor does Yates take notice of the perhaps even more important writings on Bruno's philosophy and cosmology by another French author, the Sorbonne professor, Emile Namer. This was unfortunate, for Yates would probably have changed her mind about Bruno's relevance as a cosmologist had she read the most relevant French literature on this subject.

11 Hans Blumenberg, *Aspekte der Epochenschwelle: Cusaner und Nolaner*, 2nd ed., Frankfurt am Main (Suhrkamp) 1982, p. 112.

12 The title of Frances Yates' book, *Giordano Bruno and the Hermetic Tradition*, clearly sets the boundaries of her research.

13 We shall discuss this issue more in depth in Chapter 13.

14 The deeper understanding of this strongly utopian Brunian philosophy and of his strategy to implement it, as well as of his final realization of the total impossibility of carrying it out personally in his lifetime, yields the key to understanding Bruno's otherwise incomprehensible choice of the most horrible death rather than a long life of comfortable harmlessness.

15 Cf. Lerner, Lawrence S., and Edward A. Gosselin: 'Galileo and the Specter of Bruno', in *Scientific American* (November 1986), pp. 126–133. Despite the authors' overlooking of the vast Brunian opus – they refer only to the *Supper* to prove their point – and the customary Bruno-bashing, their article has, at least, the merit of having focused on a subject – the influence of Bruno's condemnation on Galileo's trial – seldom discussed at length in major publications expressly dealing with the Galileo affair.

Chapter One

1 Nietzsche's model of the Eternal Return comes close to it, but he falls short of granting it true infinity and omnipotence by making the open spiral a closed circle; thus instead of allowing the snake to writhe for

ever, generating always new shapes and figures, he forces it to bite its tail. Bruno's spiraling cosmological model, on the other hand, is truly the first, and, perhaps, also the only one until now conceived, that proposes a congruous representation of the spiraling cosmic acentric labyrinth. See the Epilogue.

2 Roger Penrose, *The Emperor's New Mind. Concerning Computers, Minds, and the Laws of Physics*. New York (Penguin Books) 1991, p. 428.

Chapter Two

1 Bruno was fifteen years old when the Council of Trent finally came to a close in 1563. He had moved from Nola to Naples the previous year. The post-Tridentine era in Spain and most of Italy was a period of extreme intolerance and persecution not only of all presumed sympathizers of the Reformers but also of all those who held views deviating the slightest from the numerous dogmatic pronouncements of the Council. It was definitely the least propitious time for free-spiriting, and Bruno was indeed most unfortunate in having lived precisely in this time. The introduction of the Inquisition into the Spanish Kingdom of Naples had been a direct result of the counter-reformist promptings of the Council.

2 The main sources for the biographical data contained in this and the following three chapters are the biographical works of Giovanni Aquilecchia, Michele Ciliberto, Vincenzo Spampanato, and Luigi Cicuttini.

3 Dominican theologians had been entrusted by the Pope with the charge of being the principal investigators at the service of the Inquisition.

4 Brion, Marcel, *The Medici. A Great Florentine Family*. New York (Exeter Books) 1969, p. 198.

5 Luigi Cicuttini, *Giordano Bruno*. Milan (Società editrice 'Vita e pensiero') 1950, Pubblicazioni dell'università cattolica del Sacro Cuore, p. 26.

6 *'Documenti veneti'*, doc. IX, c. 8, in V. Spampanato, *Vita di Giordano Bruno*, Messina (Ed. Principato), 1921, p. 698.

7 This is Bruno's first clear statement and proclamation of his uncompromising love of freedom. It sheds a powerful light on Bruno's real motivation for his restless wanderings all over Europe. To find 'a place where he could live in freedom and feel secure' was his most ardent desire. But this, as the history of his constant displacements clearly attests, was a goal that constantly eluded him. Bruno's love of

freedom, however, is the key to understanding much of Bruno's otherwise incomprehensible behavior, his writings, and, above all, his heroic death.

8 It seems almost certain that Bruno did attend Calvinist services in Geneva, in fact, that he had become a Calvinist. He always denied this in his depositions before the Inquisition, but the evidence in support of his conversion is very strong. In order to be admitted to the Academy it was necessary to be registered in the Book of the Rector of the Community, and Bruno's name is there. Moreover, after having been pardoned and released from prison, he was admitted to the Supper, which was the name for the Calvinist Eucharist. See Ciccuttini, *op. cit.*, p. 27.

9 The Catalan Ramon Lull (c. 1234–1316), philosopher, mystic, romancer, missionary, and martyr (he was stoned to death in Bougie, Algeria), wrote some 292 works in Catalan, Arabic and Latin. After having three visions of Christ on the cross, he made the resolution to write 'the best book in the world against the errors of the infidel'. This was his *Ars Magna* written after a mystical illumination. In his book, Lull used complex semimechanical techniques involving symbolic notation and combinatory diagrams. Lull's monumental work, a universal system of knowledge, attempts to relate all forms of knowledge to the manifestation of God's attributes in the universe. It inspired Leibniz's dream of a universal algebra, and it is considered an antecedent of logic machines and symbolic logic.

10 The title of this book is *De umbris idearum* (On the Shadows of Ideas).

11 Besides his *De umbris idearum* Bruno published in Paris some treatises on mnemonics, some commentaries on the Lullian art of memory, and his comedy *Il Candelaio* (The Candle Maker). The Italian title was then a popular mock-name for homosexual, similar to the English 'fagot'.

Chapter Three

1 *Giordano Bruno and the Embassy Affair*, New Haven & London (Yale University Press) 1991, p. 14.

2 *'Senza dubio alcuno, non è chi non debba confesarla [l'Università di Oxford] prima in tutta l'Europa e per conseguenza in tutto il mondo'* ('Without any doubt there is nobody who would not consider it the first in all of Europe, and consequently in the whole world'). *Causa*, 209.

3 *Ibid.*

4 The soul and astronomy, Aristotle's subjects of philosophical inquiry in his treatises *De anima* and *De coelo* respectively.

5 *La cena de le ceneri*, Fourth Dialogue (author's translation).
6 Cardinal Robert Bellarmine, of the Society of Jesus, Saint and Doctor of the Roman Catholic Church.
7 The letter was in French, although Bruno conversed with the Queen in Italian, and Bruno's handwriting was totally different from that of the person who wrote the letter. No problem, says Bossy, Bruno simply faked his own handwriting!
8 However, very soon thereafter, Bossy forgets his initial doubts about Bruno having actually heard the confession, as well as his suspicion that Bruno had made up the story, and simply presents it as a fact. (p. 108).
9 In this truly remarkable passage, Bruno anticipates almost literally Leibniz's monadology, according to which every single monad, no matter how small, holds in itself some representation of the entire universe. If Bruno's forms are the seeds of all reality, and are, as forms, essentially representational, they must be considered true forerunners of Leibniz's monads. And since – besides this explicit conceptualization of the 'rational forms [that] shape and form in seed everything that exists' – Bruno used, more than a century before Leibniz, the term 'monad' to designate the most elementary physical entities that make up the universe, it is not difficult to guess from whom Leibniz got the inspiration for the cornerstone of his metaphysics, particularly if we consider that Leibniz had to be familiar with Bruno's Latin dialogue published in Frankfurt and widely distributed in Germany, *On the Monad, Number, and Figure.*
10 We shall discuss this further in Chapter 17.
11 *Documenti veneti*, doc. IX, c. II, in Spampanato, *op. cit.*, p. 702.
12 *De lampade combinatoria Lulliana* (1587) and *De progressu et lampade venatoria logicorum* (1587).
13 *Camoeracensis acrotismus seu rationes articulorum physicorum adversus peripateticos, parisiis propositorum* (1588).
14 *Oratio valedictoria* (1588).
15 *De specierum scrutinio et lampade combinatoria Raimundi Lullii* (1588).
16 *Centum et sexaginta articuli adversus huius tempestatis mathematicos atque philosophos* (1588).
17 'I argued my case with Monsignor the Bishop of Bergamo, Papal Nuncio in France, to whom I was introduced by don Bernardin Mendoza, the Catholic [Spanish] ambassador, whom I had met at the court of England; and not only did I argue my case with Monsignor Nuncio, but I now add that I asked him and requested insistently that he write to his Holiness in Rome and obtain the grace of being received in the bosom of the Catholic Church, but that I should not be compelled to return to my Order. And since Sixtus V was still alive,

the Nuncio did not believe he could obtain this grace and did not want to write, but he offered, should I wish to return to my Order, to write and to help me; and then he directed me to a Jesuit father; and I consulted him about my case and he resolved that it was necessary that I should procure the absolution of the censures from the Pope, and that this was impossible unless I returned to my Order, and then he warned me, that being excommunicated, I could not attend the divine offices, but that I could go and listen to the sermons and say my prayers in the church.' *Doc. veneti*, doc. XVII, c. 38, in Spampanato, *op. cit.*, p. 702 (author's translation).

18 Luigi Cicuttini, *Giordano Bruno*, p. 30.

19 *Documenti tedeschi*, doc. VI, in Spampanato, *op. cit.*, p. 665.

20 Although Copernicus was born in Polish territory, his family was of German descent, and the city where he was born, Thorn, had been founded by the German Order and was a member of the Hanseatic League until it became part of the Polish state in the fifteenth century.

Chapter Four

1 So far the author has not been successful in finding out, with certainty, the religious order to which Mocenigo's confessor belonged. Both Jesuits and Dominicans were the preferred confessors of the nobility in Venice, and both had churches, residences, and convents there where the Venetian nobility would normally seek advice, particularly in matters related to heresy and apostasy. As we mentioned earlier, it was a Jesuit to whom the Papal Nuncio referred Bruno in Paris, and Bellarmine himself was a Jesuit. In any case, the Venetian Jesuits could not but have been well aware of who Giordano Bruno was and of the serious danger he represented to orthodox faith.

2 *Doc. veneti*, doc. VI, c. 2, in Spampanato, *op. cit.*, p. 690. Nothing shows more clearly the deviousness and pettiness of Mocenigo's character than this revelation of his intentions *vis-à-vis* Bruno to his obsequious acquaintance. Their mutual trust and complicity is also sufficiently documented by these confidential revelations. Mocenigo had to be perfectly sure that Ciotto would not warn Bruno of his intentions.

3 *Doc. veneti*, doc. I, in Spampanato, *op. cit.*, p. 679 (author's translation).

4 Florence (Sansoni) 1940.

Chapter Five

1 For a more detailed report on the extradition see Corsano, *op. cit.,* pp. 35–42.

2 Mercati, Angelo [Cardinal]: *Il sommario del processo die Giordano Bruno.* Città del Vaticano (Biblioteca Apostolica Vaticana) 1942.

3 See Firpo, *op. cit.,* pp. 57–59.

4 *Op. cit.,* pp. 81–84.

5 See Firpo, *op. cit.,* p. 77.

6 *Op. cit.,* pp. 79–84.

7 *'Il* punctum dolens *del processo si incentrava ormai nella doctrina bruni-ana dell'animazione universale, sia nell'aspetto dell'*anima mundi, *iden-tificata o meno con lo Spirito Santo, sia nella definizione dell'anima individuale'* ('The sore spot of the trial was now centered in the Brunian doctrine of universal animation, either under the aspect of the soul of the world, identified more or less with the Holy Spirit, or in the definition of the individual soul'), *op. cit.,* p. 85; author's translation.

8 *Op. cit.,* pp. 48, 52, 54–56.

9 See Firpo, *op. cit.,* p. 74.

10 In Mercati's words, this was *'chiaro indizio di perturbazione di mente e fors'anco di alterazione psichica, che i guidici compresero come pervicacia e ostinazione'* ('a clear sign of mental perturbation and perhaps even of psychic derangement, which the judges understood as stubborness and obstinacy') Mercati's *Sommario,* pp. 47–51; author's translation. Firpo also quotes another Catholic clergyman who referred to Bruno's *'ingegno poderoso travolto dalla follia'* ('the powerful mind ravaged by madness') *ibid.,* footnote 1.

11 For a discussion of Bruno's proto-Nietzschean program of 'revaluation of all values' (*Umwertung aller Werte*), see Chapter 17.

12 The document has been translated by the author from the transcription thereof made by Firpo from the original Latin manuscript. See Firpo, *op. cit.,* pp. 96–97. For a more detailed description of the original manuscript and the circumstances of its discovery by Firpo see *op. cit.,* pp. 7–8.

13 Bruno's last words were faithfully recorded by an eye-witness called Scioppio, a recent convert to the Catholic faith, who, shortly after the execution, sent a detailed report of the circumstances of the final moments of Bruno's life to a correspondent in Germany. See Firpo, *op. cit.,* p. 105.

14 Paul Davies, *The Cosmic Blueprint. Quantum Physics as the Language of Nature.* New York (Bantam Books) 1984, p. 303.

Chapter Six

1 Alexandre Koyré, *From the Closed World to the Infinite Universe.* Baltimore and London (The Johns Hopkins University Press), 1987, p. 2.
2 Copernicus had already worked out the basic features of his helio-centric theory 30 years earlier, around 1514, and put them in writing in a manuscript entitled *Commentariolus*. However, it was not until 1543 that his mature and lengthy work, *De revolutionibus orbium caelestium* (On the Revolutions of the Heavenly Bodies), was pub-lished. Even this later work remained unnoticed by almost everybody except Tycho Brahe, Digges, and Bruno for another 60 years, when in 1610 Galileo finally submitted compelling evidence for the heliocentric hypothesis.
3 It is not totally clear that Nicholas of Cusa (Cusanus), before Bruno, had already stated that the universe was infinite and hence acentric, since his model retained the outermost limiting sphere, whereas Thomas Digges' allusion to an infinite heaven beyond the last sphere is clearly a theological, rather than a cosmological statement. Cf. Koyré, *op. cit.*, pp. 18–19; 35–39.
4 Ernst Bloch, *Das Prinzip Hoffnung, Gesamtausgabe* Frankfurt a. M., 1972, p. 197 (author's translation).
5 For a detailed exposition of Bruno's revolutionary concept of matter see chapter 9.

Chapter Seven

1 *On the Genealogy of Morals*, part III, section 25.
2 Only seven years elapsed between the publications of Bruno's first cosmological dialogue *La cena de le ceneri* (The Ash Wednesday Supper), London 1584, and of *De immenso*.
3 See Paul Henri Michel, *The Cosmology of Giordano Bruno*, translated by Dr. R. E. W. Maddison, F.S.A., Librarian of the Royal Astronomical Society, Ithaca, N.Y. (Cornell University Press) 1973, p. 178.
4 Most of the references, to the passages in his works, in which Bruno states and develops the cosmological and ontological insights, men-tioned in this and the following four chapters, may be found in the summary of these insights at the end of Chapter 10.
5 Although Bruno's views can, in fact, hardly avoid being considered animistic and vitalistic, they do clearly betray a strong libertarian pathos. Indeed, if the Earth and all heavenly bodies are free to move about in space spontaneously and without constraints, how could those who inhabit them be denied their freedom?

6 In his Italian dialogue *De infinito universo* Bruno does not tire of making a clear and sharp distinction between suns and earths, that is stars and planets. Stanley Jaki, however, based on some casual formulations on this subject made by Bruno in his *Ash Wednesday Supper* accuses him unjustly of not knowing the difference between stars and planets. It is unfortunate that Jaki passes judgment on Bruno's complex and evolving cosmology principally on the basis of the least rigorous and most informal of all of Bruno's cosmological dialogues.

7 *La cena de le ceneri*, pp. 305f.

8 *De immenso*, IV, vii (*Opera*, I, ii, pp. 35–36).

9 The Earth, as we know, has a central molten nickel-iron core.

10 *Ibid.*

11 *The Cosmology of Giordano Bruno*, Paris (Hermann) 1973, p. 156.

Chapter Eight

1 'Nature has neither core nor shell, it is all it is, once and for all.'

2 Lucretius' famous poem, rediscovered by Poggio in the Benedictine Abbey of St. Gallen in 1417, made a significant impact on the early Renaissance philosophers, and was a decisive factor in bringing about the turning point in cosmological thinking that Bruno was to initiate.

3 Thomas Digges was born in Kent. He matriculated at the University of Cambridge in May 1546, and died in 1595. He was the son of the astronomer Leonard Digges, author of *Prognostication Everlastinge* (London, 1576). Thomas wrote an appendix to his father's book entitled 'Perfit Description of the Caelestiall Orbes according to the most aunciene doctrine of the Pythagoreans lately revived by Copernicus and by Geometricall Demonstrations approved'. It is here that his ambiguous remark about the stars 'fixed infinitely up extendeth hit self in altitude sphericallye, and therefore immouable' is found. Digges' appendix was discovered by Professor Francis R. Johnson and Sanford V. Larkey in 1934, who were quick and eager to hail Digges as the true first modern discoverer of the infinity of the universe.

4 Alexandre Koyré, *From the Closed World to the Infinite Universe*, Baltimore and London (The Johns Hopkins University Press), 1987, p. 38.

5 Arthur O. Lovejoy, *The Great Chain of Being*, Cambridge, Mass., (Oxford University Press) 1936, p. 116.

6 Digges' text must have been known in the entourage of Queen

Elizabeth's court which Bruno began to frequent only seven years after the publication of the book; however we also know that Bruno did not speak English, so it is not unwarranted to assume that he was not reading many English books either. However, he still may have discussed Digges' views with his English friends in Latin or Italian.

7 Besides Bruno, Kepler and Descartes, as well, attributed to Cusanus the opinion that the universe is infinite. Cf. Koyré, *op. cit.*, p. 6 and footnote 8.

8 *Ibid.* p. 6–8.

9 *Ibid.*

10 Giordano Bruno, *La cena de le ceneri*, Third Dialogue, *Opere italiane*, vol. 1, ed. G. Gentile, Bari, 1907, pp. 73 sq.

11 Cf. Koyré, *op. cit.* p. 279, fn. 19, and Clemens Baemker, *Das pseudo-hermetische Buch der XXIV Meister* (Beiträge zur Geschichte der Philosophie und Theologie des Mittelalters, fasc. xxv) Münster, 1928, and Dietrich Mahnke, *Unendliche Sphaere und Allmittelpunkt*, Halle/Salle, 1937.

12 *Nicholas of Cusa (Cusanus): De docta ignorantia.* (vol. 1 of *Opera omnia, Jussu et auctoritate Academiae litterarum Heidelbergensii ad codicum fidem edita.* Eds. E. Hoffmann and R. Klibansky. Leipzig, 1932, p. 107.)

13 As Koyré points out, 'Giordano Bruno was the first man to take Lucretian cosmology seriously,' *op. cit.*, p. 6.

14 For a more detailed discussion of Cusanus' views on the infinity of the universe see Koyré, *op. cit.*, pp. 6–23.

15 *Ibid.*

16 *Op. cit.*, p. 23–24.

17 One cannot help thinking, as a sharp contrast to Bruno's demeanor, of Copernicus' timidity and Galileo's cowardice with regard to their cosmological convictions.

18 *Acrotismus*, art. xxxv.

19 P. H. Michel, *The Cosmology of Giordano Bruno*, p. 168.

20 *De infinito*, pp. 299–30.

21 *Op. cit.*, p. 245.

22 The view that God had created the world in order to manifest in and through it His greatness, beauty, wisdom, and omnipotence was generally held as a sound, orthodox theological opinion. To do so by creating a single, finite world, Bruno argued, would not be worthy of the divine intelligence, considering that he had the power to create innumerable worlds similar to ours and perhaps even greater, more beautiful and more complex than ours.

23 *De infinito, Proemiale epistola.*

24 *Op. cit.*, p. 159.

25 *De infinito*, I, p. 297; *De immenso*, VIII, iii.

26 The strong emanative flavor of this formulation, namely that 'the center of divinity amplifies itself', should not be overlooked.

27 This idea of a universe spreading forth was almost certainly inspired by Cusanus' idea of the 'possest' explicating itself.

28 We will discuss Bruno's concept of matter in the following chapter.

Chapter Nine

1 It is developed mainly in two of the three didactical poems he published in Frankfurt in 1592, namely *De triplici minimo et mensura* (On the Three Kinds of Minutest Entities and on Measure), and *De monade, numero, et figurabilibus* (On the Monad, Number, and Figure).

2 For further discussion of Galileo's mathematical conception of the atom, cf. Pietro Redondi, *Galileo Heretic* (Galileo Eretico), trans. Raymond Rosenthal. Princeton, N. J. (Princeton University Press) 1987, pp. 17–20.

3 Although Bruno's concept of the ether may now seem to us inconsequential and outmoded, after Einstein proved in 1905 that the ether hypothesis was unwarranted, we should not forget that the ether was an essential part of the revolutionary theories of electromagnetism developed by Maxwell, Hertz, and Lorentz, and that it was accepted unanimously by the scientific community until Einstein conclusively rejected it at the beginning of the twentieth century. There is, however, a widespread misconception that Newton invented the modern concept of ether. It was Bruno who first conceived and specified this notion. Based on Anaximander's *apeiron*, the infinite and eternal, perfectly homogeneous but utterly structureless and amorphous primary substance constituting everything that exists in the universe, Bruno transformed the ancient notion of the ether into a qualified void inside which atoms and bodies move. Bruno's ether is no longer the old quintessence, but also, even if he sometimes referred to it as a void, it is far from being simply nothing, a sort of absolute empty space, but rather, not unlike Anaximander's undifferentiated mass without boundaries, an extremely tenuous and subtle substance, material and infinite at the same time, pervading the entire universe, and therefore not the exclusive stuff of the heavenly bodies as Aristotle's quintessence was supposed to be. This ether supplanted Democritus' void in Bruno's atomism.

4 Cf. Redondi, *op. cit.*, p. 27.

5 This feature radically separates Bruno's atomism from Epicurus' classical atomism, which asserted that atoms differed widely in shape

and size. Paradoxically, Bruno is in the end compelled to admit perfect sphericity somewhere in physical reality, namely in its ultimate minimal components. This may be the most forgivable residue of Platonism left in him.

6 *De minimo*, I, ii (*Opera*, I, iii, p. 140).

7 In order to recognize this closeness, one needs merely to substitute the Brunian principle of movement – the center of kinetic energy immanent in every atom – by the equally immanent electromagnetic force, and the all-pervasive ether by the likewise all-pervasive electromagnetic field.

8 The irony of dualistic cosmology is that it is not orthodox enough: it shares the gnostic horror of real incarnation!

9 John Tyndall, the famous British physicist, once remarked that if matter had stepped into the world like a beggar, that was only because it had been robbed of its birthright by the Jacobs of theology. (Quoted by Bloch, *Das Prinzip Hoffnung, Gesamtausgabe*, vol. 5, p. 274.)

10 Ernst Bloch, *Das Prinzip Hoffnung, Gesamtausgabe*, Frankfurt a. M. 1972, vol. 5, pp. 540–546.

11 *Op. cit.*, p. 546.

Chapter Ten

1 Bruno calls the cosmic soul 'the soul of the universe' (*l'anima de l'universo*), and the cosmic mind 'the universal intellect' (*l'intelletto universale*).

2 Besides Stoic influence on Bruno's cosmological and ontological thinking, it is undeniable that Stoicism's call for universal brotherhood, harmony, and love, and its urge to political commitment and solidarity in order to deal with society's problems must have been a powerful source of inspiration for Bruno's plans for an ethical and social revolution. Above all, the Stoic freedom pathos as well as its strong belief in the autonomy of the human mind inspired Bruno's entire life and work. Stoic influence is also particularly noticeable in Bruno's theory of knowledge. Stoic epistemology, as well as its entire philosophy, was dominated by the thought of harmony, agreement, and accord. Thus human knowledge was considered possible only because the human mind was finely attuned to the cosmic mind. This, as we shall discuss in Chapter 12, was precisely the metaphysical foundation of Bruno's epistemology. Finally, even the Stoic concept of God may have influenced Bruno's ideas about the divinity and its relationship to the universe. The Stoic divinity was an immanent God and it was clearly identified with the cosmic mind. However, the Stoic divinity was also

a material God, a notion totally unacceptable for Bruno. Nothwithstanding, the strong panentheistic flavor of some of Bruno's formulations about the relationship between God and the universe recalls the Stoic view of the cosmos as the body of God.

3 P. H. Wicksteed's and F. N. Cornford's English translation (Loeb 1957 edition) of a passage of *Physics*, III, 4, in which Aristotle comments on Anaxagoras' *nous*.

4 This is where the influence of the Arab Aristotelian Left is more strongly felt in Bruno's ontology. According to Averroës the immortal soul that Aristotle was talking about in his treatise *On the Soul* was not the individual soul of every human being, but the universal soul common to all humankind. Only this universal soul was immortal.

5 *De la Causa*, p. 233.

6 Thomas Aquinas defined the principle of individuation as '*materia signata quantitate*', that is, matter predisposed to quantification, a view that can be interpreted as being not very foreign to Bruno's view of the universe's resulting from an unfolding of the cosmic mind into discreteness and extension, which in turn are rendered possible only by the quantum of matter.

7 Bruno arrived at this radical from of ontological monism by taking two gigantic strides away from the traditional position. First, he identified Plato's and Plotinus' *anima mundi* (Plotinus' third hypostasis) with Plotinus' *intellectus universalis* (his second hypostasis). Actually Bruno reversed the Neoplatonist hierarchy. Whereas Plotinus conceived the intellect as higher than the soul in the scale of Being and as ontologically different from it, Bruno understood the universal intellect (using here an Aristotelian rather than a Neoplatonist schema) as the faculty of the world soul, thus merging the two distinct Plotinian hypostases into one single substance. As Leen Spruit points out, 'Bruno integrates the universal intellect and the world soul into one single hypostasis. By regarding the intellect as a faculty of the soul, he applies, in effect, an Aristotelian scheme to a Neoplatonic doctrine. The result is that in this construction the intellect no longer requires the mediation of the soul since it is in direct contact with nature,' (author's translation) Leen Spruit, *Il problema della conoscenza in Giordano Bruno* (The Problem of Knowledge in Giordano Bruno), Naples (Bibliopolis) 1988, p. 194, fn. 124.

8 Richard Dawkins, *The Blind Watchmaker, Why the Evidence of Evolution Reveals a Universe without Design*, New York (W. W. Norton & Co.) 1987.

9 One of the most obscure and puzzling traits of the cosmic mind is its boundless vanity – the need for infinite display of its resourcefulness, power, and intelligence.

10 This acentric and aimless universe in its awesome absurdity is precisely what the Jesuit paleontologist and theologian Teilhard de
Chardin refused to accept, even if he had no doubts about the fact of
universal evolution. Instead, he proposed a goal, a *telos*, the eschatological Omega point towards which the entire universe, as the mystical body of Christ, is relentlessly heading for.

11 As Hegel pointed out, nature, 'profoundly understood', is ultimately
nothing but the concept (*der Begriff*), since it is the phenomenon or
appearance of the concept. However, despite the striking similarities,
Bruno's idea of the Absolute is very different from Hegel's. Although
for both thinkers the Absolute is mind, for Hegel Mind (*Geist*) is a
conscious and self-conscious subject. Moreover it has a *telos* (a goal),
which is to achieve absolute self-knowledge through the experience
of all the phenomena it brings forth. This is precisely the crucial and
most important feature of Hegel's Absolute, as opposed to
Schelling's, who conceived it as nature, and hence not specifically as
subject, but rather merely as substance (in Hegel's scornful metaphor,
'the night where all cows are black'). In this point Bruno is completely
in agreement with Hegel, for Bruno's Absolute, like Hegel's, is the
mind in and with the totality of phenomena it brings forth. Hegel
further contends that the phenomenal world, deeply understood, is
nothing but the Spirit since Spirit is the very essence of the universe
as long as it is understood as 'concept'.

12 *Steps to an Ecology of Mind*, New York (Ballantine), p. 461.

13 According to Schelling, the immutable, immanent, and infinite Absolute is the ultimate principle of organized complexity observable
in the physical universe. It is indifferent to difference, although it is
at the same time and paradoxically the principle of all difference. The
ultimate reason for this indifference to difference is precisely Nicholas of Cusa's principle of the coincidence of opposites, which was to
become the very foundation of Hegel's dialectics. One of the main
reasons for Schelling's admiration of Bruno was his acceptance and
incorporation of this dialectical principle into his philosophy.

14 *De la causa*, 287, 319, 325, 376; *Infinito*, 376, 394, 433, et passim.

15 *De la causa*, 336; *Infinito*, 382, 485.

16 '*L'universo è tutto centro e tutto circumferenza.*' ('The universe is all
center and all circumference.') *La cena*, 73, 164; *De immenso*, I, iii, v; *De
la causa. Proemiale epistola*

17 *Infinito*, 378, 380, 414, 520.

18 '*Aether vero idem est quod coelum, inane, spacium absolutum, qui insitus
est corporibus, et qui omnia corpora complectitur infinitus.*' ('The ether,
however, is the same as the heavens, empty, absolute space, which
pervades the bodies and, being infinite, contains all the bodies.')

19 '*Non ergo absurda est vacui sententia.*' (The assertion that the void exist is therefore not absurd.')

20 *De immenso*, IV, xiv.

21 *Infinito*, 373, 374, 378.

22 *De la causa*, 287, *Infinito*, 411.

23 *Infinito*, 389, 425, 432.

24 . . . *dall'infinito sempre nova copia di materia sottonasce. Infinito*, 361.

25 *De immenso*, III, 1, 510–516.

26 '*Non più la luna è cielo a noi, che noi a la luna.*' (No more is the Moon heaven to us then we are heaven to the Moon.) *Infinito*, 438, 464, *Cena*, I, p. 100.

27 '*Nessuno di que' moti è fatto regolare e capace di lima geometrica.*' (None of those movements is regular and capable of a geometrical measurement.) *La cena*, V, p. 227.

28 *Infinito*, 424.

29 *Acrotismus*, art. xxxviii.

30 *De magia* (Biondi), 36, 38.

31 *De magia*, 38.

32 *Infinito*, 376, 387, 409, 411, 415, 436.

33 *De la causa*, 282; *Infinito*, 382.

34 *Infinito*, 472; *La cena*, I, pp. 99–100.

35 *Infinito*, 389.

36 *De immenso*, IV, vii (*Opera*, I, ii, p. 42).

37 *De immenso*, IV, vii (*Opera*, I, ii, pp. 35–36).

38 *Infinito*, 436; *De immenso*, I, iii.

39 *Infinito*, 436.

40 *Infinito*, 437.

41 *Acrotismus* (*Opera*, I, p. 69); *De immenso*, IV (*Opera*, I, ii, pp. 1–3).

42 *De immenso*, IV, xvii.

43 *Infinito*, IV.

44 *Causa*, 231, 236.

45 *Causa*, 228.

46 *Causa*, II, 188.

47 *Ibid.*

48 '*Mens, deus, ens, unum, verum, fatum, ratio, ordo.*' *De immenso*, VIII, x.

49 *Causa*, 183, 231, 232, 236.

50 *Causa*, 235, 282; *Infinito*, 350, 381.

51 *Causa*, 282; *Infinito*, 395.

52 *Sigillus sigillorum* (*Opera* II, ii, 203).

53 *De vinculis in genere* (*Opera*, III, 695–696); *Infinito*, V, 399, 415; *De immenso*, VII, vi, xv.

54 *Causa*, IV, 238.

55 *Infinito*, 361.

56 *Causa*, IV, 231.
57 *Infinito*, 412, 425.
58 *Infinito*, II, 32–33; *De magia*, 36, 38; *Infinito*, 492; *De minimo*, II, iv (*Opera*, I, iii, 200).
59 *De magia*, 36, 38.
60 *Infinito*, 492.

Chapter Eleven

1 'Atheist' and 'atheism' were the terms used in the sixteenth and seventeenth centuries by the Roman Catholic theologians to denote pantheism, panentheism, and, in general, any doctrine that did not hold the universe to be a separate and different creation of the Creator-God. The word 'pantheism' was used for the first time in 1709, more than 100 years after Bruno's death, and the term 'panentheism' appeared even later, in 1828.
2 Author's literal translation of the document as referred by Ciliberto, *op. cit.*, p. 275. Cf. also L. Firpo, *Il processo di Giordano Bruno*, pp. 101f.
3 The Lament was that part of the Hermetic book titled *Asclepius*; it prophesied the decline and disappearance of the true religion of Hermes Trismegistos from the world.
4 *De la causa*, 234.
5 The 'negative way' of theology, maintains that the human mind is totally incapable of knowing anything at all about the essence of the divinity, which is not subject to rational description. The most it can do is to affirm what God is not, never what He actually is, not even by way of analogy.
6 Panentheism, as opposed to pantheism, does not totally identify the universe with God. It does hold, however, that the universe is a finite creation within the infinite being of God. Hence, the universe is conceived as an essential part of God, and therefore divine, but it still basically maintains a dualistic perspective by making a distinction between God's essence and the finite universe. The analogy frequently used by a cruder form of panentheism to express this distinction is that of the universe as the 'body of God'. However, Bruno's conviction that the universe is infinite separates his position from that of panentheism. On the other hand, his repeated insistence on the difference between God and the universe clearly places him at a safe distance from pantheism. However, although Bruno never referred to the universe as the body of God, his affirmation of the actual infinity of the universe, of the immanence of God in the universe, and

of the divinity of both the cosmic mind and nature bring him very close to the more subtle forms of panentheism.

7 *'Dio è infinito nell'infinito, dovunque e in tutte le cose, non al di sopra di esse né fuori di esse, ma ad esse assolutamente intimo.'* De immenso, in *Opere latine*, p. 804.

8 This view would imply that the universe is the body of God and would clearly make Bruno a panentheist.

9 Hegel would later agree with both Bruno and Cusanus: freedom, he pointed out, is 'the insight into necessity'.

10 Blumenberg, *Aspekte der Epochenschwelle*, p. 140.

11 'Open systems can also display ordered and lawlike behavior in spite of being indeterministic and at the mercy of seemingly random outside perturbations.' Paul Davies, *The Mind of God. Science and the Search for Ultimate Meaning*. London (Simon & Schuster) 1992, p. 182.

12 Pietro Angelo Manzoli, called Marcellus Stellatus Palingenius, was born in Stellata, Italy, in 1502, and died in 1543. He composed a cosmological treatise in verse called *Zodiacus vitae*.

13 *De immenso*, VIII, ii (author's translation).

14 Nowhere in his writings does Bruno's rejection of gnosticism appear more vigorous than in these last pages of *De immenso* (VIII, vi).

15 Paul Henri Michel, *The Cosmology of Giordano Bruno*, p. 241.

Chapter Twelve

1 It is true, however, that Galileo did not admit the limitation of the world – its enclosure – by a real sphere of fixed stars. In fact, he believed it was impossible to know whether the orb of fixed stars, or 'firmament' as it was called, has any shape at all. Infinite space beyond fixed stars, he argued, is not possible, and if it were, any star placed there would be imperceptible to us anyway. He explicitly stated that it will ever be undecided for human knowledge whether the universe is finite or infinite, thus anticipating with this keen insight Kant's famous antinomy.

2 *The Cosmic Code. Quantum Physics as the Language of Nature*. New York (Simon and Schuster) 1982, p. 65.

3 Pagels, *op. cit.*, p. 61.

4 The strong Neoplatonic roots of the early Bruno (*il primo Bruno*) have been clearly exposed and solidly documented by A. Ingegno in his article 'Il primo Bruno e l'influenza di Marsilio Ficino', in *Rivista critica di storia della filosofia*, 23 (1968), 149–170. Although in disagreement with Ingegno's main thesis, Leen Spruit, too, sheds considerable light on these early Neoplatonic influences on Bruno in *Il*

problema della conoscenza in Giordano Bruno, Naples (Bibliopolis) 1988, passim.

5 *'Senza voler arrivare a parlare di una frattura, possiamo affermare che tra* Sigillus *e* De la causa *il pensiero bruniano matura un'evoluzione importantissima.'* ('Without wanting to hint at a rupture, we can affirm that between *Sigillus* and *De la causa* Bruno's thought undergoes an evolution towards maturity.') Spruit, *op. cit.* p. 161.

6 *De infinito*, p. 254.

7 Here we must disagree with Leen Spruit's main thesis that the foundation of Bruno's epistemology was his metaphysics. See *Il problema della conoscenza in Giordano Bruno*, Naples (Bibliopolis) 1988.

8 Heinz R. Pagels, *The Cosmic Blueprint. Quantum Physics as the Language of Nature*. New York (Bantam Books) 1984, p. 306.

Chapter Thirteen

1 Giordano Bruno, *De magia. De vinculis in genere*. A cura di Albano Biondi. Pordenone (Edizioni Biblioteca dell'Immagine) 1986, pp. 7–11.

2 Cf. Albano Biondi's 'La caccia magica di Giordano Bruno' in his Introduction to *De magia. De vinculis in genere*, pp. X–XIII.

3 *Lo Spaccio*, pp. 236f.

4 *Lo Spaccio*, pp. 240 and 242.

5 *Dialoghi*, p. 778, (author's translation).

6 *Op. cit.*, p. 239.

7 Plotinus, *Ennead II, 9. Against the Gnostics*.

8 Footnote to p. xi.

9 *Op. cit.*, p. 398.

10 Yates, *Giordano Bruno and the Hermetic Tradition*, p. 401.

Chapter Fourteen

1 See John Horgan, 'The Universal Wizard', in *Discover*, March 1992, pp. 81–85.

2 The thinker that has probably delved more deeply, from a psychological point of view, into the roots of this obsession of mankind with centers was C. G. Jung. As is well known, one of Jung's most fundamental archetypes is the mandala.

Chapter Fifteen

1 *The Mind of God. Science and the Search for Ultimate Meaning.* London (Simon & Schuster) 1992, p. 197.
2 Although the word 'blueprint' does suggest a two-dimensional, static layout, which could be somewhat misleading, I have preferred it to other possible metaphors, such as 'scheme' or 'plan', which convey a stronger sense of intentionality. I was delighted to discover that Paul Davies had used it in the title of his book, *The Cosmic Blueprint*, New York (Simon & Schuster) 1989.
3 There is a passage in Plato's *Phaedrus* that marvelously illustrates his concept of 'world soul'. It reads thus: 'Soul taken as a whole is in charge of all that is inanimate, and traverses the entire universe, appearing at different times in different forms.' This quotation is taken from *Phaedrus and Letters VII and VIII*, translated by Walter Hamilton, London (Penguin Books) 1973, p. 31. Earlier Plato had identified this world soul with *arche*, that is, principle (Walter Hamilton prefers to translate it as 'source and prime origin', which is perhaps more understandable than 'principle' to modern readers).
4 This is the term Gregory Bateson used to characterize the cosmic mind. We shall discuss Bateson's concept of the larger mind later in this chapter.
5 The dialectical interdependence of chaos and order has recently received the strongest boost from the discovery of chaos-theory that order underlies certain forms of chaos.
6 This principle states that the result of cosmic evolution must necessarily appear to us as a *telos* (goal and purpose) of evolution because we are the observers and witnesses of the universe, so that everything looks as if conditions were initially set in such a way as to produce this particular effect, whereas the truth of the matter is that things could not have been arranged in any other way since we are here to observe them.
7 Gregory Bateson, *Steps to an Ecology of Mind*. New York (Ballantine Books) 1972, pp. 450 and 461.
8 *Ibid.*, p. 466.

Chapter Sixteen

1 *The Cosmic Blueprint*, New York (Simon & Schuster) 1989, p. 138.
2 *Ibid.*, p. 139.
3 Kenneth Denbigh, London (Hutchinson) 1975.
4 Eric Jantsch, Oxford (Pergamon) 1980.

5 David Bohm, London (Routledge & Kegan Paul) 1980.
6 Rupert Sheldrake, London (Blond & Briggs) 1981.
7 Paul Davies, New York (Simon & Schuster) 1982.
8 Fred Hoyle, London (Michael Joseph) 1983.
9 John Barrow and Joseph Silk, New York (Basic Books) 1983.
10 Ilya Prigogine and Isabelle Stengers, London (Heinemann) 1984.
11 Louise B. Young, New York (Simon & Schuster) 1986.
12 John Barrow and Frank Tipler, Oxford (Oxford University Press) 1986.
13 Arthur Peacocke, London (J. M. Dent) 1986.
14 Roger Penrose, Oxford (Oxford University Press) 1989.
15 Paul Davies, New York (Simon & Schuster) 1989.
16 Paul Davies, New York (Simon & Schuster) 1992.
17 Ernst Mayr defines teleonomy as 'a goal-directed activity or behavior that is controlled by a program'. For a thorough discussion of the terms teleology and teleonomy cf. Mayr's book *Toward a New Philosophy of Biology. Observations of a Biologist.* Cambridge (Harvard University Press) 1988, pp. 47f.
18 *The Mind of God. Science and the Search for Ultimate Meaning.* London (Simon & Schuster) 1992, pp. 190f.
19 Paul Davies, *The Mind of God*, pp. 140f.
20 *Disturbing the Universe.* New York (Harper and Row) 1979, p. 249.
21 *The Cosmic Blueprint*, p. 200.
22 Paul Davies, *God & the New Physics*, New York (Simon and Schuster) 1983, pp. 210f.
23 *Infinity and the Mind*, Boston (Birklhauser) 1982, p. 170.
24 *The Mind of God*, pp. 218, 220.
25 *Infinity and the Mind*, p. 183.

Chapter Seventeen

1 In Walter Kaufmann's and R. J. Hollingdale's translation, edited by Walter Kaufmann, New York (Random House) 1868, p. 8.
2 This is how Nietzsche characterized Christianity.
3 Von Bülow was a celebrated German conductor and a personal friend of Wagner.
4 In this, Nietzsche shows a remarkably close similarity with Franz Kafka. Both men grew up in a household dominated by five women and an absent father. In Nietzsche's case it was his mother and sister, two aunts, and the grandmother (the father had died when he was only four). In Kafka's case, it was the mother, three sisters, and the cook (although the father was physically there too in the evenings,

he was virtually absent as far as his troubled son was concerned). It is also interesting to note how this search for the missing Ariadne in both cases leads to the same type of 'woman of stature' Kaufmann is referring to: Cosima for Nietzsche and Milena for Kafka. Neither one of them succeeded in getting their Ariadne – Nietzsche broke with Wagner over some personal derogatory remark Wagner made to a common friend, and for the rest of his life, until he went mad, he was terribly jealous of Wagner not only because of Cosima, but also, and perhaps even more so, because of the colossal musical genius Nietzsche knew he could never match. Kafka, for his part, was rejected by clever Milena, and then settled for kind little Dora who nursed him until his deathbed.

5 Walter Kaufmann, *Nietzsche. Philosopher, Psychologist, Antichrist.* 4th ed. Princeton, N.J. (Princeton University Press) 1974, p. 32.

6 *Ibid.*, p. 34.

7 Walter Kaufmann and several other interpreters of Nietzsche's doctrine of the Eternal Return refuse to understand it as a metaphysical statement; the author disagrees with this interpretation, based on numerous texts proving the contrary in Nietzsche's *Will to Power*, and on Heidegger's understanding of Nietzsche as well.

8 *De minimo* in *Opere Latine* p. 45.

9 Cf. Ciliberto, *op. cit.* p. 233f.

10 *Opere Latine* p. 556.

11 *Opere Latine* p. 556.

12 Bruno believed that all atoms had one and the same spherical form. In this he disagreed with both Democritus and Epicurus who believed that the forms of the atoms were either infinite or at least indefinite.

13 *De immenso*, in *Opere Latine*, pp. 478–80.

14 Bruno himself never used the spiral as a symbol of his image of the universe. However, it is strongly suggested by his rejection of a cyclical, eternally returning universe, as well as by his conception of an eternally evolving universe constantly renewing itself by the incessant creation of new forms. Indeed, the symbol of the spiral most successfully blends the idea of constant change with that of the infinite resourcefulness of true omnipotence. It is also the symbol most congruous with the image of an acentric infinite labyrinth eternally generating itself towards no definite goal other than relentless self-unfolding and self-transcending.

15 It is interesting to note that nature shows a remarkable preference for the spiral configuration. In the macrocosm it forms spiral galaxies, and the orbits of planets around their respective stars, if they resemble the Earth's orbit around the Sun, are not closed ellipses but

helices, according to general relativity. In the microcosm nature produces all forms of life through the double helix of the DNA.

Epilogue

1 Author's ode to Bruno.
2 The theme and the symbol of the labyrinth have fascinated many modern authors, like Joyce, Borges, Gide, Robbe-Grillet, Durrell, Nin, Camus, Cortázar, Donoso, and Eco. See Wendy B. Farris, *Labyrinths of Language: Symbolic Landscape and Narrative Design in Modern Fiction*, Baltimore and London (The Johns Hopkins University Press) 1988.
3 Borges, *Labyrinths*, p. ix. Borges does not mention the fact that Nicholas of Cusa had adopted, before Bruno, the image of the sphere whose center is everywhere and its circumference nowhere, although for Cusanus this was only an image, and he applied it only to divine thought, not to the universe. Bruno then borrowed Cusanus's image and applied it, for the first time, to the universe. See 'L'univers de Giordano Bruno et la destinée humaine', in *L'univers à la Renaissance: microcosme et macrocosme*, Brussels (Presses Universitaires de Bruxelles) 1970, p. 103.
4 *'El universo [que otros llaman la Biblioteca] se compone de un número indefinido, y tal vez infinito, de galerías hexagonales ...'* Jorge Luis Borges, 'La biblioteca de Babel', in *Ficciones*, Buenos Aires (Emecé) 1968, p. 85. The English translations of Borges's texts are taken from *Labyrinths: Selected Stories & Other Writings*, ed. Donald A. Yates & James E. Irby, New York (New Directions Publishing Corporation) 1964.
5 *'La Biblioteca es una esfera cuyo centro cabal es cualquier hexágono, cuya circunferencia es inaccesible.'* Borges, *Ficciones*, p. 86.
6 *'La cifra y el compendio perfecto de todos los demás: algún bibliotecario lo ha recorrido y es análogo a un dios.'* The English version translates *cifra* as 'formula'.
7 *'Muchos peregrinaron en busca de Él. Durante un siglo fatigaron en vano los más diversos rumbos.'* Borges, *Ficciones* p. 92.
8 New York (Warner Books) 1986.
9 *Op. cit.*, p. 181, 195–207.
10 Borges' hexagons become heptagons and octagons in Eco's library. The Aedificium itself, where the library is located, is octagonal (p. 15), but the center of the labyrinth is heptagonal (p. 563). Eco's model was the octagonal labyrinth on the floor of the cathedral at Reims. Umberto Eco, *Postscript to The Name of the Rose*, trans. William Weaver San Diego, (Harcourt Brace Jovanovich) 1984, p. 55.
11 Eco acknowledges his indebtedness to Borges in *Postscript to The*

Name of the Rose, pp. 7–8, where he writes: 'Everyone asks me why my Jorge, with his name, suggests Borges, and why Borges is so wicked. But I cannot say. I wanted a blind man who guarded a library (it seemed a good narrative idea to me), and library plus blind man can only equal Borges, also because debts must be paid.'

12 The inaccessible center of Eco's labyrinth-library is the grandiose parody of a well-known institution in Roman Catholic ecclesiastical libraries: the *infiernillo* or 'little hell'. This is the secluded part of the library where books considered to be dangerous to the faith were safely kept and zealously guarded. Only in special cases, if weighty reasons backed the request, permission for perusal (sometimes reserved only to the bishop) was granted. *Infiernillos* are now rapidly becoming obsolete, due in part to spectacular advances in library technology.

13 For a discussion of the importance of mirrors in his theory of semiotics, see Umberto Eco, *Semiotics and the Philosophy of Language*, pp. 202–226.

14 Borges, *Labyrinths*, p. xiii.

15 Final words of Camus' *The Myth of Sisyphus*.

Glossary of Proper Names

Actaeon: mythical hunter.

Anaxagoras: Greek Pre-Socratic philosopher (500–428 BCE); he saw the mind (*nous*) as the force that caused every knowable being.

Anaximander: Greek Pre-Socratic philosopher (610–546 BCE); the first to write a philosophical work; he asserted that things originate in pairs of opposites from the Unlimited (*apeiron*) and disappear in it.

Aquinas, Thomas: Dominican priest, philosopher, and theologian, the most powerful intellect of medieval Scholastic philosophy (1225–1274). He embraced Aristotelian philosophy in support of Christian dogmatic theology. His most important work is the monumental *Summa theologiae* and the *Summa contra gentiles* in which he tries to reconcile the natural with the supernatural order.

Aristotle: Greek philosopher (384–322 BCE) a disciple of Plato; took the whole field of knowledge as his subject, giving it unity, and providing a philosophy which held its own for 2,000 years.

Bellarmine, Robert (Roberto Bellarmino): Jesuit priest and eminent theologian (1542–1621). He distinguished himself in the Council of Trent and as principal consultor in the Roman Inquisition trials of Bruno and Galileo. He was made a Cardinal by Pope Clement VIII in 1599 and later canonized in 1930 by Pope Pius XI.

Bloch, Ernst: Marxist reformist philosopher (1885–1977), author of *Das Prinzip Hoffnung* (The Hope-Principle) in three volumes (1954–56). Great admirer of Bruno; Bloch favored Bruno's concept of matter over dialectical materialism's more rigid concept.

Brahe, Tycho: Danish astronomer (1546–1601); he carried out systematic observations, which enabled Kepler to work out his planetary laws.

Cartesian: refers to Cartesius, the Latin name of René Descartes.

Clement VIII: Ippolito Aldobrandini (1536–1605), Pope from 1592 to his death. He favored the Counter-Reformation, pressed for Bruno's trial, and approved his condemnation by the Roman Inquisition.

Copernicus, Nicolas: astronomer (1473–1543) who put forward the novel theory that the planets, including the Earth, revolve around the Sun.

Cusanus: see Nicholas of Cusa.

Darwin, Charles: (1809–1882) argued that nature evolved according to the principle of natural selection.

Democritus: Greek Pre-Socratic philosopher (460–371 BCE), disciple of Leucippus, and co-founder of atomism.

Descartes, René: (Cartesius in Latin) French philosopher and mathematician (1596–1650), the first critical and systematic thinker of Modern times. He sought a firm foundation and starting point of philosophical discourse in the proposition '*Cogito ergo sum*' (I think therefore I am). He laid the foundations for rationalism, determinism, and a strong dualism that upheld the irreconcilable difference between the thinking substance (soul) and the extended substance (matter).

Dominicans: members of a Catholic mendicant religious Order founded in 1216 by the Spaniard Domingo de Guzman (Saint Dominic). The Dominican priests received from the Pope the authority to hear confessions and to preach everywhere, and they became the main officials and theologians of the medieval Inquisition. Both Bruno and Thomas Aquinas were Dominican priests.

Einstein, Albert: mathematical physicist (1879–1955) whose theory of relativity superseded Newton's theory of gravitation; he refused to challenge the stable-state universe.

Epicurus: Greek philosopher (341–271 BCE). He modified Pre-Socratic atomism by holding that the atoms spontaneously swerved and hence were not caught up in a necessary, irresistible causality. This allowed him to uphold human freedom. He asserted further that the greatest evils of humanity were fear and pain, and his philosophy aimed at delivering mankind from these evils. His friends and disciples met in the Garden, which became a symbol for his school.

Erasmus, Desiderius: Dutch Renaissance Humanist (1466–1536).

Ficino, Marsilio: Florentine Neoplatonic Renaissance priest, philosopher, theologian, and linguist (1433–1499), founder of the Florentine Neoplatonic Academy and translator of Plato's *Dialogues*, Plotinus, and the *Corpus Hermeticum* (a collection of writings falsely attributed to Hermes Trismegistos) into Latin. He envisioned Platonism as a safeguard against what he considered the degenerate and antireligious Aristotelianism of the fifteenth century. He conceived the universe as a hierarchy of beings that descended from God to matter and formed a living organism held together by a vital unity (vitalism).

Galileo Galilei: Italian scientist (1564–1642) who proved the superiority of the Copernican over the Ptolemaic theory, facilitated by his discovery of the telescope.

Goethe, Johann Wolfgang von: (1749–1832) German poet, playwright, and philosopher.

Gassendi, Pierre: (1592–1655) one of the founders of modern atomism.

Hegel, G. F. W.: German philosopher (1770–1831). He constructed the most comprehensive doctrinal edifice of German Idealism. Hegel's idealistic pantheism holds that 'Being' and 'Thought' are identical, that the Absolute Spirit is the essence of the universe, which builds itself from the Absolute Spirit in a necessary dialectical process as it brings forth successively nature, history, art, religion, and philosophy – the self-knowledge of the Spirit.

Heracleitus: Greek Pre-Socratic philosopher (around 500 BCE) saw in fire and war the essence of all things; he taught the Eternal Return of the Same – everything is in flow (*panta rei*). He denied the existence of the One defended by his rival Parmenides, and affirmed the existence only of the Many.

Hermes Trismegistos: (from the Greek: Hermes, the thrice greatest).

Greek title for the Egyptian God Thot, the god of knowledge and wisdom, to whom the Hermetic writings (*Corpus Hermeticum*) were attributed. He was considered by the Renaissance Neoplatonic philosophers to be a semi-divine sage contemporary of Moses who, because his teachings were in remarkable agreement with those of Plato and Plotinus, was an authority worthy of the highest veneration. However, in the early seventeenth century, the French philologist Isaac Casaubon dealt the death blow to the authority of the *Corpus Hermeticum* by proving that the Hermetic books were merely Neoplatonic writings from the third century of the common era.

Holy Office: The Congregation of the Holy Office is another name for the Roman Inquisition.

Hubble, Edwin: American astronomer (1889–1953). 1929 is known as the birthyear of contemporary cosmology, because of Hubble's discovery that the universe is expanding.

Inquisition: There are three Inquisitions: the medieval, the Roman, and the Spanish. Founded in 1231 to combat the spreading heresies of the Cathari and the Waldenses, the medieval Inquisition was put in charge of the Dominicans to search out heretics, witches, and sorcerers, to try the culprits, and to punish them if found guilty or upon their confession of their crimes. Bruno was tried first by the Venetian (medieval) and later by the Roman Inquisition.

Jesuits: members of the Catholic religious Order called the Society of Jesus founded by the Basque (Saint) Ignatius of Loyola in 1541 to defend the Catholic faith and the Papacy and to spread Catholicism all over the world with missions and colleges. They considered themselves the Light Cavalry of the Pope, bound to him with a fourth vow (of obedience) and thus exempt from the ordinary jurisdiction of the bishops.

Kepler, Johann: German astronomer and mystic (1571–1630), assisted Tycho Brahe, for a short time, establishing laws of planetary motion.

Laplace, Pierre: French mathematician and astronomer (1749–1827) who advanced the hypothesis that the solar system had condensed out of a vast rotating gaseous nebula.

Leibniz, G. W.: German rationalist-idealist philosopher (1646–1716) and mathematician. He tried to reconcile Descartes' mechanistic philosophy of nature with the Christian faith. Thus, instead of dead atoms he postulated animated monads (a concept he borrowed from Bruno) – simple, living entities which made up everything that existed in the universe. God, the principal Monad, ordered a perfect universe by means of a 'pre-established harmony'. Leibniz's world view was dynamic rather than mechanistic since the concept of 'force' played a decisive role in his philosophy of nature. He invented calculus almost simultaneously with Newton.

Lucretius (Titus Lucretius Caro): Roman poet and Epicurean philosopher (died in 55 BCE). He composed the didactical poem *De rerum natura* (On the Nature of Things) which decisively influenced Bruno's philosophy of nature.

Newton, Sir Isaac: (1642–1727) showed by his theory of gravitation that the universe was regulated by mathematical laws.

Nicholas of Cusa (Cusanus): cardinal and philosopher (1401–1464), precursor of Modernity, influenced considerably Bruno's thought.

Nietzche, Friedrich: German philosopher (1844–1900). In common with Bruno he planned a revaluation of traditional values.

Occam, (William of): English Franciscan philosopher (1285–1349), founder of Nominalism.

Palingenius: Pietro Angelo Manzoli, called Marcellus Stellatus Palingenius, was born in Stellata, Italy, in 1502, and died in 1543. He composed a cosmological treatise in verse called *Zodiacus vitae* in which he allegedly defended the infinity of the universe.

Parmenides: Greek Pre-Socratic philosopher (around 500 BCE). He taught that only thought leads to true knowledge and that sensorial perceptions deceive us. Multiplicity is only an illusion, only the One true being exists. The One is at the same time the All – *hen kai pan* (One and All). His main adversary was Heracleitus.

Peripatetic: (from a Greek verb meaning walking around and referring to the public hall in Athens where Aristotle taught) is another name for the Aristotelian school of philosophy.

Pico della Mirandola, Giovanni, Count: Italian scholar and Renaissance Platonist philosopher (1463–1494), friend of Marsilio Ficino and member of the Florentine Platonist Academy. He used the Hebrew Cabala in support of Christian theology. His *Oration on the Dignity of Man* sets the foundations of Renaissance Humanism. In 1486 he invited scholars from all over Europe to Rome to attend his defense of 900 theses he had drawn from Greek, Latin, Hebrew and Arabic writers. The defense never took place because thirteen of his theses were denounced as heretical by a Papal Commission. Bruno was very familiar with Pico's writings and was accused in Oxford of plagiarizing him. Pico died when he was only 31, probably already the most erudite man in Europe.

Plotinus: Greek Platonist philosopher (205–270 CE), the founder and most important thinker of Neoplatonism. His main work is the *Enneads*, which Marsilio Ficino translated into Latin. Plotinus' thought had a powerful influence on the Florentine Platonist Academy.

Pre-Socratics: Greek natural philosophers of the sixth and fifth century BCE, most of them from Ionia, Magna Graecia, and Sicily, whose fragmentary writings give us only a glimpse of their elaborate and profound metaphysics and cosmology.

Ptolemy: second-century Egyptian astronomer, geographer and mathematician, whose work supported the 'geocentric' idea that the earth is the fixed center of the universe.

Schelling, F. W.: German idealist philosopher (1775–1854). He defended the identity of nature and spirit, a sort of idealistic pantheism. He was very influential in directing his contemporaries' attention to Bruno's philosophy. One of his most important dialogues is titled *Bruno*.

Spinoza, Baruch: rationalist philosopher (1632–1677) defender of pantheism. He had considerable influence on German philosophy.

Suárez, Francisco: Spanish Jesuit theologian (1548–1617), the most powerful and productive mind of the late Scholastic and the Counterreformation. Based on Thomas Aquinas' philosophy but sometimes sharply disagreeing with it, Suárez's works were enormously influential in the philosophical and theological tradition of seventeenth and eighteenth century Europe.

Glossary of Philosophical Terms

acentric: centerless, without a center.

Age of Reason: refers to a period during the eighteenth century when philosophy was in vogue.

animism: (from the Latin *anima*, 'soul'). doctrine that considers all objects of physical reality as animated or having souls, either individual souls or a universal cosmic soul.

anthropocentric: regarding mankind as the centre of existence.

anthropology: the study of mankind, especially of its societies and customs.

anthropomorphic: attribution of human form or personality to god, animal or thing.

antinomy: the irreconcilable contradiction between two propositions.

aphorism: a brief statement of principle.

apodictic: clearly established.

apostasy: renunciation of a belief or faith, especially religious.

astrophysics: a branch of astronomy concerned with the physics and chemistry of celestial bodies.

atomism: philosophical theory which holds that all bodies are made up of countless minute, indivisible particles called atoms, and that all natural phenomena are caused by them. The first atomists were the Greek Pre-Socratic philosophers Leucippus and Democritus, followed by the Greek Epicurus and the Roman Lucretius. The first modern atomists were Bruno, Galileo, Gassendi, and Descartes.

Big Bang singularity: see singularity.

Cabala: collection of medieval Jewish secret doctrines about God and the universe.

chaos-theory: the theory concerning the potential for patterning in apparent chaos.

Corpus Hermeticum: see Hermetic writings.

cosmogony: doctrine or theory about the origin and evolution of the universe.

cosmology: part of metaphysics and philosophy of nature that deals with the structure, composition, and order of the universe, and the laws that regulate them.

Counter-Reformation: the reform of the Church of Rome, in the six-teenth and seventeenth centuries, which took place in response to the Protestant Reformation.

demiurge: Plato's creator of the universe.

determinism: doctrine that holds that every event has a cause and that everything is rigorously determined to be what it is the way it is.

dialectics: inquiry into metaphysical contradictions and their solutions, especially in the thought of Kant and Hegel.

dialectical materialism: comprehensive philosophical system based on Hegel's Dialectics and Marx's Historical Materialism, elaborated par-tially by Marx and Engels themselves, and later by Plechanow and Lenin in Russia. 'Diamat' understands the universe as purely mate-rial, and its natural laws as involved in a dialectical process analogous to the one developed by Hegel for the Absolute Spirit.

docetism: early gnostic belief which maintained Jesus Christ was divine only and that his visible form was merely an illusion.

Doppler effect: an increase, or decrease, in the frequency of sound, light, or other waves as the source and the observer move towards, or away from, each other.

dualism: philosophical doctrine that holds that reality can be explained by two radically different principles, substances, or forces, such as God and universe, matter and spirit (mind), body and soul. Its opposite is monism.

empiricism: epistemological doctrine that holds that all knowledge is derived from experience.

empyrean: highest heaven.

epigone: one of a later and less distinguished generation.

epistemology: philosophical theory that investigates the nature and origin of knowledge.

eschatology: Christian doctrine about the end of the world and the fate of human beings after death.

geocentric: considering the Earth as the center of the universe.

general theory of relativity: Einstein's theory about the structure of spacetime, according to which gravitation is considered a property of spacetime.

gnoseology: see epistemology.

gnosticism: moverment, strong around the first three conturies of the common era, which held that salvation could be attained only through man's knowledge of the mysteries of God and the universe.

heliocentric: considering the Sun as the center of the universe.

heresiarch: the leader or founder of a heresy.

Hermetic writings (*Corpus Hermeticum*): collection of books falsely attributed to Hermes Trismegistos and containing gnostic, Neoplatonic doctrines about the origin, immortality, and salvation of the soul and about the origin of the universe.

homogeneity (cosmic): property of the universe stating that the same laws apply indifferently to all cosmic phenomena, and similar elements and structure exist everywhere in the universe.

hylemorphism: metaphysical doctrine first conceived by Aristotle which asserts that physical reality is composed of two metaphysical, inseparable, complementary principles, one of them utterly indeterminate: matter (*hyle*), and the other totally determining: form (*morphê*).

immanent: intrinsic, abiding within.

isotropy (cosmic): property of the universe according to which it would look approximately the same in all directions from wherever an observer would look at it.

magus: magician or sorcerer.

maxima (as opposed to Bruno's minima): the largest bodies of the universe, such as planets, comets, and suns.

metaphysics: part of philosophy that inquires about being as such, and about both immanent principles and transcendent causes of all beings, within or beyond perceptible physical reality, and accessible only to reason, mind, or intellect.

mimesis: in general, imitation or representation of nature.

minima (according to Bruno): the minutest elements that constitute physical reality, such as atoms and monads.

monism: metaphysical doctrine that explains physical reality by one single principle, either purely material (materialistic monism), or purely spiritual (idealistic monism), or by the indissoluble and interdependent unity of spirit (mind) and matter (hylemorphic monism).

morphology: the study of the forms of things.

***nous*:** Greek for mind, intellect, reason. First used by Heracleitus to explain the immanent principle of physical reality, and then adopted and widely used by the Stoics and Neoplatonists.

nuclear physics: the physics of atomic nuclei and their interactions, especially in the generation of nuclear power.

Occam's razor: the principle of fewest possible assumptions, supposed to have put an end to the pedentary of Scholasticism.

ontology: part of metaphysics that focuses on being as such and the kinds, principles, and causes of beings in general. This concept is more universal than metaphysics since it does not necessarily include (nor exclude) such particular metaphysical entities as God and the soul (ego).

opuscle: a minor work.

oxymoron: a figure of speech in which apparently contradictory terms appear in conjunction.

panegyric: a laudatory discourse.

panentheism: doctrine that asserts the immanence of the universe in God or of God in the universe and generally understands the universe as the body of God. Unlike pantheism it does not deny the existence of a personal God.

panpsychism: the theory that all nature has a psychic side.

pantheism: philosophical or religious doctrine that outright identifies God with the universe thereby denying the existence of a transcendent, personal God.

positivism: philosophical movement founded by Auguste Comte (1798–1857). It rejects metaphysics and takes what is immediately perceived as the only reliable foundation for knowledge.

possest: neologism coined by Nicholas of Cusa to denote God as pure actuality (*esse*) and true omnipotence (*posse*) whereby nothing that God is capable of doing is left undone; accordingly the universe cannot but exist; it is absolutely necessary.

quantum mechanics: a system or theory using the assumption that energy exists in discrete units.

quintessence: The fifth and highest extraterrestrial element or essence (after the terrestrial four elements of earth, water, air, and fire) thought to be the exclusive substance of all heavenly bodies.

rhizome: underground root-like stem, bearing both roots and shoots.

Scholasticism: the philosophy and theology of the late Middle Ages. It sought to explain Christian doctrine rationally with the support of Aristotelian and Neoplatonic philosophy. Its most important representative is Thomas Aquinas.

singularity: the infinitely condensed mass at the center of a black hole; it has no dimensions. The universe is believed to have originated from the Big Bang singularity.

spacetime: the fusion of the concepts of space and time, especially as a 4D continuum.

stochastic: determined by a random distribution of problems.

supercolliders: Device, usually in a long underground tunnel, for firing sub-atomic particles on a collision course.

teleology: the doctrine of the final causes of things: interpretation in terms of purpose.

teleonomy: 'a goal-directed activity or behavior that is controlled by a program' (see Chapter 16, note 17).

theism: doctrine of a Creator-God, who is also provident, caring, heeding of prayer, and a miracle-worker, as opposed to deism, which is the doctrine of a Creator-God, who does not interfere either with the course of nature or with human affairs.

theurgic magic: magic, popular in Neoplatonism, based on conjuring beneficent deities to intervene in natural phenomena, by using occult languages.

transcendent: beyond the grasp of experimental knowledge. When applied to the divinity it denotes a God utterly different and separate from the universe. The transcendent omnipotent God creates the universe freely out of nothing and hence is not compelled by his essence to create it.

Tridentine: relating to the Council of Trent (1545–1563) in Trento, Italy, concerning Roman Catholic doctrine.

vitalism: philosophical doctrine that asserts that everything in the universe is alive either because it is animated by individual souls or by the cosmic soul or intellect, or because it is driven by a vital force such as the one Bergson called *élan vital*. With regard to living organisms vitalism denies that all biological phenomena can be adequately explained by strictly physical and chemical forces and laws, and postulates additionally (or instead) a special immanent life-force or life-principle irreducible to those laws.

Bibliography

A: Bibliography of literature on Bruno

Salvestrini, Virgilio: *Bibliografia di Giordano Bruno (1582–1950)*. Ed. Luigi Firpo (2nd. posthumous ed.). Florence (Sansoni Antiquariato) 1958 (= Biblioteca Bibliografica Italica).

1 Bruno's Collected Works:

Opere di Giordano Bruno Nolano ora per la prima volta raccolte e pubblicate in due volumi. Ed. Adolf Wagner. Leipzig (Weidmann) 1830, 2 vols.

Jordani Bruni Nolani, *Opera latine conscripta*, publicis sumptibus edita. [recensebant F. Fiorentino, F. Tocco, H. Vitelli, V. Imbriani et C. M. Tallarigo]. Naples (Dom. Morano) and Florence (Le Monnier) 1879–1891, 3 vols. in 8 parts (Large Italian state edition). Facsimile reproduction (ed. Günther Holzboog) Stuttgart-Bad Cannstatt (Friedrich Frommann) 1962, 3 vols.

Volume 1:

Part I:

1 *Oratio valedictoria*. Wittenberg 1588.
2 *Oratio consolatoria*. Wittenberg 1588.
3 *Acrotismus camoeracensis*. Wittenberg 1588.
4 *De immenso et innumerabilibus* (bks. 1–3).

Part II:

1 *De immenso et innumerabilibus* (bks. 4–8). Frankfurt 1591.
2 *De monade, numero et figura*. Frankfurt 1591.

Part III:

1 *Articuli adversus mathematicos.* Prague 1588.
2 *De triplici minimo et mensura.* Frankfurt 1591.

Part IV:

1 *Summa terminorum metaphysicorum.* Zürich 1595.
2 *Figuratio physici auditus Aristotelis.* Paris 1586.
3 *Mordentius et de Mordentii circino.* Paris 1586.

Volume 2:

Part I:

1 *De umbris idearum.* Paris 1582.
2 *Ars memoriae.* Paris 1582.
3 *Cantus circaeus.* Paris 1582.

Part II:

1 *De architectura lulliana.*
2 *Ars reminiscendi, Triginta sigilli,* etc.
3 *Sigillus sigillorum.* London 1583?
4 *Centum et viginti articuli de natura et mundo.*
5 *De lampade combinatoria, De specierum scrutinio.* Wittenberg 1587.
6 *Animadversiones in lampadem lullianam.* 1587.

Part III:

1 *De lampade venatoria.* Wittenberg 1587.
2 *De imaginum compositione.* Frankfurt 1591.
3 *Artificium perorandi.* Frankfurt 1612 (posthumous work).

Volume 3:

1 *Lampas triginta statuarum.* 1587.
2 *Libri physicorum Aristotelis explanati.* 1587?
3 *De magia, Theses de magia.* 1589?
4 *De magia mathematica.* 1590?
5 *De principiis rerum, elementis et causis.* 1590.
6 *Medicina lulliana.*
7 *De vinculis in genere.*

Le opere italiane di Giordano Bruno ristampate. Ed. Paul de Lagarde. Göttingen (Dieterichsche Universitätsbuchhandlung (Lüder Horstman) 1888–1889, 2 vols.

Le opere italiane di Giordano Bruno. Critica testuale e oltre. Ed. Giovanni Aquilecchia. Naples (Bibliopolis) 1991.

Giordano Bruno: Gesammelte Werke. Trans. Ludwig Kuhlenbeck. I–II Leipzig (Eugen Diederichs) and Berlin (H. Zossen) 1904; III–VI Jena (Eugen Diederichs) and Leipzig (O. Brandstetter) 1904–1909, 6 vols.

Giordano Bruno, opere italiane. Ed. Giovanni Gentile. 3 vols. Bari (Laterza) 1907–1908.

Volume I (metaphysical dialogues):

1 *La cena de le ceneri.* London 1584.
2 *De la causa, principio e uno.* Venice 1584.
3 *De l'infinito universo e mondi.* Venice 1584.

Volume II (moral dialogues):

1 *Spaccio de la bestia trionfante.* Paris 1584.
2 *Cabala del cavallo pegaseo, con l'aggiunta dell'asino cillenico.* Paris 1585.

Volume III (*II candelaio.* Commedia):

1 *Candelaio* Paris 1582.

Giordano Bruno, opere italiane. Ed. Giovanni Gentile and Vincenzo Spampanato (improved and enlarged edition). 3 vols. Bari (Gius. Laterza & Figli) 1925–1927.

Giordano Bruno: Dialoghi italiani. Ed. Giovanni Aquilecchia, 3rd. ed. Florence (Sansoni) n.d. [1958] (= Classici della Filosofia VIII).

Opere latine di Giordano Bruno: II triplice minimo e la misura, La monade, il numero e la figura, L'immenso e gli innumerevoli. Ed. Carlo Monti. Turin, (Unione tipografico-editrice torinense) 1980.

Opere di Giordano Bruno e di Tommaso Campanella. Ed. Augusto Guzzo. Milan and Naples (Ricardo Ricciardi) 1956.

Giordano Bruno: Heroische Leidenschaften und individuelles Leben. Auswahl und Interpretationen. Reinbeck bei Hamburg (Rowohlts Taschenbuch Verlag) 1957 (= Rowohlts Klassiker 16).

2 Giordano Bruno's works:

La cena de le ceneri. Ed. Giovanni Aquilecchia, Turin (Giulio Einaudi) 1955.

La cena de le ceneri. Milan (G. Daelli e como) 1864.

The Ash Wednesday Supper. (La cena de le ceneri). Trans. Stanley L. Jaki, with introduction and notes. The Hague and Paris (Mouton) 1975.

De la causa, principio e uno. Introduction and commentary by Augusto Guzzo. Florence (G. C. Sansoni) 1955.

De umbris idearum. A cura de Rita Sturlese. Florence (Leo S. Olschki) 1991.

The Expulsion of the Triumphant Beast. Trans. Arthur D. Imerti, with an introduction and notes. New Brunswick, N.J. (Rutgers University Press) 1964.

B: Secondary sources

Aquilecchia, Giovanni: *Giordano Bruno*. Roma (Enciclopedia Italiana) 1971 (= Biblioteca Biographica).

Atanasijevic, Ksenija: *The Metaphysical and Geometrical Doctrine of Bruno as given in his work De Triplice Minimo*. Trans. George Vid Tomashevich from French original edition [Belgrade 1923]). St. Louis, Mo. (Warren H. Green, Inc.) 1972.

Badaloni, Nicola: *La filosofia di Giordano Bruno*. Florence (Parenti) 1955 (= Saggi di cultura moderna 12).

Bloch, Ernst: *Gesamtausgabe*. Frankfurt am Main 1972, vol. 5,1, *Das Prinzip Hoffnung*, vol. 1, 'Die Schichten der Kategorie Möglichkeit. Das objektiv-reale Mögliche', 271–278; 'Erinnerung: Logischstatistischer Kampf gegen das Mögliche', 278–281 'Die technischen Utopien. Bacons Ars inveniendi', 760–763; vol. 5,2, *Das Prinzip Hoffnung*, vol. 2, 'Bruno und das unendliche Kunstwerk; Spinoza und die Welt als Kristall', 993–1001; vol. 7, *Das Materialismus Problem, seine Geschichte und Substanz,* 'Zweiter Kursus: 25. Materie als Grösse und Ausdehnung' 169–172; '26. Materie, gesehen in Gott: als Ausdehnungs-Attribut Gottes (Malebranche; Spinoza)' 172–179; '30. Materie als Nicht-Ich und im Aufstieg Schwere-Licht-Leben (Fichte, Schelling)' 211–229; '48. Anhang/Avicenna und die Aristotelische Linke: Texte und Erläuterungen. Giordano Bruno', 538–546; vol. 12, *Philosophie der Renaissance,* '3. Giordano Bruno', 188–206; vol. 14, *Aut Logos aut Kosmos.* 'Keine Parallele, doch folgerichtige Seltsamkeit', 303–307; vol. 15, *Drehung/Hebung: Gebiete und Prinzip.* '44. Objektkraft Chiffriertes. Ohnekopf Natur und Wunschbild Sphinx', 214–223.

Blumenberg, Hans: *Aspekte der Epochenschwelle: Cusaner und Nolaner.* Revised new edition of *Die Legitimität der Neuzeit,* Part 4. Frankfurt a. M. (Suhrkamp) 1976 (= suhrkamp taschenbuch wissenschaft 174).

Brunnhofer, Hermann: *G. Brunos' Lehre vom Kleinsten als die Quelle der prästabilierten Harmonie von Leibniz.* Leipzig (Rauert u. Rocco) 1890.

Broad, C. D.: 'The New Philosophy: Bruno to Descartes', in *Cambridge Historical Review,* VIII, (1944–1945), 36–54.

Ciliberto, Michele: *Giordano Bruno.* Rome-Bari (Laterza) 1990.

Ciliberto, Michele: *Lessico di Giordano Bruno.* 2 vols. Rome, 1979.

Ciliberto, Michele: *La ruota del tempo. Interpretazione di Giordano Bruno.* Rome, 1986.

Cicuttini, Luigi: *Giordano Bruno.* Milan (Società editrice 'Vita e pensiero') 1950. Pubblicazioni dell'università cattolica del Sacro Cuore.

Clemens, Franz Jakob: *Giordano Bruno und Nikolaus von Cusa. Eine philosophische Abhandlung.* Bonn (Wittmann) 1847.

Corsano, A.: *Il pensiero di Giordano Bruno nel suo svolgimento storico.* Florence (Sansoni) 1940.

Deregibus, Arturo: *Bruno e Spinoza. La realtà dell'infinito e il problema della sua unità.* Vol. I: 'Il concetto dell'infinito nel pensiero filosofico di Bruno.' Turin 1980.

Firpo, Luigi: *Il processo di Giordano Bruno.* Naples (Edizioni Scientifiche Italiane) 1949.

Garin, E.: *Giordano Bruno*. Milan, 1966.

Garin, E. *Ermetismo del Rinascimento*. Rome, 1988.

Gatti, Hilary: 'Minimum and Maximum, Finite and Infinite. Bruno and the Northumberland Circle' in *Journal of the Warburg and Courtland Institutes*, vol. 48, 1985, 144–163.

Gentile, Giovanni: 'Giordano Bruno', 'Le fasi della filosofia bruniana', and 'Veritas filia temporis' in *Il pensiero italiano del Rinascimento*, Giovanni Gentile, Florence (Sansoni) 4th ed. 1968 (= G. G. Opere 14) 259–355.

Grassi, Ernesto: *Giordano Bruno. Heroische Leidenschaften und individuelles Leben. Eine Auswahl und Interpretation*. Bern (A. Francke A.G.) 1947.

Greenberg, Sidney: *The Infinite in Giordano Bruno*. 1950.

Groce, Abel: *Giordano Bruno, der Ketzer von Nola*. Versuch einer Deutung. 1. Teil: Werdegang und Untergang. Vienna (Europäischer Verlag) 1970.

Guzzo, Augusto: *Giordano Bruno*. Turin (Ed. Filosofia) 1960.

Heipcke, K., Neuser, W., and Wicke, E. (eds.): *Die Frankfurter Schriften Giordano Brunos und ihre Voraussetzungen*. Weinheim (VCH, Acta Humaniora) 1991.

Ingegno, Alfonso: *Cosmologia e filosofia nel pensiero di Giordano Bruno*. Florence (La nuova Italia) 1978.

Kirchhoff, Jochen: *Giordano Bruno*. Reinbeck bei Hamburg (Rowohlt Taschenbuch Verlag) 1980 (= Rowohlts Monographien).

Kuhlenbeck, Ludwig (ed.): *Giordano Bruno: Kabbala, Kyllenischer Esel, Reden,Inquisitionsakten* (Proceedings of the Venetian Inquisition's trial for heresy of Giordano Bruno). Trans. Ludwig Kuhlenbeck. Jena (Eugen Diederichs) 1909, 145–234.

Kuhlenbeck, Ludwig: *Giordano Bruno*. Berlin-Schöneberg (Protestantischer Schriftenvertrieb G.m.b.H.) 1913 (= Die Religion der Klassiker. Ed. Gustav Pfannmüller. Vol. 1).

Lovejoy, Arthur O.: 'The Dialectic of Bruno and Spinoza' in *University of California Publications in Philosophy*, I (1904) 141–174.

Kristeller, Paul Oskar: *Eight Philosophers of the Italian Renaissance*. Stanford (Stanford University Press) 1964.

Mercati, Angelo [Cardinal]: *Il sommario del processo die Giordano Bruno*. Città del Vaticano (Biblioteca Apostolica Vaticana) 1942.

Michel, Paul Henri: *The Cosmology of Giordano Bruno*. Trans. R. E. W. Maddison (from the French edition, *La cosmologie de Giordano Bruno*. Paris (Hermann) 1962). Paris (Hermann), London (Methuen), Ithaca, N.Y. (Cornell U.P.) 1973.

Namer, Émile: *L'univers de Giordano Bruno et la destinée humaine*. Paris (Presses universitaires de France) 1926.

Namer, Émile: *La pensée de Giordano Bruno et sa signification dans la nouvelle image du monde*. Paris (Centre de Documentation Universitaire) 1959.

Namer, Émile: *Les aspects de dieu dans la philosophie de Giordano Bruno*. Paris (Librairie Félix Alcan) 1926.

Namer, Émile: *Giordano Bruno ou l'univers infini comme fondement de la philosophie moderne*. Paris (Éditions Seghers) 1966.

Nicholas of Cusa (Cusanus): *De docta ignorantia*. (vol. 1 of *Opera omnia, Jussu et auctoritate Academiae litterarum Heidelbergensii ad codicum fidem edita*.) Eds. E. Hoffmann and R. Klibansky. Leipzig, 1932.

Previti Luigi S.I.: *Giordano Bruno e i suoi tempi*. Prato (Giachetti, Figlio e C.) 1889.

Paterson, Antoinette Mann: *The Infinite Worlds of Giordano Bruno*. Springfield, Ill. (Charles C. Thomas) n.d.

Saitta, Giuseppe: 'Il Rinascimento' in *Il pensiero italiano nell'umanesimo e nel rinascimento*. 2nd. ed. Florence (G. C. Sansoni Editore). 'II. Giordano Bruno' 81–193.

Saracista, Maria: *La filosofia di Giordano Bruno nei suoi motivi plotiniani*. Florence (Vallecchi) 1935.

Schelling, F. W. J. v.: *Bruno, oder über das göttliche und natürliche Prinzip der Dinge*. Berlin (Unger) 1802.

Singer, Dorothea Waley: *Giordano Bruno: His Life and Thought*. With annotated translation of his work *On the Infinite Universe and Worlds*. New York (Henry Schuman) 1950.

Schmitt, Charles B. (editor): *The Cambridge History of Renaissance Philosophy*. Cambridge (Cambridge U.P.) 1988. 'The Renaissance Concept of Philosophy' by Cesare Vasoli, 57–73; 'Humanism' by Oskar Kristeller, 113–137; 'The New Philosophy of Nature' by Alfonso Ingegno, 236–263; 'Astrology and Magic' by Brian P. Copenhaver, 264–300; 'Metaphysics' by Charles H. Lohr, 537–638; 'Theories of Knowledge' by Richard H. Popkin, 668–684; and 'Epistemology and the Sciences' by Nicholas Jardine, 685–713.

Spampanato, Vincenzo: *Vita di Giordano Bruno, con documenti editi e inediti*. Messina (Principato) 1921 (= Studi filosofici 10).

Spruit, Leen: *Il problema della conoscenza in Giordano Bruno*. Naples (Bibliopolis) 1988.

Stern, Fred B.: *Giordano Bruno: Vision einer Weltsicht*. Meisenheim am Glan (Verlag Anton Hain) 1977.

Sturlese, Rita: *Bibliografia, Censimento e Storia delle Antiche Stampe di Giordano Bruno*. Florence (Leo S. Olschki) 1987.

Thorndike, Lynn: *History of Magic and Experimental Science*, vol. VI: Sixteenth Century. New York (Columbia University Press) 1941, 423–428.

Védrine, Hélène: *La conception de la nature chez Giordano Bruno*. Paris (Librairie Philosophique J. Vrin) 1967 (= De Pétrarque à Descartes).

Veillard-Baron, Jean-Louis: 'De la connaissance de Giordano Bruno à l'époque de "l'idéalisme allemand" ' in *Revue de Métaphysique et de Morale* 76 (1971), 406–423.

Walker, Daniel Pickering: *Spiritual and Demonic Magic from Ficino to Campanella*. London (Studies of the Warburg Institute 22) 1958.

Westman, Robert S.: 'Magical Reform and Astronomical Reform: The

Yates Thesis Reconsidered' in *Hermeticism and the Scientific Revolution*. Papers read at a Clark Library Seminar, March 9, 1974. Ed. by Robert S. Westman and J. E. McGuire. Los Angeles (William Andrews Clark Memorial Library. UCLA) 1977.

Wilde, Georg: *Giordano Brunos Philosophie in den Hauptbegriffen Materie und Form dargestellt*. Breslau (Marcus) 1901.

Yates, Frances A.: 'Giordano Bruno's Conflict with Oxford' in *Journal of the Warburg Institute*, vol II, 1938–39, 227–242.

Yates, Frances A.: 'The Religious Policy of Giordano Bruno' in *Journal of the Warburg Institute*, vol. III, 1939–40, 181–207.

Yates, Frances A.: 'The Emblematic Conceit in Giordano Bruno's De Gli Eroici Furori and the Elizabethan Sonnet Sequences' in *Journal of the Warburg and Courtland Institutes*, vol. VI, 1943, 101–121.

Yates, Frances A.: *Giordano Bruno and the Hermetic Tradition*, London-Chicago (Paul) 1964.

Yates, Frances A.: *The Art of Memory*. London (University of Chicago Press) 1964.

C: Modern and contemporary cosmology

Bavink, Bernhard: *Ergebnisse und Probleme der Naturwissenschaften. Eine Einführung in die heutige Naturphilosophie*. 8th. ed. Leipzig (Hirzel) 1944.

Boslough, John: *Masters of Time. Cosmology at the End of Innocence*. Reading, Mass. (Addison-Wesley) 1992.

Burtt, Edwin A.: *The Metaphysical Foundations of Modern Physical Science*. 2nd. ed. Garden City, N.Y. (Doubleday) 1932.

Capek, Milic: *The Philosophical Impact of Contemporary Physics*. Princeton (Van Nostrand) 1961.

Cassirer, Ernst: *The Individual and the Cosmos in Renaissance Philosophy*. Trans. Mario Domandi, with introduction and notes. New York (Harper) 1963.

Davies, Paul: *God & the New Physics*. London/New York (Simon and Schuster) 1984.

Davies, Paul: *The Mind of God. Science and the Search for Ultimate Meaning*. New York/London (Simon & Schuster) 1992.

Davies, Paul: 'Is the Universe a Machine?' in Nina Hall (ed.), *The New Scientist Guide to Chaos*, London (Penguin 1990, pp. 213–229).

Davies, Paul: *The Cosmic Blueprint. New Discoveries in Nature's Creative Ability to Order the Universe*. New York/London (Simon and Schuster) 1988.

Davies, Paul and Gribbin, J.: *The Matter Myth. Dramatic Discoveries That Challenge Our Understanding of Physical Reality*. New York/London (Simon and Schuster) 1992.

Ferris, Timothy (ed.): *The World Treasury of Physics, Astronomy, and Mathematics*. Boston, Toronto, London (Little, Brown and Company) 1991.

Gleick, James: *Chaos. Making a New Science*. New York (Penguin) 1988.

Hall, Nina (ed.): *The New Scientist Guide to Chaos*. London (Penguin) 1990.

Hawking, Stephen W.: *A Brief History of Time. From the Big Bang to Black Holes*. London (Bantam) 1988.

Heimendahl, Eckart: *Dialog des Abendlandes. Physik und Philosophie*. Munich (List) 1966.

Heisenberg, Werner: *Das Naturbild der heutigen Physik*. Hamburg 1955 (= rowohlts deutsche enzyklopädie 8).

Heisenberg, Werner: *Physik und Philosophie*. Frankfurt a. M. (Ullstein) 1959.

Heisenberg, Werner: *Der Teil und das Ganze. Gespräche im Umkreis der Atomphysik*. Munich (Piper) 1969.

Jeans, Sir James: *Physics and Philosophy*. Cambridge (Cambridge University Press) 1942.

Koyré, Alexandre: *From the Closed World to the Infinite Universe*. New York (Harper) 1958.

Kuhn, Thomas S.: *The Copernican Revolution*. New York (Modern Library) 1957.

Kuhn, Thomas S.: *The Structure of Scientific Revolutions*. Chicago (University of Chicago Press) 1962.

Layzer, David: *Cosmogenesis. The Growth of Order in the Universe*. New York, Oxford (Oxford University Press) 1990.

Lederman, Leon: *The God Particle. If the Universe Is the Answer, What Is the Question?* Boston, New York (Houghton Mifflin Co.) 1993.

Lightman, Alan and Brawer, Roberta (eds.): *Origins. The Lives and Worlds of Modern Cosmologists*. Cambridge, Mass. (Harvard University Press) 1990.

Lovejoy, Arthur O.: *The Great Chain of Being*. Cambridge, Mass. 1936.

Pagels, Heinz R.: *The Cosmic Code. Quantum Physics as the Language of Nature*. New York (Bantam Books) 1983.

Riordan, Michael and Schramm, David N.: *The Shadows of Creation. Dark Matter and the Structure of the Universe*. New York (W. H. Freeman & Co.) 1991.

Stewart, Ian: *Does God Play Dice? The Mathematics of Chaos*. London (Penguin) 1989.

Weyl, Hermann: *Philosophy of Mathematics and Natural Science*. Princeton (Princeton University Press) 1966.

White, Michael and Gribbin, John: *Stephen Hawking. A Life in Science*. London (Viking) 1992.

D: Literature on Mind

Bateson, Gregory: *Steps to an Ecology of Mind*. New York (Ballantine Books) 1972.

Johnson, George: *Machinery of the Mind. Inside the New Science of Artificial Intelligence*. Redmond, Wash. (Microsoft) 1986.

Körner, Stephan: *Metaphysics: Its Structure and Function*. Cambridge, (Cambridge U.P.) 1984.

Miller, Arthur I.: *Imagery in Scientific Thought. Creating 20th Century Physics*. Cambridge, Mass. (MIT Press) 1986.

Penrose, Roger: *The Emperor's New Mind. Concerning Computers, Minds, and the Laws of Physics*. New York (Penguin Books) 1991.

Rucker, Rudy: *Infinity and the Mind: The Science and Philosophy of the Infinite*. Cambridge, Mass. (Birkhäuser) 1982.

Russell, Peter: *The Global Brain. Speculations on the Evolutionary Leap to Planetary Consciousness*. Los Angeles (J. P. Tarcher, Inc.) 1982.

Wilber, Ken (ed.): *The Holographic Paradigm and Other Paradoxes*. Boulder, Co. & London (Shambhala) 1982.

E: Other

Deleuze, Gilles: *Nietzsche and Philosophy*. New York (Columbia University Press) 1983.

Eco, Umberto: *Postscript to The Name of the Rose*, trans. William Weaver. San Diego (Harcourt Brace Jovanovich) 1984.

Keith, Thomas: *Religion and the Decline of Magic*. New York (Penguin) 1971.

Kaufmann, Walter: *Nietzsche. Philosopher, Psychologist, Antichrist*. 4th ed. Princeton, N.J. (Princeton University Press) 1974.

Mayr, Ernst: *Toward a New Philosophy of Biology. Observations of an Evolutionist*. Cambridge, Mass. (Harvard University Press) 1988.

Rorty, Richard: *Philosophy and the Mirror of Nature*. Princeton, N.J. (Princeton University Press) 1979.

Index

multiplicity of worlds 9, 55, 57,
92, 99, 100, 125, 134–5
mundus ideatus 163
mysticism 194, 210

Namer, Emile xiv
Naples 13, 188
Napoleon I 52
NASA 152
natural philosophy xiv, 111, 142, 154
natural selection 197
nature 86, 100, 125, 131, 139,
144–5, 150–1, 170–1, 172–6,
187, 202, 217, 226
laws of xii, 86, 116–17, 189,
203, 206
necromancy 170–1
negentropy 191, 195
Neoplatonism xxii, 45, 46, 76, 79,
84, 90, 98, 140, 143–4, 147, 157,
161, 163, 169, 171, 178
Neptune 88
neurons 204
Newton, Isaac xii, xvi, 4, 6, 8, 75,
78, 84–5, 87, 88, 89, 91, 92, 113,
116, 156, 157–8, 198, 199, 201
Nicholas of Cusa xii, xx, 4, 36, 92,
95, 96, 97, 98, 110, 119–20, 130,
136, 140, 143–4, 145, 161, 207, 208
Nietzsche, Friedrich xxi, xxiv, 32,
61, 73, 81, 131, 187, 216, 217,
218–24, 228, 230, 231
Nola xvii, xxiii, 13
Nolan *see* Bruno
Noli 16, 24
nous see mind, cosmic
numbers 140, 158, 175, 176

Occam's razor 210
occult 172, 174, 176
Oedipus xxiv
omnipotence 43, 100, 102, 130, 131,
145, 146, 162, 206, 222, 224, 228

One 140–1, 163–4, 210, 211
*One Hundred and Twenty Articles
on Nature and the World Against
the Peripatetics* 33
ontology xxiii, 9, 31, 67, 75, 86,
109, 114, 119, 124, 133, 143,
149, 161, 169, 170, 174, 176,
186, 190–1, 203, 215, 217
Oratorio valedictoria 36
organization, principle of
complex 22–3, 204–5, 206
Overman 231–2
Oxford 23–6, 54

Padua 17, 39, 48, 56
Pagels, Heinz R. 159, 168
Palingenius 148, 149
Pan 120
panentheism 133, 141, 142, 146, 206
panpsychism 127, 208
pantheism 36, 93, 124, 131, 138–9,
140–2, 143, 144, 145, 147, 149,
173–4, 206
Pan-theology 170, 174
panzooism 127
Papal States 16
Paracelsus 36
Paris 19–22, 23, 31, 33, 52, 161, 163
Parmenides 31, 100, 105, 130, 164
particle accelerators 6, 9
particles 158, 189, 190–1, 193, 202
Pascal, Blaise 93, 226
Paterson, Antoinette Mann xiv-xv
Paul 218
Paul III 81
Penrose, Roger 8, 206
Peripatetics *see* Aristotelianism
physics 109, 110, 112, 113, 146,
152, 153, 156, 157, 158, 159,
160, 164, 198, 201, 202, 203
atomic 114
nuclear xi, 111, 157, 190
particle 204, 209